Ba... ...n

*Sex, drugs
and rock'n'roll
was never like this*

by
Jeff Baker

*Still Reeling
After All These Years*
Loosely Based on the Truth

OTK Books

First published in Great Britain in 2005 by OTK Books Ltd

Cover design by Bernt Kristiansen

A CIP catalogue record for this book
is available from the British Library.

ISBN 0-9548073-6-7

Printed in Great Britain by
TJ International Ltd, Padstow, Cornwall

Distribution by Central Books, 99 Wallis Rd., London E9 5LN
Tel: (0)20 8986 4854 e-mail:orders@centralbooks.com

OTK Books Ltd
One Friar Street
Reading RG1 1DA
e-mail:otkbooks@online.no

To Joan
with very Best Wishes

Jeff Baker (AKA "Biffo")

Ta! A lot for BABYSITTING
for me all those years ago!

Contents

Countdown
to the
Great Adventure

The air was crisp and clean, and the golden leaves in the trees glistened in the rays of the morning sun as it dried the dew from the grass and raised the moisture from the ground. *Isn't life wonderful,* I thought. It was the first week of October 1966, and The Four Tops were topping the charts. That evening we drove the green band van along familiar roads to that night's booking with Joey concentrating on the road ahead as he brought us to our destination. We had both been in local beat groups since the beginning of that glorious decade, so I had known him for many years.

Joe was a very good lead guitarist, and played his Fender Telecaster with gusto, if little panache. Such was his nature that he had assumed the leadership of the group, The Charters, due to the fact that he was unquestionably the most outspoken of us, and happened to own the van. He had a mop of ginger-red hair, and an equally red and bulbous nose. Joey was full of confidence, and was a wise-cracking, amiable bloke, but if you ever annoyed him he could become very aggressive indeed.

I put this down to his genes, or more likely, his red hair, which I'd been told was a sign of a fiery temperament. So I tried not to irritate him too much, contenting myself with commenting on the size and colour of his nose and other abnormalities

That year had been a time of upheaval in the group, and the band had literally dissolved in a matter of days. First, "Bill the Bass" told us he'd had enough, complaining that his heart was no longer in it. Besides, he reasoned, "I'm far too old for this lark now." I suppose he was really. He was a good ten years older than the rest of us, who were mere youngsters in our early twenties.

While the rest of us where barely literate no-hopers who only worked to pay for the booze of the day and a few laughs along the way, Bill was well-educated, with a good job and enough cash to keep him in comfort in his sizable, detached property on the outskirts of town. All we really had in common was a love of rock and roll, and a crazy sense of humour. But he could really play that bass!

He explained, "I really want to spend more time with Ellie." Ellie was his wife. I thought *you're a bit late to think about that now, mate*, for his missus was an extremely beautiful woman who attracted men to her ample charms like moths to a flame.

As bad as the news was that Bill had decided to hang up his Fender Precision Bass after three years with the group, I reckoned we could overcome the loss, as I knew someone who would fit the bill for Bill. My old mate Dave "Lodder" Lloyd had stood in for him on previous occasions when Bill couldn't make it, and he did have some things going for him compared to Bill, because he was young, good-looking, and didn't smoke a pipe, which were all preferable in a rock and roll outfit like ours. I thought the problem was sorted and laid my mind to rest.

The following day however, the group literally fell apart when a knock on the door announced the arrival of Mick John, our legendary lead guitarist.

"Y'alright, Mick!" I greeted him, "Come in. I've got something to tell you …"

"If it's about Bill, then save your breath, because he told me himself last night."

"Well, what d'ya think?" I asked to gauge his reaction to the news.

"Well..," he drew on it, evidently feeling uncomfortable "given the news about Bill, I've decided to jack it in too …"

My jaw dropped at this unexpected announcement. "Tell me you're joking, Mick!" I pleaded, but the shaking of his head and the set expression on his face clearly showed he wasn't.

"You see," he explained almost embarrassed, "I've been offered a job in a proper band, and since hearing from Bill, I've decided to take them up on their offer. So that's it. Sorry about giving you such short notice, but that's how it is."

No amount of persuasion by our eminent manager and van-driver, who also happened to be my Old Fellah, could make Mick change his mind, and with that, he just turned on his heel and left. Just like that. Gone! It was a shattering blow, not only to the group, or what was now left of it, but also to me personally, for I admired Mick as a great musician, and liked him as a friend.

Within a couple of hours our telephone rang. It was Roy Fullwood, our charismatic electric keyboard player, enquiring about the following day's rehearsal. I had to tell him that there wouldn't be one. "Why's that then Jeff, you haven't got the shits again, have you?" laughing as he said it.

"It's nowt to do with my bowels," I assured him, pausing for a few seconds to build myself up to tell him the bad news, "but apart from me and thee, we haven't got a group anymore," I told him, and went on to explain. "Mick and Bill knocked it on the head, I'm very sad to say."

"Really …?" he replied with surprise in his voice, "Now that is a bloody shame."

There then followed a long pause. "Roy, are you still there?" I asked into the mouthpiece. He confirmed the fact. "Well tell me," I asked him, "where do we go from here?"

"To be perfectly honest," came his reply, "not very far, I would imagine. It's a real shame," he said again, "I was seriously thinking of buying a brand new keyboard, but not now. It's not worth it if it's just the two of us having to play between the bingo sessions somewhere on a Saturday night, or busking outside Marks and Sparks to earn a few bob, then, well …" He left the end of the sentence hanging in the air. As though collecting his thoughts, and coming to a decision, he sighed, then assured me, "I'll tell you what," he said, "I'll have a good think about the situation, and I'll get back to you." And with that he hung up. He must still be considering it, for I never heard from him again.

Looking at my totally devastated face, the Old Fellah said "Well, you've got no group, so now you don't need a manager either, do you."

"Stop being so negative, will you!" I told him in a desperate attempt to inject some positive inspiration into the conversation. "I'll form another group. I've done it before and I can do it again, no problem." He nodded his head in acceptance of that fact, but I could see there was little conviction or enthusiasm in the expression on his face. Still, I bore on, "Well, there you go then. That means we still need a manager and a van driver."

"I don't know son," he replied with a resigned sigh. "I'm getting too old for all this group malarkey. I've bought myself some angling gear, and from now on I'm going to use my free time to nip out and do a bit of fishing. They say it's supposed to be relaxing."

"Fishing!" I howled. "What the frigging hell do you know about fishing!?"

"Nothing at all, son," he admitted with a twinkle in his eyes, "but at least it will get me out of the house and away from your mother's moaning and nagging. Come to think about it, that's why I became your manager in the first place," he said. "I tell you son, she could moan with the best of them.

In fact she could have won the Olympic Gold in moaning and nagging. It's enough to drive a man to drink!"

"I know dad," I had to agree. "Why d'ya think I spend so much time in the pub these days?" We both chuckled and gave a smile, for we both knew that she really wasn't such a bad old stick. Anyway, I never needed an excuse to go to the pub.

Over the next few weeks I did manage to form another group. We kept the old name – The Charters – but it now had new faces in the line-up. I contacted Joey first, to sound him out on the project. It turned out that he had two mates in North Wales who fancied the idea of forming a group. Firstly, there was Stuart, who was a friendly and easy-going expatriate Scouser who hailed from Holywell. He had a mop of unkempt straggly hair, a grinning moon-like face, and was a married man with a couple of kids, and a penchant for drinking vodka straight from the bottle. He was a great character, with a John Lennon edge to his singing voice, and handled his guitar with consummate ease. Stu was to become our rhythm guitarist.

Secondly, there was Dave, who came from a small place called Greenfield on the coast road. It was so small and nonedescript that you would miss it if you blinked. He was a vain and vaguely handsome character who seemed to take his good looks for granted. He had bleached, blonde hair in a length that was fashionable at the time. Despite being married, he clearly had an eye for the girls. Although the dim, half-wit expression on his handsome face belied the fact, I suspected that Greenfield's own super stud had dabbled with the affections of every other woman in the area, and some who just happened to be passing through.

He later confided in me, and confirmed that my initial suspicions had been quite accurate. I admit I was jealous at the time, for where he seemed to be jockeying through life in the land of milk and honey, I was still very much crawling on my knees through the dry and arid desert in search of a spot of t'other. I thought at the time that he might have been bragging about his conquests, but soon concluded that the boy was the real McCoy. As I got to know him better, there was no longer any doubt about the fact. I only hoped he would be as adept at playing the bass guitar as he was at making women hum. As it transpired, he was. In fact, he was good at everything he did, as long as it didn't put too much strain on his brain, which seemed to be securely located between his legs.

All of these thoughts came flooding back to me as we continued on our way to that particular night's booking. I smiled to myself at the recollections as I concentrated on the lyrics of the songs we'd rehearsed the previous evening, while Dave and Stu ran through the chord sequences on their guitars, in the back seat of the van. Then Joey interrupted my thoughts by correcting the avid musicians in the back seat in his own encouragingly pedagogical way, "The chord changes to D after the middle eight, not frigging E, you pair of dick heads!"

"Fuck off, Joey," Stu retorted over the noise of the engine, "and just concentrate on your driving will you!"

Joey chuckled to himself. "Them pair of idiots are just winding me up, I know damn well they are.."

Would they even have the temerity? I mused, with a smile on my face …

Apart from the noise of the engine and the sounds of the guitars, not a word was spoken as we continued towards our destination. Looking out of the window I saw a sign announcing the fact that there were six miles to go. Without looking at me Joey suddenly says "Oi, you! Soft lad!"

"Who you calling soft lad, mush?" I replied

"You, that's who! Who the fuck do you think I'm talking to?" said Joey grinning like a madman, with his great red hooter only inches from my face. "Tell me summat," he continued, "have you got a passport?"

In a carefully considered response, I asked, "Now, why would I be in need of a passport? We're only playing at the Memorial Hall in Nantwich."

"Yes, now we are," he said smirking. "But our agent rang me earlier, saying he's got us a six week gig, if we're all up for it." He gave me a sideways glance to see my reaction. "And as such, you're going to need a current passport."

"And where exactly is this proposed gig that requires us to have a valid passport," I enquired. Dave and Stu had both stopped strumming in the back of the van, as they too took a sudden interest in this unexpected information.

"Germany!" Joe informed us with glee. "To be precise, it's Northern Germany, on the Star Palast Dance Club circuit. The agent told me that the boss over there, some bloke called Manfred, had heard so much about us, he'd rung him up and demanded we should get ourselves over there as soon as possible. He reckons our brand of stuff should go down a storm with the locals."

"Bollocks!" sneered Stu. "Heard so much about us, indeed!" He gave a snort of derision, "How could this Manfred character have heard of us for crying out loud? We only play around these parts, you daft sod!"

"Okay then, I lied," admitted Joey, grinning sheepishly. "But our agent does think we'll do okay over there, honest!"

"And what makes him think that then?" Dave chipped in, apparently becoming fearful that his Greenfield harem would be deprived of his services for the duration, and that a rival might benefit from his absence to take over his duties among the local beauties he had been serving so well.

"Germany, eh?" I said, gleefully casting my mind back to that exciting day earlier in the summer when we had stuffed the Krauts 4-2 to win the World Cup. I positively glowed with pride at the memories. "Germany!" I exclaimed again. "We can't go there. It's full of bloody Germans! Anyway, it's a long way, isn't it?" The furthest I'd been at the time was to Margate a couple of years earlier.

"Okay, Joey! Just tell them we're up for this particular jaunt," Stu announced, as he lit up a cigarette, having made the decision there and then, with no tangible sign of concern or consideration. "When exactly are we supposed to be going?"

"Well," said Red Nose, "according to the agent, we have to leave on the Twenty-Eighth of October, and be there ready to take up the contract from the First of November."

"Christ," exclaimed Dave, "that doesn't leave us much time to get everything ready for the trip does it!" Even Stu nodded his head in agreement at this piece of wisdom.

"Oh, and by the way, Joey," I said, suddenly regaining my senses, "just to remind you before you get too carried away; I haven't got a passport. And another relevant point – what about my job? I can't just swan off for six weeks," I told him. "I've got a career to think of," I wailed, like an aging stage diva refusing to do the Omo ad.

"Career my arse!" Joey snorted derisively. "You're just a bloody labourer, you thick sod!"

"I beg your pardon?" I said, somewhat taken aback, "I'll have you know that I'm a … I'm an artist!" I stammered, with some semblance of indignation, and not a little hurt pride.

"Listen to yourself! You're nothing but a gofer. In other words, a fucking labourer!" he chided me. "A bloody snowman's got better career prospects than you have, you daft sod! Nobody, but nobody, is even going to notice you're gone."

"Ah, but …" I countered.

"Look, I don't want anymore lame excuses. We're going as a group or not at all!"

Suddenly, *Not at all* seemed quite appealing.

"It's going to be a great adventure," he announced enthusiastically, as we reached our destination and began to unload our gear. Joey continued to wax lyrical about the trip as we began to set up on the stage. "Our agent's even going to pay our ferry-crossing, which is good of him, eh? Must cost him a few bob."

"Aye," Stu chuckled, "he probably thinks it's money well spent, so he doesn't have to look at our ugly mugs for a month or two."

"Speak for yourself, Stu," said Dashing Dave, admiring himself in the dressing-room mirror as he combed his golden, bleached locks.

But nothing was going to stop Joey now, not while he was in full flow. "We'll be getting twenty-five quid a week each, free digs and as much rumpy-pumpy as we can handle," he told us with relish.

Drawing on a cigarette, I looked at him aghast, and asked, "Rumpy pumpy, Joe? What's that when it's about? Some kind of German sausage?"

"A German sausage? You soft sod! It's a euphemism for screwing. D'ya get my drift, or do I have to draw you a picture?"

"Oh," I remarked, "and, just so we know the score, is this a compulsory part of the contract, or purely optional?" I enquired in the most innocent voice I could muster.

"Compulsory, you dozy git? Once you get over there, you'll be frolicking with those frauleins like there's no tomorrow, just mark my words. They're all gorgeous blue-eyed blondes, and absolutely gagging for fine fellahs like us!"

I thought aye, it'll be alright for you, you horny bastard. I could never get over the fact that Joey, possibly the ugliest guitarist in the North West, could pull so many women. Mind you, it could have had something to do with his tackle, for it was absolutely huge. It reminded me of a baby's arm holding a shiny red apple, and that was when it was flaccid, so God only knows what it must have been like when it was angry! It was a well known fact that if it was available, Joey would screw it, whatever and whoever it was. He'd probably fuck a frog if he could stop it hopping.

Finally happy with his gear set up and his Telecaster tuned, he turned to me again "It'll do you good, Jeff. It'll take your mind off moping over that hairdresser bird who gave you the elbow. What was her name again?"

I hadn't been expecting him to drag this particular moth-eaten piece of my life out of the closet, and I could feel my stomach muscles tighten with tension. He was referring to the one and only girl I had ever had a relationship with. I had been happy for the year it lasted, and devastated when she unceremoniously broke it off without a word of warning or a sign of regret. I thought I had finally been able to put her out of my mind and forget, but now Joey had suddenly dragged her into the conversation to confront me with love lost, and the pain and insecurity that had followed as a result of that loss.

"Ann," I weakly replied, suddenly sad and wary at the same time, readying myself for whatever new humiliation he would spout out at me.

"Aye, Anne," he said. "You let her lead you a right merry dance, didn't you? And you let her walk all over you, you daft sod. She was a right little gold digger. Everyone warned you about her, didn't they? But you took no bloody notice, you daft bugger! She was too hoity toity for a bit of rough like you mate. You'd have been better off, and a whole lot happier, if you'd picked a sort like my girl, Mandy."

16

I shuddered at the thought of Joey's girlfriend. Mandy, was known to the rest of the group and others who knew her, as many did, as Randy Mandy. The mere mention of Mandy provoked gales of laughter from Stu and Dave. "Don't wish for anything like that for the poor lad here. She's as rough as rust," chuckled Stuart.

"Aye, she's a right dog, that one," said the Greenfield Stud, "I wouldn't touch her with a barge-pole." Coming from him, that was certainly saying a lot about the poor lass. "You could enter her in Crufts and not only win, but possibly end up Best in Show!"

"Hang on, you bastards, you're talking about the woman I love," pleaded Joey.

"She's probably the only girl in North Wales with a crevice deep enough to cater for that weapon of yours. I'm only surprised you don't strap a plank across your arse to stop yourself from falling in."

I roared with laughter at this barbed repartee.

"You bastards!" Joey snarled. "When you've finished, it's time for a few beers in the bar, because we're on in half-an-hour." And that took our minds off Randy Mandy for the moment, and onto more pressing matters.

Lonnie Donegan!
The Old Fellah's
Never Gonna Believe me …

With so much to do and prepare for, the following few weeks passed in a blur of activity. After what seemed like an awful lot of wheedling and wrangling, I eventually did get permission to swan off work for the period of time required, under some kind of ruling called "Leave of Absence", and I left the department in the more than capable hands of John Wilson, the Geordie boss, and young Terry Pitt, a guy who, had he been any sharper, would surely have cut himself. But most importantly, I now had in my sweaty grasp, a pristine new passport, and was ready to go. Yippee!

It was finally time to leave on our great adventure, or it would be as soon as the van arrived with the others. I stood on the pavement outside our house with my drum-kit and luggage, like a marooned sailor searching the horizon for a vessel to appear, as I nervously checked my watch and wondered if they had forgotten me.

Besides my parents, who no doubt where there only to ensure that they were actually rid of me, quite a few of the neighbours and their kids had gathered to see me off on my travels. *Good luck, Jeff*, seemed to be the message of the day. Even Johnny Burns, the former singer in my earlier group, The Dateliners, had turned up for the occasion, telling me to have a great time and not to do anything he wouldn't do. I assumed by that, he meant chasing a bit of skirt, and I sighed at the thought, thinking that aye, now that really would be something, wouldn't it! Because, for some reason, I never seemed able to pull the birds, however much I tried.

You'd think by all the commotion, that I was going off to war to kill the Jerries, instead of hopefully trying to entertain them.

Albeit, ten minutes late, Joey duly arrived. The van was crammed to the roof with all the gear and luggage, with Stuart's moonlike face grinning at me through the side window. I couldn't believe there would be any room for my gear, and, more importantly, for me.

Joey jumped out of the driver's seat to give me a hand, and greeted me with a smile, "Y'allright?"

"Yeah," I lied, for I wasn't really.

"Well, come on and shift yourself, will you, and get your arse in the van!"

As we finally pulled away there was a great cheer and much waving from the assembled throng, followed by gales of laughter as all and sundry spotted the large lettering emblazoned across the back of the van, reading, *R.SEND*. Yeah, I know. Infantile, right? Then again, that was us; immature, inexperienced and naïve young men, with an infantile outlook on life and little experience of it.

It was getting dark as we travelled across the country en route for our destination, which was the port of Harwich. As I slumped in the back seat of the van, amongst all the gear, my mind was racing with thoughts of events yet to come.

After a few hours of mind-numbing travel Joey slowed down to pull into a garage forecourt. I idly wondered where we were, then wondered, with somewhat more concern, if I had time to ease the pressure on my bladder. "I thought you filled the tank up before we left," moaned Stuart, as he fumbled in his pocket for petrol money. Dave and I joined in, whining away at having to contribute to the petrol kitty. Joey uncoupled the cap of the petrol tank and sniggered, "Do you load of idiots reckon this vehicle runs on fresh air, or summat!" Then he explained that it was all the extra weight we were carrying. "Consequently being, we're not getting the mileage, as we'd normally do".

I was mightily impressed. *Consequently*, eh? I never even thought that Joey knew such a long word, let alone knowing what it meant, and actually being able to use it in the right context. Truly mind- boggling!

None of us actually knew were this particular garage was on our route to Harwich, and as Joey fussed about, filling the tank before going on to pay at the cash-desk, we took the opportunity to have a quick smoke, well away from the petrol pumps I might add. If we were going to go up in flames, we would at least like to know where we were at the time. Not necessary, I admit, but nice to know …

"Bloody hell!" Stu suddenly gasped. "Do you see who that is over there at the next pump?"

"Who? Where?" Dave and I stammered, taken aback by the excitement in his voice.

"There! Can't you see him?" said Stu pointing in the direction of someone filling up his car. "It's him, isn't it!" he said excitedly. "It's Lonnie Donegan!"

"Frigging heck!" I said. "It is an' all. Lonnie Donegan … Wait till I tell the Old Fellah, that I've seen Lonnie Donegan in the flesh!" For he'd bought all his records – *Rock Island Line, My Old Man's A Dustman*, etc. He had them all. He's never going to believe me, I thought. I actually found it hard to believe it myself, even though the King of Skiffle was actually standing there, right in front of me. "Fuckin hell!" I repeated, "Lonnie Donegan!"

"Y'alright, lads," he greeted us, as he noticed the excitement his appearance had caused among the slack-jawed, star-struck cretins staring at him. He cast a glance at our van and saw the gear stacked inside it. "I take it you're a group off to some gig," he stated, rather than asked.

"Er, yes Lonnie," we confirmed in chorus, then, awe-struck as we were, corrected ourselves, still in wide-eyed chorus,

"Sorry. Mr. Donegan." Then I gave him the thrilling information, "We're The Charters from Chester."

"Ah, yes," said the King of Skiffle. "I think I've been there. As I recall it's a nice place with black and white buildings and that. Very picturesque." There was what you might call a pregnant pause, for we didn't know what to say in the presence of the great man. So he broke the silence to make us feel more comfortable. "Anyway, lads," he continued, "where are you off to at this late hour?"

Suddenly finding his voice, Joey piped up to inform him that we were on our way to Germany. "We're playing on the Star Palast circuit," he told him with some pride in his voice, apparently hoping that the great man would be impressed.

"Germany?" He gave a short laugh. "What a drag, man!"

As he climbed into his car, he wound down the window to wish us luck. "All the best with your trip lads," he said smiling at us. "Believe me, you're going to need it." As an afterthought, he then added some advice. "Be careful with your dealings with Manfred," he warned, "he's a frigging gangster, and if he can shaft you out of money, believe me, he will. Oh! And keep your eye on Black Bob, his second in command," he said, tapping the side of his nose, as though we were supposed to understand what that meant. "Keep a very good eye on Black Bob!" he repeated, as he rammed the car into gear, and began to accelerate. "Right then, see you lads!" And with that he was gone.

"'Ere Joey," said Stuart, with a dark frown on his face, "you never told me that this Manfred geezer was a fucking gangster. And what about this Black Bob character?"

Joey slammed the van door shut and started the engine, then turned to the rest of us. "*Manfred a gangster? Black Bob, who we've got to keep an eye on,*" he mimicked. "How the fuck would I know what he was on about. What d'ya think I am, bloody septic or something?"

"Don't you mean psychic, Joe?" chortled Stu.

"Oh, fuck off!" snarled Joey, and pulled out of the brightly-lit garage and into the dark night. I wasn't really listening, for my mind was still preoccupied with the fact that I had actually spoken to Lonnie Donegan himself. I knew the Old fellah was never going to believe me, but I knew it was true, and that's what really mattered. Lonnie Donegan, eh! I thought, now that was really something to write home about!

Dawn was breaking when we finally reached the port of Harwich. A chilly mist hovered over the dock area, creating a surrealistic atmosphere that was almost intense. There wasn't a soul about except for the four of us sitting in our trusty van, with its headlights cutting a swathe through the swirling mist.

Yawning loudly, and stretching the muscles of his tired body, Joey informed us that we were early, and wondered what we should do while we waited. This prompted Stuart to offer to find his guitar and give us all a rendition of *Sitting on the Dock of the Bay*, which, all things considered, was quite appropriate.

But Joey wasn't in a jokey mood. "It's too early in the day to listen to you murder a perfectly good song," he sneered.

"Please yourself," cackled Stu.

It was then just a case of trying to settle down within the cramped confines of the van, and try to get a brief nap before the port offices opened for business. The windows quickly fogged up with the condensation of our breath. Our nap was cut short by a sharp tapping on the windscreen, and we looked out at two port officials peering suspiciously back at us as they blinded us with torches that shone into our screwed up faces. They called through the window to enquire about our business, and why we were parked where we were.

Joey rolled down the side window. "We're booked on the five o'clock sailing to Bremerhaven with the Prinzenlinen

Ferry. I think it's called the Viking III," he informed them. Then a sudden rush of dismay showed on his face. "Don't tell me we've missed the boat?" he wailed, and glanced nervously at his watch.

"No, you haven't missed your boat, as you so succinctly put it," one official assured him. "Actually, you're a little early, because it doesn't sail until five o'clock this afternoon, not five in the morning, like it is now."

The pregnant silence that followed this information was broken by Stuart. "You dozy ginger bugger!" he exploded, "You've got us here half a day early, you useless git. I could have spent last night in a warm bed, with my nice warm missus, you bloody arsehole!"

"I'm sure the tickets said …" Joey began, lamely trying for forgiveness, but then allowed his words to trail off into silence, as Stu gave him a fixed stare that could have killed the cat and the kittens with it.

"Okay lads," I interjected, recognising the necessity of inserting some degree of diplomacy into the proceedings, before they came out of control. "As it transpires, Joey here has made a bit of a faux pas," I told them. The expressions on the faces before me made it clear that it was still too early in the morning for any sign of intelligence, not that my fellow musicians were especially noted for showing any such signs at any time of the day. So, to make sure they knew what I was going on about, and generally enlighten them, I added, "The ginger nut has made a right bloody cock-up." I then went on to dilute the anger that was understandably raging within them, by informing them, "But, this particular fiasco does have one redeeming feature going for it …"

"You don't half talk some bollocks Baker," sneered Stuart, interrupting me in mid-stride so to speak. "What d'ya mean, redeeming thing going for it?"

"Well, think about it lads," I told them, "if this soft prick hadn't driven us here tonight, we wouldn't have met Lonnie Donegan, now would we?"

Joey, always astute at recognising a way out of trouble, grinned and grabbed the opportunity eagerly. Nodding his head approvingly at what I had said, he confirmed my assumption. "Yeah! You tell 'em Biffo! We wouldn't have met Lonnie!" and he turned to smile triumphantly at all and sundry.

There was some mumbling and grumbling from the Greenfield Gigolo and the Holywell Hooligan in the back, but in the end, they slowly came to the same conclusion. "Yeah. Okay. I suppose you're right..." Not happy, you see, but grudgingly conceding a valid point.

A sharp tap on the window was followed by an exaggerated "Ahem!" We looked at a new face with a uniform cap on top of it. "Far be it for me to break up this early morning meeting of the Lonnie whats-his-name's fan club," the official informed us sarcastically, "but you'll have to move this rusty old van, because the port is about to swing into action very shortly."

Even as he spoke, I could see the lights coming on in the port offices, and people beginning to scurry about their business. Then I suddenly noticed that we were straddled across a set of railway lines for the dock train. "I think he's right," I told Joey. "As he so tactfully put it, we'd better move away from here."

"Where to?" Joey was becoming agitated.

"Anywhere you like son," hissed the official, "just not here, okay? Just stay off the area until later this afternoon. If my memory serves me right, they'll start loading your ferry around three forty-five for the afternoon departure. In the meantime enjoy your day in Harwich lads," he said, as he suspiciously surveyed the shifty characters within the van with his torch. "A word of advice," he offered, "behave yourselves, because the coppers around here don't take kindly to trouble-makers." So that was what we were, I thought. I sometimes wondered …

He pointed to the dock entrance and informed us, "There's a café just around the corner called Sid's Café. It's a bit rough, but it's okay. All the port lads use it, and it's reasonably cheap."

As we sat forlornly in the fume-filled café, with the stench of cigarette smoke and burned bacon permeating the room, I felt reasonably content. The greasy fry up, supplemented by a big mug of steaming coffee and a smoke, certainly hit the spot, and I was beginning to feel more relaxed. I turned to the others. "Well," I said, just to make conversation, "it's still early, so what are we going to do now?"

"Downing his coffee, Stu grinned and repeated his earlier suggestion, "I could fetch my guitar and give you a quick burst of *Sitting on the Dock of the Bay*." The response was short and brutal, and he chuckled to himself at having got the reaction he had wanted.

Someone sitting at the next table overheard our little repartee, and piped in. "You've got a guitar then, have you mate? Tell me, do you know any Lonnie Donegan songs?" I didn't have the heart to tell him …

It was with great excitement that we finally rolled down the loading ramp into the bowels of the Viking III. Ascending the stairs that led to the top decks, we happily chatted among ourselves like excited kids on a school outing, which wasn't far off the mark, for none of us had been outside the confines of Old Blighty before, and we were very excited at the prospect of every knew experience, and the anticipation of what the next few weeks would offer us. On reaching the main deck area we made our way to the reception desk where Joey produced the travel tickets and enquired about the whereabouts of our cabin. The receptionist scanned the tickets over the top of his glasses, then informed us, with an overbearing air of officialdom, "There is no cabin allocated to these tickets".

"No cabin..?" Joey wailed. "Then where the fuck do we get our heads down for the night?"

The official frostily informed us. "These tickets are just for basic travel, and as such you'll be allowed to use the reclining seats at the rear of the ship," he pointed in the general direction of the stump end, "and you will of course be given a blanket to keep warm during the night."

"A seat and an effing blanket!" Joey cried, clearly rankled, as indeed were we all. Stuart then joined in to berate the man, "I haven't had a kip now for almost two days, and I'm telling you mush, I'm bloody knackered, and you're telling us we have to sleep in a bleeding seat! You're having me on, aren't you!"

The shaking of the official's head clearly indicated that he wasn't.

"At least they're giving us a blanket," I said cheerily, "it shouldn't be too bad, lads!"

"Bollocks to that!" Joey snarled. Taking control of his temper and his frustration, I could see from the cunning glint of his eyes that his mind was beginning to stir up some kind of devilment. "Let's sit at that table by the bar," he said, pointing, "because I've got a plan ..." Being Joey, he would have, I thought. As we sat down, he nodded his head towards the bar and eyed Stuart, "Nip to the bar and get a round in, will you Stu."

"What did your last slave die of, you grinning git," chuckled the moon-faced one, as he left for the bar. He was back in double quick time, looking somewhat put-out.

"Where's the beer?" we all asked, wondering what was wrong.

"I can't get any because I don't have any German money. They're called marks, or summat like that. I gave the bloke a pound note but he wouldn't take it." He seemed quite crestfallen.

"Wouldn't take it!" Joey nearly exploded. "We're still in frigging England aren't we!" he snarled. "Fucking marks indeed!" So we all set off once more for the reception desk, to find out where we could change our cash.

The receptionist we had spoken to earlier saw us coming, and quickly decided he had pressing business elsewhere, leaving his assistant to our mercy. This young man courteously pointed in the direction of the Bureau de Change or whatever they call it in Kraut, where I emptied my pockets of the princely sum of nine pounds four shilling and sixpence, which was all the money I had. This was then exchanged for what looked like differing coloured soap coupons and a handful of coins. "Shit, is that all?" I enquired of the cashier, feeling even poorer than I had before.

"Yes, that's all there is," she answered in the affirmative.

She even gave me a smile when I asked "Are you sure, because it certainly doesn't look much to me!"

"Well, that depends on how long you are going to be in Germany," she answered politely.

"Six weeks," I informed her, which brought an even wider smile to her face.

"Then you're right," she confirmed my doubts, chuckling quietly. "It's certainly not enough for six weeks."

"Aha!" I said, seeing an opportunity to impress, and perhaps land a cosy crossing with this delectable damsel, "but we'll be earning money when we're over there, playing the dancehalls," I told her. "We're a group. The famous Charters from Chester," I informed her with some small pride in my voice."

Judging by her glazed expression, I would have to say that she was less than impressed. I could hardly blame her considering the fact that the apparition standing before her was a somewhat dishevelled character who hadn't slept for twenty-four hours and had spent that time cramped inside an old van with three other layabouts, and now stared at her like a simpleton claiming fame and fortune, when both commodities were so obviously not part of my luggage. I also had to concede that The Charters were really only famous in Chester, and hardly likely to raise eyebrows on a North Sea ferry-crossing.

With our money changed it was back to the bar. "Four beers, my good man," Stu aristocratically ordered, flourishing a fifty mark note he nonchalantly held between two fingers.

I turned to Joey, and demanded to know what his cunning plan was. "Well, I don't know about you lot, but I'm not kipping in a seat tonight, blanket or no blanket. The way I see it is this …," he furtively looked around to check that nobody overheard us, then leaned forward across the table, bridging the gap between us, and four heads closed to join in the conspiracy, as he continued. "Looking around, I'd say that this ship is hardly full, so there must be some empty cabins. It stands to reason, doesn't it?" We all nodded our heads in silent agreement, and not a little admiration for such astute power of observation, already knowing where he was heading, and thinking that this was the best idea the grinning idiot had had all day.

He lowered his voice. "As soon as we leave port, we'll go and have a look-see for one," he said. "Agreed?" It was like the four musketeers, one for all and all for one, but our answer was drowned by the sharp blast of the ships horn and the rumbling sound of the engines bursting into life and making the whole ship vibrate so our glasses danced precariously towards the edge of the table where we quickly rescued them before they fell off. I looked at my watch. We were right on time. "Keep an eye on my beer, will you," I told them, "I'm just nipping out on the deck to have a look."

The sky was grey and leaded as we made our way out of the harbour. The seagulls wheeled and dived, emanating their mournful cries, as I pulled up the collar of my donkey jacket to ward off the chill in the air. I must have spent several minutes out on deck lost in my thoughts. We finally made the open sea and the ship began to rise and fall with the waves. It was darker by then, and I watched the twinkling lights of Harwich slowly fading into the distance. I shivered with the cold and the excitement of the adventure we had embarked upon, and wondered what it held in store for us. Then, realising that this was the very first time I was to experience crossing a large expanse of water – going on the Royal Iris across the Mersey from Birkenhead to Liverpool didn't really count – I looked back at the fading outline of the coast, and suddenly felt a sense of freedom coursing through me, making me feel warm and content in spite of the chilly sea breeze that was getting colder by the minute.

I rejoined the others back in the warmth of the bar, and found a new beer placed next to my half-full glass. Feeling somewhat elated after my time alone on the deck, I raised the half to my lips and toasted the four of us, "Cheers, lads. Here's to a good trip, and a great adventure!" I said, with genuine enthusiasm, feeling uncharacteristically optimistic and happy.

Nobody seemed too inclined to join in my enthusiasm, but they all took a swallow for show, hardly needing an excuse for that.

"What was it like out there?" enquired Stu.

"Cold, mate!" I replied. "Not to put too fine a point on it, it was bleeding freezing!"

The bar was quickly filling up, mostly with British squaddies returning to their bases in Germany. They were all in boisterous mood, and obviously up to sinking a few brews in what was left of their leave. Ten minutes later, Joey decided it was time to put his deviously cunning plan into action. "Right, grab your bags, and let's find ourselves some accommodation for the night," he said, and lurked off, with the rest of us bringing up the rearguard behind him.

As it turned out, Joey's reasoning had been sound, and there were a number of empty cabins just waiting for us to fill them. So, with no further ado, we dived into the one closest to the bar, reasoning that it would be easier to find after a night on the beer, which was the logical outcome for the evening before us. I flung myself on the nearest bunk and closed my eyes as I listened to the rumbling of the engines below, and the excited chatter of the others. I don't know how long I lay there, but I noticed that I was in the process of dozing off. The fact that the voices around me gradually calmed, indicated that the others were also enjoying their moment of peace. After all we had been through, the cosy warmth of the cabin and the soft inviting mattresses had obviously gone a long way towards inducing this state of mind,.

I was suddenly disturbed from my slumber by Dave's voice asking our red-nosed hero, "Hey, Joe, I've just been thinking." That alone was worth waking up for, because our eminent bass player was not too well known for thought. "What if someone finds us in here?"

Joey wasn't concerned. It took more to put a frown of worry on that lad's face. Considering the size of his konk, there wouldn't have been any room for one, anyway. "If anyone looks in," he surmised, "they'll just see our coats and luggage and think that we've booked a cabin," he said, completely unfazed.

"Ah, but," Dave moaned on, "what if they've got a passenger list, and they ask our names and we're not on it?" That lad was easily worried when away from the safe security of Greenfield's boudoirs.

Stretching himself and yawning, Stu admitted, "He's got a point there, you know, Joe."

Clearly getting irritated, not least because they'd brought him out of his beauty sleep, of which he was understandably in deep need, Joey acidly berated them. "What's the matter with you daft sods? What's the worst they can do to us, anyway, make us walk the fucking plank?

"Or," I pointed out, pausing for effect, and stating the obvious, "they can tell us to get our sorry arses out of here and back to the seats and blankets."

"Precisely!" said Joey with an air of triumph. "So stop whining." He seemed to consider his options for a moment, then jumped out of his bunk, full of spunk again. "Let's go to the bar," he demanded, rather than suggested, "The barman told me they've got a bit of a band on, so we can see if they're any good, and have a few pints." He grabbed Stu by his straggly hair and eased him out of the bunk, "So move yourself, you lazy sod," he said, "it's your frigging round!"

"No it isn't!" howled Stu in anguish. "I've already got the first two in. It's your round now you grinning git, so put your hand in your own pocket for once, will you, and find the cash."

We had a convivial evening of mirth, mayhem, music and laughter. Why, after some encouragement from the squaddies, I even indulged in a few glasses of schnapps. As the hours passed I began to feel a little woozy. In fact, I was as tired as a newt, and began to mumble nonsense, in a heavily slurred voice. So I staggered to my feet, wished everyone in the company a good night and headed unsteadily towards the cabin, followed by the chiding comments and ribald laughter of the others ringing in my ears, as I fought my way in a beeline in an attempt to reach my destination safely, like a cork in a stormy ocean, rocking all over the place and completely in the hands of fate and the elements, and with neither succour nor pity forthcoming from the shipmates I had left behind at the bar. The bastards!

My desperate departure was certainly down to too much beer, and too many schnapps, but the rolling of the ship didn't exactly help either, and it was obvious to anyone following my slow progress that I didn't have sea legs. I literally fell into the cabin when I finally reached it, and crawled unto my bunk, then fell into a comatose state of sleep, with only the constant throbbing of the ships engines to keep me company.

Getting from A to B
(eventually)

I was awakened from my deep slumber by the resounding sound of the ship's fog horn. Rubbing my eyes and gingerly easing m head from side to side in an attempt to get back to the land of the living, I slowly prised myself into the sitting position on the edge of the bunk. Still basically half-asleep, I was confronted by the sight of Stu pulling a yellow and black shirt over his ample body. "Shit, Stuart!" I managed, "You look like a frigging wasp!"

He chuckled to himself, and a broad grin spread across his moon-like features. "So you are alive then," he said. "I was really beginning to wonder, because you looked like death just now."

Actually feeling like death warmed up, I could understand his comments, for I didn't for the life of me know which was throbbing the most, the ships engines or the inside of my head. I found out a few minutes later when the engines suddenly stopped, whereas the pistons inside my head remorselessly kept pounding away at full throttle.

My self-pitying remorse was interrupted by Dave, who excitedly informed us that he could see land. This announcement had us all scrambling to the cabin window to look for ourselves. Despite the grey murk of the early morning, we could see buildings and the shadowy outlines of dock cranes in the distance, as we slowly approached the harbour.

"Frauleins, here we come!" Joey gleefully exclaimed. "Get the girls ready for The Charters, 'cos here we come!" How he could possibly think of sex whilst hopping around the tight confines of the cabin on one foot while trying to get his socks on, was a mystery to me, but then Joey was a mystery to everyone, and *always* had sex on his mind, regardless.

I slumped back on the bunk and closed my eyes to ward off the pain inside my head, then whispered a plea to Joey "Give your voice a rest, will you Joey," I begged, "I've got a splitting headache here."

"Bollocks!" exclaimed the red-nosed one, even louder, grinning at my pain and enjoying it, there isn't a headache big enough to fill that big fat head of yours!"

"Sod off, you red-nosed bugger!" I cursed with a vengeance, but the words only came out in a hoarse and miserable whimper.

We rolled off the ferry at seven o'clock in the morning and drove into a swirling mist that enveloped the port of Bremerhaven. We passed through the passport control and customs without any problem, but were then waved down by the police as we reached the dock exit. "Now what!" moaned Joey, to nobody in particular. He was obviously irritated by this new delay, for we were all eager to press on with the journey, and there was still a helluva long way to go.

We were confronted by four, somewhat bored, policemen. One checked the front of the vehicle, another controlled the tax disc, while the other two gave the bodywork a cursory glance and nonchalantly kicked at the tyres. When there were no more tyres to kick, one of them indicated that Joey should open his window. "Papers and documents please," he was asked in an accent taken right out of a war film from the fifties. Joey duly complied with this request.

With a sharp intake of breath, Dave exclaimed with some concern in his voice, "Shit, they're all wearing guns!"

"Maybe they're the SS Dock Korps," sniggered Stu in his nasal Scouse dialect. He had a special love/hate relationship to all things German – he loved to hate them, but liked even better to mimic and mock them, and all their ways.

"Shut your cake hole, Stuart, or you'll have us all arrested!" I hissed.

It turned out that the paperwork was in order, and Joey took the opportunity to ask for directions.

"Schleswig?" one policeman said, apparently quite impressed. "That is quite a long way to drive." Then he gave us the gist of which way to take out of the port to get us moving in the general direction of where we wanted to go. It was just as well, because we didn't have a clue which way to go, and the plethora of German signposts were very confusing, to say the least.

As he watched them through the van windows, Dave was heard to grumble, "It's like being in a foreign country, isn't it." His innocent boyish face couldn't hide the fact that he found it hard to accept the fact that he actually was in a foreign county.

"It is a foreign country you dozy bugger!" Joey sneered at him, as he stared ahead, concentrating hard to find the way.

After half an hour or so, our red-nosed leader pulled up on the outskirts of a small village, and began to rummage through the contents of the glove compartment. "Ah, here it is!" he said in triumph, and not a little relief. He brought out a rather tatty map that was held together with tape, and looked decidedly dog-eared. He then proceeded to lay the map across the steering wheel and stared at it blankly, before coming with the comforting words, "Where the fuck are we?"

The unexpected revelation that the leader in whom we had placed our unquestioning trust had led us into the wilderness instead of to the land of milk and honey, did not do a lot for the morale of the rest of the van inmates, who were wont to rely on Joey for inspirational leadership. Sadly, at this vulnerable stage of our adventure, it was not forthcoming, something that was more than evident by observing how his blank face became even blanker by the minute. After considering our predicament for some time, concentrating hard, he finally came to a conclusion. "We're lost!" he wailed.

"Stop being so bloody melodramatic," I told him melodramatically. "We've got a map, so all we need to do is find out where we are now, and take it from there." Peering ahead, I could just make out a signpost by the roadside. I managed to read out the letters on it. "There you go," I said, bucking up considerably. "This place is called Bremervorde." I turned towards the leader of the expedition fretting in the driver's seat next to me, and asked if he could find it on the map.

Joey scanned the map again. "Yeah, got it!" he gleefully yelped, suddenly wreathed in smiles of relief.

"There you are," I told him, feeling quite pleased with myself, "that wasn't too hard, now was it?" I patronised him with a comforting pat on his head.

"I wasn't really worried," he smirked, "'cos I had a rough idea of where we were going."

"Did you?" asked Dave, all wide-eyed innocence, and already impressed by Joey's claim.

"No you didn't, you lying bugger!" Stu sniggered from the back.

"I did, really!" insisted Joey, "I was only having you on."

"Yeah, right!" came the response from the two of us with brains enough to know, while Dave stayed silent as he looked from one to the other with a dim expression on his face, trying to figure out what this was all about. I dare say, he's still thinking about it, now.

"The way I see it," Joey said, already regaining his confidence and grinning broadly, "if we stay on this road, we'll reach a town called Stade." He was engrossed in the map as he spoke, with his finger scouting the trail we were to follow. "Then we get to a place called Stadersand Holm, and then ..." His voice trailed off momentarily, before he continued, more uncertain now, "then we reach this blue wiggly thing ..."

"Blue wiggly thing!" I almost chocked in disbelief, amazed by what I had just heard. "What blue wiggly thing?" I grabbed the map from him, to see for myself.

"There," he said, stabbing his finger at it to show me.

I looked at where his grubby finger pointed, and laughed aloud. Then I howled at him, "It's a river, you daft dick!" I shook my head in pity as I studied the map, and mumbled, "A blue wiggly thing, indeed …" Then I found it again, and informed all and sundry that it was the Elbe river. "I suppose we'll just have to cross that problem when we get to it," I said, and got a short chuckle for my trouble from Stuart, who was the only one with half a brain enough to understand my little joke, as he sat in the back seat, happily strumming away on his guitar.

We pressed on safe in the knowledge that we were at least heading in the right direction, and that we had one among us who at least knew the difference between a river and the town hall clock.

As the map had indicated, we eventually came to a ferry-crossing. This is when new doubts began to form in my mind, for this stretch of water seemed a lot narrower than the river Elbe appeared to be on Joey's crumpled old road map. None-theless, we knew we had to cross a stretch of water to continue our journey, and there was certainly a stretch of water before us, so …

As we rolled on to the flat ferry and parked where a ferry-man had ushered us, he approached us for the twenty mark ferry fare. "Twenty marks!" Joey moaned loudly. "That's what, over two frigging quid!" he decided. "I reckon we could clear this bit of water with a good run at it with the van, no problem, and save the money." It was only the fact that we were boxed in by other vehicles that stopped him from trying.

Apart from the wheelhouse, there was a smallish cabin area that served snacks and coffee. I was gagging for a brew and informed the others that the coffee was on me. So we sat at a table supping our steaming coffee and enjoying a smoke while we discussed the journey we had made so far. "Not too bad, I suppose," Stu laconically admitted, "apart from this ginger sod here, getting us lost, the useless bugger!"

Joey was going to let these cutting remarks go, but then changed his mind, and decided to berate us after all. "It's alright for you bastards. All you've got to do is sit there and take the piss. It's me that has to do all the frigging driving and has to concentrate on the road, while you lazy buggers nod off, because none of you idiots can drive!"

This was a very relevant point indeed, as none of us knew the arse-end from the tit of a car, and would even have problems starting one up. So with discretion being the better part of valour, we decided to stop trading insults with the Man of the Day, and allow him time to simmer down. This was always a sensible attitude to take when confronted with Joey's nose getting redder than usual, which was always a bad sign and a luminous and potent warning.

Joey was the kind of bloke who was up and down like a yo-yo, and could threaten you with death and damnation one moment, and be your friend for life the next. "D'ya know," he said, by now calm and content, "considering the short stretch of water we're supposed to cross, we've been on board this ferry for a hell of a long time."

Old Red Nose was right; it did seem to be taking its time across. Emerging from the cabin, the sight that met us smacked us right between the eyes, and we stood transfixed as we stared about us. For, looking around, we could just about make out the sight of land far in the distance on both sides of the ferry.

None of us said a word. We didn't need to; we could see our own dismay reflected on the faces of the others as we stood there and stared, open-mouthed and wide-eyed, feeling dejection and apathy creeping over us.

However, half an hour later, the ferry pulled into its terminal, which provoked the phrase that had been much-used of late, "Now where the fuck are we …?"

Feeling the burden of leadership weighing heavily on his shoulders, Joey decided to take control. "I'll check the map when we get back in the van," he told us with an air of cool assurance and control, that was supposedly meant to make us relax the tension that had been building up inside us, for we were certainly concerned, and not a little worried, about what we had now managed to dump into.

As it transpired, we had landed at a place called Gluckstadt. Studying the map with an air of new-found confidence, Joey airily announced, "We've got to head for Itzehoe and follow the road to Rendsburg, and then it's straight on to Schleswig." He looked up with a smug expression on his face. "It couldn't be easier, now could it?"

Perhaps, I thought to myself, but with your driving and sense of direction, it's a knocking bet that there'll be a few more twists and turns and we'll probably end up in Gibraltar before we're finished. I loved the sad sod, but had lost all faith in his navigational skills. My thoughts were interrupted by Dave, who demanded to know just where this Schleswig place was.

I only hoped he had finally managed to register the fact that our little excursion was to Germany and not Skegness, for by now, it was more than apparent that he had no idea at all about anything that did not have some bearing on the local antics of the Greenfield houries. I'm sure that if we had told him that Schelswig was in Cumbria, he would have accepted that knowledge as fact, then asked why they all spoke so funny there, when we finally arrived. Whatever was happening in David's head, it wasn't much.

Stabbing his finger at the map, and holding it up for him to see, Joey acidly informed him, "There!"

"Bloody hell," exclaimed the Greenfield Stud, "that's miles away from here!" Then he turned his innocent eyes on Joey, suddenly uncertain, after all. "Isn't it …?"

Taking a sudden interest, Stuart piped up, "Exactly how many miles is it, Joe?"

By using the scale on the map and his finger to measure the distance, Joey concentrated hard, biting his lips to give added inspiration as he worked out the mathematics, and finally decided that it was roughly ninety kilometres.

"Kilometres?" I didn't ask you to tell me in effing continental lingo!" Stu wasn't happy with the answer. "Now, tell me in miles?"

Joey counted on his fingers, rolled his eyes and stared at the roof of the van in deep concentration as he grappled with this new problem. "As near as damn it, I'd say about sixty miles," he decided. "That's not so bad," he said, sounding pleased with himself. "We'll be there in about an hour or so."

So with renewed faith in our leader and van driver, we set off on the last leg of our momentous journey, with a new air of optimism and a modicum of cheerfulness. Unbeknown to us however, somewhere along the way, we managed to take a wrong turn. This first became apparent when we found ourselves approaching a sizable town called Neumunster. I tapped Joey on the shoulder. "Pull over a minute, will you," I began, "I think …" but got no further.

A sudden screeching of tyres as the van slammed to a sharp and hazardous halt and almost forced me through the windscreen, was followed by a manic scream from our driver. "Now what!!" he snarled. "What the fuck's up now?" He was not a happy red-head!

Looking at the map, I tried to calm him. "It's not a complete disaster mate, but I think we've missed the road to Rendsburg," I held the map up for him. "See …?"

After a couple of minutes of grumbling and moaning, we finally had a bit of luck, for our eyes fell on a huge road sign a hundred yards away, that pointed the way to the Autobahn and informed us that this was just a couple of kilometres down the road from where we were. The towns on it read: Kiel, Rendsburg, Flensburg, and most importantly, Schleswig (Nord).

"That's where we're going!" we all shouted in unison, suddenly feeling elated, and we set off again as though we truly were on a mission to destiny, for after having negotiated what seemed to be hundreds of minor roads before eventually arriving at this point, we could finally travel with some degree of confidence, and we now felt that even Joey, bless him, could not get lost on an Autobahn. Could he …?

We roared down the Autobahn making good time, and now in such a good mood, knowing that we were finally coming to the end of our long and arduous journey, that we were actually singing with gusto. Then Stuart's voice trailed off in the middle of *Nine Green Bottles,* and broke off both the song and the exhilaration with the words, "Hei, Joe," he said, with some concern, "shouldn't we be going north …?"

After the initial reaction at this discovery, which, although quite understandable under the circumstances is best forgotten, we drove in simmering silence for a few more miles before we found a turn-off that enabled us to change our direction and return the way we had come. There was no more singing on the way back, and the only sound came from the screaming frustration we heard within our own heads.

An hour or so later we came across road signs for Schleswig: 1000m … 500m … 200m … There!

"There it is, Joe!" we shouted excitedly, our frustration forgotten.

"Yeah, I can see it, you morons," he confirmed in his own charming way, fed up and surly as he was. "Do you think I'm blind or daft or something?"

Well, after all we had been through, there was certainly an answer to that, but none of us had the temerity to respond; not now when we were so close to our destination. Knowing him, he was likely to kick us all out to walk the rest of the way, just to make a point.

"Shit!" Joey cursed. "According to that last sign there's still five kilometres to Schleswig." We were all tired, and nobody said a word, disappointed that we weren't closer, but glad that we were at least that close.

Dusk was coming on as we came off the feeder road, and we could see the lights of Schleswig coming on, as though to welcome us at the end of our long journey. "I wonder where this place is, we're going to?" asked Joe to nobody in particular.

Stu took up the challenge by telling him to stop driving around in circles, which he had by now been doing for some time, and to ask someone for directions, instead. That didn't go down too well in Joey's present state of mind. "That's brilliant, that is, Einstein," he sneered. "And just how long have you been able to converse in frigging German, Stuart?" Stu had to admit that he couldn't. "Well, there you are then!" snarled Joe. "Well, I'll let you into a little secret, mate. I frigging well fucking can't either, so what's the point of stopping to ask someone?"

So we continued to drive aimlessly around in circles, straining our eyes and hoping to spot something that might actually look like a dancehall. My frustration finally boiled over, and I snarled, "Joey, give me that piece of paper with the address on it, because this is the fifth time we've gone round that bloody roundabout!"

We found someone walking along the pavement, and I rolled down the window and showed him the piece of paper. He pointed out the building for us, and informed us, "It is only one hundred metres, no more. There, it is, on the right, okay?"

"Danke," I said, proud to be showing off my lingual abilities to the others, who no doubt didn't even know that word, which was the only one I had in my vocabulary.

"No problem," he replied, and continued on his way.

I turned to Joey, with a smug and arrogant look on my face. "There you are, mate. That wasn't too difficult, now was it?"

Grinning wickedly, he suggested that I stick my head up another part of my anatomy to see the view, before we gently rolled up before a large and imposing building which was in complete darkness, apart from the street-level bar that was nicely lit up and obviously open for business. I suppose we must have stayed in the van for ten minutes or so, relaxing with a smoke and savouring the moment – we had finally made it!

There had certainly been times during the previous day or two when we had had serious doubts that we would ever arrive. But here we were. Finally ...

Joey took charge, as was his wont. He stubbed out his cigarette and casually tossed it out of the window. "Well," he said, "are we going to sit here all night, or are we going to show our faces?" So we tiredly climbed out of the van, stretching our cramped muscles, and mounted the short flight of steps leading to the main door, where Joey turned to inform us, "You lot leave the talking to me."

"God help us!" muttered Stuart under his breath.

"I heard that, you fat bugger," Joey calmly informed him.

"Oh, charming!" chuckled Stu, who nothing, and nobody could faze.

The general noise inside stopped as we swung open the door and entered to find all eyes fastened on us, apparently unsure of what to make of the four dysfunctional, somewhat scruffy characters who had suddenly invaded their premises.

"Evening all," Joey cheerfully called out to the general assembly, "we're the …"

He didn't have time to finish. A man in his fifties rose from a table and called back, interrupting him in mid-sentence. "Good evening, gentlemen!" he called, in perfect English. He was obviously expecting us, and actually seemed pleased to see us. "My name is Ernst Schmidt and I am the owner of this establishment," he introduced himself. "And you must be The Charters, from England," he said, taking it for granted. No doubt he was used to dishevelled apparitions arriving on his doorstep claiming to be musicians but looking more like something the cat dragged in on a wet night. "We've been waiting for you to make an appearance," he told us with a smile. "Welcome, welcome." He shook our hands in turn. "Let me get you all a drink," he offered.

"If it's okay with you, Mr. Schmidt, we should be getting the gear and luggage into the building first," we told him, then hurriedly added, "We'll enjoy the drink later," lest he should forget.

Her Schmidt clicked his fingers, and called to two younger men who were drinking by the bar. "Heinz, Peter, help the boys with their equipment," he ordered. He then turned towards a grey-faced, balding man behind the bar, Otto by name. "You go with them," he told him, "and show them where to put it all, then show them to their living quarters." And they all scuttled off to do as they had been told, as though their lives depended on it, which may very well have been the case.

Otto led us up the stairs to the dancehall, with a microphone-stand in one hand and a case in the other, as he cheerfully repeated, "The Beatles! Liverpool!" like a psychedelic on speed. It was quite unnerving, I must admit, being led through the dark corridors of this imposing old building, in a strange town, in a strange country filled with what I felt were old Nazis with a collective chip on their shoulders, by some obviously demented character, gleefully repeating "Beatles! Liverpool!" over and again, like the giant up the beanstalk fe-fi-fo-fumming at the prospect of new blood. It reminded me of one of those old Vincent Price films, but now I was in it myself, and not too happy about it.

The dancehall was quite spacious. It had a raised stage at one end, with tables and chairs arranged around the edge, and had another carpeted seating area at the other end, where a large window allowed us a view into the night outside. Surveying the general ambience of the place, we all agreed that this looked okay. "It'll look even better when it's full of people drinking and dancing," Joey enthused. He was obviously delighted with himself for having got this gig for us.

With all the gear in place, we thanked Heinz and Peter for their help, whilst Otto the barman, still in a happy and agitated state of mind, kept muttering "The Beatles … Liverpool …" and didn't seem to want to be interrupted in whatever thoughts were claiming his attention. Whatever they were, the way he was handling them, made us somewhat uneasy. "Come gentlemen," coaxed Otto, "and I will show you to your rooms."

We followed him down a narrow passage, all of us curious to see our living quarters, and uncertain what to expect. "Here you are," he said, smiling and rubbing his hands together, as though gleefully anticipating our reaction. He handed us the key to the outside door, bowed slightly, then stumped off down the wooden stairs, repeating over and over, "The Beatles …! Liverpool …! The Beatles …! Liverpool …!" until he was thankfully, finally out of earshot.

"There's something wrong with that bloke," Dave observed, as though he had suddenly become aware of him. It was a revelation in itself that he had actually noticed anything at all, as his normal state of mind was one of whimsical vacuum. He didn't look too comfortable, and was probably wishing he had stayed at home with his harem. And who could blame him?

"You might be right," Stu concurred. "On the other hand, perhaps he's just pleased to see us."

"Oh, aye?" sneered Joey. "The soft bugger looks a bit simple if you ask me." Observant as always.

What was simple however, were our living quarters. They were dark and dingy, and had definitely seen better days, with damp-stained wallpaper hanging forlornly off the walls here, there, and almost everywhere. We spent several moments staring in miserable disbelief at what confronted us, and we were undoubtedly in a state of shock. The silence was eventually broken by Stuart. "I wasn't exactly expecting the Ritz, but this is completely beyond belief!"

"Right," I said, coming to my senses, "I'm bagging the anteroom, because I'm not kipping in here with you lot, having to endure your snuffling, snoring and farting all night." And with that, I flung my gear in, and threw myself on the lumpy cast-iron bed to the unmusical sound of twanging springs. I stared despondently around the sparsely furnished room and frowned at the cracks in the ceiling, and felt depression claiming me.

I knew from the moaning and grumbling I could hear from the larger room, that the others were sharing my misgivings. My self-pity was interrupted by the strident voice of David, the Greenfield Jockey, howling like a vestal virgin who's pricked herself, "Joey, come here and look at the state of this fucking wash room, will you!" The panic and disgust in his clarion call made us all respond, and what a sight it was that greeted us there!

The wash-basin was cracked and engrained green. The cold tap couldn't be turned off, whereas the hot tap didn't even have a turning key to turn it either on or off. The mirror was so cracked and mouldy that we could hardly see our reflections in it, which was just as well under the circumstances, because we were not looking too good any of us. But worst of all was the toilet. The chain was lying on the floor in an unpleasant puddle, and the contents of the bowl defied description. Not to put too fine a point on it, it was absolutely disgusting! We shook our heads in disbelief. After a particularly fraught and tiring day, this really curled our tonsils.

We sat on the beds, totally disenchanted, inhaling deeply from cigarettes that had somehow all been lit simultaneously, deep in our own thoughts, dejected and miserable as hell, without a word uttered. As usual, it was Joey who pulled us out of our lethargy. "Right!" he snapped, jumping to his feet and looking determined. "Let's go to the bar," he ordered. "I could murder a beer!" By the looks of him, that wasn't all he could murder. "And I'm hungry enough to eat a scabby rat!" he informed us.

"Well you won't have a problem finding one here," Stu mumbled, as he stared disconsolately at the grease-stained floor.

"What about that frigging toilet, Joe?" whined Dave. He had already pissed in the sink, presumably thinking that it was more hygienic. "I'm not sitting down on that thing," he informed all who cared to listen, "I'd probably get the bloody scurvy!"

"And the rest of us wouldn't, eh?" chuckled Joey. "You've obviously never worked on a building site, mate. Compared to some of those karzies, this is shit heaven!"

He noticed David's forlorn look, and decided he needed some encouragement. He patted him on the back. "Look, if it makes you feel any better, I'll have a word about it, and failing that, I'll fix the bleeding thing myself. So come on, shift yourselves and let's get to the bar."

Although the place had filled up quite considerably since our arrival, our second appearance in the bar didn't have the same effect as our first entrance, and we only got the odd passing glance from one or two of the new arrivals. Otto the barman positively glowed when he spotted us. "Beer, gentlemen?" he asked and got four nods in reply.

We found an empty table and sat down to survey the scene and become acclimatised. "It looks like this place has been done up recently," Joey remarked, with a nod of approval.

"Pity they didn't do our rooms at the same time," moaned Stu the Wasp, still clad in his yellow and black striped shirt.

"Aye, and that bleeding bog!" Dave still hadn't come over the shock. "I've never seen anything like it in my life," he moaned, "It's … it's …"

Before he could find the words to describe his disgust, I broke in. "Okay, Dave. Spare us all the graphic details," I begged him, simply not wanting to be reminded of what lay in wait for us when we returned to our penthouse suite. "We've all seen it, you know," I reminded him.

Otto arrived and plonked four beers down on the table, then found a beer mat and marked down four lines on it "What was all that about?" Stu enquired when he had gone. He was puzzled and worried, and the combination of the two showing on his moony face wasn't a pretty sight.

"He's just making a note of how many beers we have," Joey, the man of the world, informed him. He turned to me with a scowl on his face. "So don't you go confusing the issue by doing all your little doodles all over the mats like you usually do. That'll totally screw up old Otto trying to keep tabs on us."

Just then Ernst entered the bar and came up to us smiling. "You must be hungry after travelling all day," he stated, "would you like something to eat?"

"Not half!" I said, patting my stomach and ready to eat a horse. "What have you got?"

"How does roast chicken and chips sound?" asked our smiling host. We all nodded in agreement, and he clicked his fingers at Otto and indicated the order.

"How much?" asked wily Joey, suddenly wary, as though he had been around the canal a time or two before, and knew the score.

Ernst held up the flat palms of his hands and, smiling sweetly, he shook his head. "Nothing, my friend. The meal is on me," he told us. "Enjoy it!" It might have been the effect of his wartime service, but there was definitely a hint of Gestapo in the command, enough to make me want to whimper "I will! I will!"

After finishing off the repast, which I actually did enjoy, and after several more rounds of beer, I began to feel much more relaxed. Even the prospect of bedding down in the dive upstairs no longer seemed quite so daunting. The bar regulars were drinking with gusto, and much banter and laughter filled the cosy oasis and gave it warmth. The jukebox merrily blared out the pop songs of the day. I remember one particular Sandie Shaw record which seemed to be played over and over again. The thing was, that shoeless Sandie was singing in German, which I found quite unnerving.

After we'd heard the same song about twenty times, Joey wondered if there was anything else in the juke, to which Stuart chuckled, and piped up with the suggestion that we'd probably find the Horst Wessell song there, along with numerous Werhmacht marching songs from the war. We all fell about laughing at this piece of irrelevant wit, the booze inside us making it seem funnier than it probably was, when Stu sobered up sufficiently to inform us that he'd hated the Germans ever since he had been a nipper. We looked at him, wondering what had brought this on. "Well, the bleeding Luftwaffe bombed our chippie in Smithdown Road in Liverpool," he informed us, still obviously offended by the fact. We all broke down in tears of laughter at the thought of the Luftwaffe crossing the Channel in the dead of night to bomb a chip shop. I thought Joey was going to wet his pants, I really did. Our levity was however, quickly curtailed, when an older man, probably around the sixty mark, gave us a fixed stare, rose to his feet and came towards us.

"Fucking hell, Stu," Joe hissed, "you and your big gob. We've only been here five minutes and it looks like you're already about to start World War III!"

Stuart looked uncomfortable, probably expecting genuine trouble, and not in the mood for it after being cramped in the van for what felt like half a lifetime. The man came over and hovered above us. "Guten abend, gentlemen!" he hailed us. "I assume you are the group from England who are to play for us in the dancehall, yes?"

"Aye …" we warily replied, wondering what was coming, and not sure of what to say next.

He took a sip of his beer without taking his eyes off us, giving himself good time, as though he was unaware of the silence that had fallen upon our little group. "I could not help but overhear your comments about the records on the jukebox," he said, pronouncing it *yuk*, which somehow gave it a sinister air. "I particularly found your comments about the Horst Wessell song, and what you call the Werhmacht marching songs, interesting." He allowed his gaze to rest on each of us in turn as he spoke. "Although the war has been over for twenty years, the subject is still very much a sore subject here," he lectured us. "Your RAF bombers virtually erased the city of Kiel with blanket bombing. Many, many people were killed and horribly disfigured. It was a terrifying time for the "Volk" …"

Stuart interrupted him by jumping to his feet to harangue him. "Hang on mush," he said, a bit too loudly for my peace of mind, "you lot started the whole shooting match in the first place!" Stuart was an easy-going guy, who wouldn't say boo to a fly, but he didn't come from Liverpool without a temperament and the grit to back it up if he felt for it. "And while we're on the subject of blanket bombing, mate, I don't suppose those Scousers waiting in queue for their cod and chips were all that chuffed about it either!"

I looked around and saw the faces turned towards us. We had the undivided attention of the whole establishment, and I thought, for God's sake Stu, put a sock in it will you, before they lynch us.

But the veteran gave an overbearing smile, and shrugged. "Yes, of course," he graciously admitted. "I understand. But, happily we are friends now, yes?" He saluted us with the remnants of his drink splashing against the glass, as he spoke. "Please let me introduce myself," he said. "My name is Johann Strauss," he held up his hand to silence us. "Before you make the usual jokes about musical composers and suchlike, I would like to point out that I am neither a relative nor a musical composer, but only a humble toilet attendant."

Brightening considerably at this information, Stuart, who had already calmed down and seemed to have forgotten that he had just been about to give him a Scouse kiss, actually had the audacity to ask if he would care to bring his bristle brush and have a go at the bog in our quarters. If it wasn't the booze talking, it must have been desperation at the thought of what awaited him when the evening was over.

Our new-found friend shook his head regretfully, "I am afraid that is not on my list of duties," he informed us, and I quickly gave Stu a hefty kick on the leg to stop him saying what I saw was coming, and his *I only follow orders!* was broken off by a cry of pain instead. Herr Strauss continued unabashed, "but, let me get you more to drink," he said, and we gladly allowed ourselves to be talked into it, collaborating with the enemy and happy to do so.

We're Cool
– We Are the Kiddies

As I lay there, I couldn't be sure if I was awake or not, for the mental images were bouncing around in my subconscious, with Johan Strauss in SS uniform, standing with one foot in a filthy toilet bowl while conducting a Vienna-waltz with a bristle-headed toilet brush, and snarling at me, accusing me of bombing Dresden.

Thankfully, my eyes flickered open and the nightmare disappeared, only to be replaced by the depressing sight of my surroundings closing in on me, and my claustrophobia only alleviated by the pain in my head from the potent German beer I had enjoyed too much, just a few hours earlier.

The bedsprings creaked and groaned under my weight as I carefully manoeuvred my aching body into the sitting position, then held my head in my hands, swearing that I would never again drink. I felt terrible. Although I had experienced hangovers in my sinful past, this was the king of them all. When I noticed that I was still fully dressed, right down to my donkey- jacket and boots, I could understand why. I decided that I must have drunk the bar dry to be in such a state, and promised myself, never again!

I stared empty-eyed at the damp wall before me, and registered the writing and general graffiti scribbled on it. My eyes managed to focus – just – and I noticed one particular line of scribble, that may have been a cry for help, because it read: *We gotta get out of this place if it's the last thing we ever do!* I squinted closer to read the author's signature scribbled underneath it, and almost choked on the cigarette I had just about managed to light with my trembling hands, for it read *Eric Burdon Newcastle 1963.*

The Animals! Here? Eric Burdon had actually been sleeping in the same creaking bed that I had just spent the last few hours in, swinging between life and death? I managed a smile at the thought that a superstar like that had also had to live in such squalor. And look at him now! I decided that if he could take it, I'd have to do the same. I looked at his cry for help, written just a few years earlier, and told him, as though he was there before me, "Yes, Eric, I understand your feelings, mate, believe me!" Eric Burdon, eh! The Old Fellah was never going to believe me!

I was brought back by the sound of voices murmuring in the other room, and a guitar gingerly being strummed, then I winced as the pain in my head jarred at the sound of Joey's harsh voice screaming out, "Not bleeding *G*! How many times d'ya want telling? It's not frigging *G*!" followed by his maniacal laughter.

As I stumbled to my feet and went in to join the others, I noticed the enticing smell of beans being cooked, and saw Joey, like a good housewife, stirring the contents of a pan full to the brim of Heinz's finest, on a small primus stove. "That smells great, Joe," I said, suddenly wanting to live again. "For breakfast is it?"

He didn't look up. "No, you daft bugger," he replied, "I'm going to decorate the bloody wall with them!"

I bore on regardless. "Are we having them on toast, and all?" I asked hopefully.

"Toast?" he grumbled, "How am I going to do toast with nothing to toast the bread with, you chuff! What d'ya think this is, a frigging café?" He scooped the beans onto three tin dishes and stuck a slice of bread in each heap, along with a spoon. "There you go," he said with a smile on his face, "bon appetite or whatever it is in Kraut."

I tucked in with a vengeance for I was really hungry, and then had the temerity to ask the chef if he had remembered to bring some salt and pepper. He gave me a withering look that answered my question better than a thousand words. I finally finished my meal with a flourish by mopping up the juice with my bread, and sighed contentedly as I felt my body coming back to life. It was first then that I noticed that one of our comrades was missing; Dashing Dave, the Greenfield Gigolo and blonde-bleached bass, had not partaken of his breakfast with the rest of us and was nowhere to be seen. "Where's Dave?" I enquired, mildly curious.

"He went to find the toilet downstairs in the bar," Stu informed me. "He says he's not parking his bum on that cesspool in there," and he nodded his head towards the bathroom. I could understand him, and completely shared his views on that particular issue. Just then, our heterosexual hero made his appearance, which prompted Stuart to dash for the door to follow his performance.

Joey scraped the remnants from the pan and splashed it on a plate for Dave, who began to refill himself ravenously, while Joey then headed for the bathroom with the pan, informing us that he was going to rinse it out so we could use it to boil water for some coffee.

"Not that water, from in there!" I whined, showing panic on my creased face. "It's probably contaminated or even worse!"

"Give over!" The Nose snorted. "Once it's been boiled it'll kill off all the germs and stuff."

Fortunately, or unfortunately, depending on our point of view, we were saved from a dose of something-pretty-bad-and-German-at-that, for just as he returned with the pan filled to the brim and slopping over, we became aware of a phutt-phutting noise that emanated from the primus, and saw how the flame rapidly dwindled and went out.

Joey stared blankly at the apparatus, as though he couldn't believe his eyes. He cursed. "That's just fucking great!" There was a scowl on his face as he continued. "You know what this means, don't you?"

"No coffee?" I offered innocently, trying to suppress a smirk.

"Worse than that, mate! It means there'll be no beans for breakfast tomorrow, and we'll have to make do with corn-flakes."

Our bright bass player had actually been following the conversation, which was no mean feat in itself, and observed, "So what you're saying is that the choice is strictly limited." He was in the process of sorting out the contents of what looked like a medicine bag, as he spoke. This was quite impressive for a lad of his calibre, actually doing two things simultaneously; speaking and thinking at the same time. Perhaps there was hope for him after all.

Joey seemed quite crestfallen, and sat on his bed as though he had nothing more to live for. I hardly noticed, for I was completely fascinated as I watched as Dave took out pills, potions and medicines from his bag and placed them on a small table by his bed. Even Joey became interested as the table began to fill to overflowing. He looked on in mild amusement as Dave arranged it all in rows. "Bloody hell," he commented with some awe, "you've got more stuff there than Boots the Chemists!" He was impressed, and interested despite himself. "What's it all for?" he asked.

I wished he hadn't asked that question. Dave went through every medication, giving all the details, and it never seemed to end. *Kill me now!* I thought, begging for it to end, but he just droned on and on, apparently enjoying his little lecture, until he finally picked up one of the potions and informed us that "These are for piles." He didn't even blush when he said it.

Joey's face creased into a broad grin. "Well," he said, "that explains it then, doesn't it?"

"Explains what?" Dave asked, with a more puzzled expression on his face than usual.

Joey chuckled to himself, and the grin almost fell off his face, it was that wide. "Well, Stu always told us that you were a pain in the arse!" Then he almost fell on the floor laughing.

I decided to get my two pence in. "I can't see any rhino-powder in that mini-pharmacy of yours there, Dave," I observed.

"Rhino-powder?" he asked, looking blanker than usual.

"Yes, with you being a super stud, you must need something to support your staying power, and a bit of rhino is supposed to help."

A hint of pride introduced itself into his voice as he replied, "Believe me, I don't need anything like that to keep Willy happy." A twinkle came to his eyes. "Mind you, I did try once."

"Really?" I was interested in hearing more. "Did it do you any good, like making you even more rampant?" I enquired, wondering if that could be possible.

"Not really," he replied. "I'm horny enough as it is. But it did have one interesting side-effect after I'd taken it."

"Side-effect?" said Joey, becoming engrossed, and waiting for some sexual revelation that he could himself put to use. "What sort of side-effect?"

Dave suppressed a smile, and replied, "I kept getting this uncontrollable urge to charge at passing Land Rovers."

The lad couldn't have been as daft as I thought, after all, and obviously had his moments. But just then, Joey didn't. "Land Rovers?" The frown that had appeared on his face confirmed that he was lost. "What the frigging hell do Land Rovers have to do with it?" Then it dawned on him as he saw us laughing at him. "Okay," he acknowledged, "you got me. It's a joke, right?"

"Yes," Davis confirmed, "just like you, Big Nose!"

Just then Stuart returned from his sojourn in the bar's toilet-facilities. It must have done him good, because he was really chirpy. "Morning campers!" he greeted us. "What's up? Owt or nowt?" It turned out that he had enjoyed a chat in the bar, and could tell us that this particular dancehall was the only one for miles around, so there would be plenty of people coming to hear us play.

That was the good part. The bad part was that the owner was apparently a stickler for rules, and Stu related what he had been told: If we were late on stage we would be fined; if we smoked, drank or swore on stage, we would be fined; and more of the same. "Typical bloody Kraut!" Joey smirked, and gave a Nazi salute. "Jawohl herr Obersturmfuhrer!" he snapped, and clicked his heels. Getting back to being just Joey, he asked Stuart, "Haven't you got some good news to brighten our day?"

"Well, I was told that a lot of willing young frauleins usually come to the dances to check out the groups." I noticed how Dave began to take notice, and brighten up, even allowing his attention to wander away from his apothecary kit for a moment. "I was told that some of them like to fraternise with the English groups, with a bit of rumpy-bumpy," and he moved his hips in what was supposed to be a provocative movement, but didn't quite work out that way, with it being Stu doing the business.

By now, Dave was positively salivating. "Well, I hope there'll be enough to go around, so you lot will get a chance, too," he told us, making it quite clear that he would be first in line.

Joey, always full of himself and ready to take on any challenge, grinned and offered the odds. "I'll bet I get stuck in before any of you other wankers," he said, and was obviously confident that he would.

Before we could retort to this challenge, Stuart changed the subject, and brought up matters even more pressing. "And, for all you coffee-lovers," he told us, "there's a café just across the road." His news had us all scrambling down the stairs within seconds, and we soon sat at a table in the warmth of the little eatery with steaming coffee before us, finally out of the rat-hole that was our home. An added bonus for me was the beautiful young waitress who served us. I thought she was absolutely gorgeous. My eyes followed her wherever she moved, and I found myself smiling inanely at her like a love-sick teenager. I hardly dare think of what impression I must have given if she noticed me at all, because I must have looked like a simpleton with his tongue hanging out. I thought the coffee she brought me was the best I had ever tasted, just because she had brought it. I'd only been in the place five minutes, and I was already in love.

Apart from this, we all liked the place well enough to decide that we would eat breakfast there from then on. This decision was, in no small way, helped on its way by Joey declaring that he wasn't going to make any more baked beans for us. "I'm not going through that bloody performance every morning, while you lazy sods just sit and watch," he informed us.

"That's all very well," Stuart told him, "but looking at this menu here, it's not going to be cheap, and we haven't got much money with us, so we're going to have be careful with the cash," he pointed out.

Joey nodded his head in agreement, and a thoughtful expression filled his face. "You're right," he decided, "so we'll just spend it on the important things, like beer and cigarettes." Decisions! Decisions! All the time, decisions! But then, Joey was a true leader of men, and knew the priorities necessary to lead them.

"Hang on," said Stuart, suddenly coming to his senses, "I'm a married man, and I have to send some cash back for the wife and kids," which was an admirable thought.

"Yeah, and me," Dave decided, after thinking about it.

"What!" Joey was becoming irritated by all this penny-pinching talk. Out of sight and out of mind, suited him better, and let the little waifs starve if they have to, but he didn't say as much. Instead he scowled into his coffee, probably regretting not having brought with him more compatible company. He finally gave a shrug and a resigned smile, knowing only too well that they were right, and talking sense for once. "Right then, is there anything else we need to think about?"

"Aye," I said, grabbing the opportunity with both hands, "another cup of coffee!" I was genuinely disappointed when it was brought by another waitress, a stout, ruddy-faced woman with a hint of moustache and a huge wart on her chin. The coffee no longer tasted as well, and I didn't try to hide my despondency, not for the coffee, but for the girl who didn't bring it.

When we eventually prepared to leave, our red-headed hero took command. "Right, lads," he told us, "once we're out there on the mean streets of this Schleswig place, we've got to look the part. He thumped his breast like Tarzan loosening phlegm as he continued, "We're a British band," he said with enough pride in his voice to have done the briefing before the Battle of Britain, "and we've got to show these Krauts what's what, see," I could almost hear Rule Britannia somewhere in the background, "and project an image and look cool, and stuff like that."

"Listen to yourself, you barmy bugger!" Stuart chuckled. "There are times when you don't half talk a load of bullshit!"

But Joey was right about the image thing, because, as we walked through the streets, everyone stopped to look at us. I automatically checked if my fly was open, but with the chill in the air, I suppose I would have noticed if it had been. People still stared, and I found it somewhat unsettling, and wondered why. We felt like something that had dropped out of the sky from another planet; they weren't just glancing at us, but actually stopping to openly stare at us without a hint of embarrassment. *Ringo*, I thought, *now I know how you guys must feel like when you pop down the pavement for a wrap of the greasy stuff at the chippie!*

Had our fame preceded us? That was taking it a bit far and a bit further. Or could it be our appearance? I was wearing a building-site donkey jacket, a woolly cap, checked trousers and heavy boots; nothing special about that, surely? Joey had his oversized, green parka-coat with a fur-lined hood that was zipped up so tight around his head that only his bulbous red nose showed from the fur, while Stuart looked like a marooned pirate in his striped T-shirt and battered leather jacket, and Dave was dressed from head to foot in white – a short and trendy white jacket, white polo-neck pullover, and tailored white jeans. It was as well it wasn't snowing or you wouldn't have seen him at all. So, I would have thought that our appearance was quite normal, but the good people of Schleswig seemed to disagree.

We decided to pop into a cosy little bar we happened to be passing, just to get out of sight from our audience, but our entrance brought us new attention and after the first moments of utter silence had passed, caused some considerable animated conversation among the locals.

With a beer a piece before us, our mood lightened as we sat at a table by an open fire that crackled merrily away, bringing a rosy glow to our cheeks. We settled back in the seats and relaxed. "It's not bad here, lads," I said, sighing with contentment, "almost cosy."

The other customers continued to stare at us, and there were close whispered conversations as they eyed us, followed by laughter. This was clearly getting to Joey. "If those two geezers over there stare at me again, I'll fuckin' duff 'em!" he told us, belligerently staring back at them with daggers in his eyes. "I mean, what are they looking at?"

"Maybe they like puzzles," Stuart suggested.

"Puzzles?" Joey said, feeling puzzled, and showing it. "What do you mean, puzzles?"

"You, you red-headed sod," Stu laughed at him, "'cos face it mate, you are a bit of an enigma aren't you!"

"What's that?" Dave enquired, suddenly showing some interest.

"What's what?" we asked, wondering what he was on about.

"Enema," Dave said, waiting for an explanation.

"What?" we called in unison, suddenly puzzled ourselves.

Then I understood. I shook my head in disbelief, and patiently began to explain to Dave. "Enigma, Dave, not enema," I spoke slowly and distinctly so he would hear the difference. "Now, Joey here, he's an enigma, that's like a puzzle, or something that you don't understand." He was concentrating hard, trying to understand. "An enema, is like when you're full of shit," I began, but Dave's face lit up and he broke me off before I could finish.

"That's what I said," he said enthusiastically, with a daft smile smeared across his face, "Joey's like an enema – he's full of shit!"

I decided that I might have done that bloke an injustice by thinking he was slow, because in this case at least, he was right on the mark.

As we sat and joked, I couldn't help but notice a rather stern-looking older woman who sat at a table near the fireplace. She was entirely dressed in black, topped by a black hat that she wore at a jaunty angle. She had small glasses perched on the end of her nose as she read a newspaper. Whenever she thought we weren't looking, she would lower the newspaper and intently stare at us over it, then quickly raise it again if she caught us looking back at her; now you see me, now you don't! We were certainly making an impression on the good people of Schleswig, and that, before we had even struck a note.

The easy banter gradually slowed to the more serious prospect of how our first-night debut later that evening would go down. Stuart laconically observed, "We're here now, so they'll have to like it or lump it, because what they see is what they get!" He wasn't worried.

Ever the optimist, Joey stated as fact, "They're going to love us, just wait and see!" then downed the last of his beer, slammed his glass on the table, and announced, "Right, I'm off! I've got things to do. Babies to wash and all that. I'm a man on a mission, so I'll see you shower later!" and with that he was gone.

"What the heck was that all about?" Dave wondered aloud. "Babies to wash? Man on a mission? Has he gone daft?" Well, he would know about that, now wouldn't he?

"Who knows," cackled Stuart. "You know what he's like once he's got summat in that thick skull of his, nothing will stop him." Then he suddenly laughed out loud.

"What's tickling you?" Dave enquired, already smiling at the joke, even before he had heard it.

"I was just wondering who's servicing Randy Mandy now that King Dong is over here, because she's insatiable, that one."

"It wouldn't be anyone with any taste, that's for sure," guffawed Dave, involving himself in the conversation for the first time, since it was talk of women, and considering himself an authority on the subject.

I shuddered at the thought of Randy Mandy, and decided to change the subject. "Another beer, lads?" The answer was as expected, and I showed three fingers to Fritz at the bar, who acknowledged the order with a nod of his head, and we waited patiently for our refills with the warmth from the fire making us feel quite at ease.

It was snowing by the time we began to walk back to our dismal digs. I wondered where Joey had gone off to. Stu didn't really care. "At least we've been spared from the grinning idiot for a while, not to mention that big, red, shiny hooter of his," he said, smiling as he spoke, for he really liked Joey. "I only hope he remembered to buy some milk and bread for tomorrow."

We came to a small café and decided we needed to eat, so we went inside, eager to put some food inside us. When we compared the prices and the little cash we had in our pockets, our choice was severely limited, and we ended up with a bratwurst sausage and a bowl of pea soup with a roll of bread. It went down well, and we could afford it – just – and for the next couple of weeks this was to be our main source of nourishment, for our rapidly diminishing supply of marks and pfennigs had to be spent sparingly, so we would have enough for the important things such as beer and cigarettes, for without those, our stay would truly be dreadful.

When we finally entered the downstairs bar, Otto informed us that Mr. Joey had come in an hour earlier with a couple of large plastic shopping-bags, which made Dave wonder how much bread and milk he had actually bought. Otto was more interested in the fact that he had heard a lot of shouting and banging, and not a little frustrated cursing coming from our rooms after Mr. Joey had gone upstairs. I was a little concerned by this news, fearing that our red-nosed leader might finally have gone crazy under the strain of responsibility he had taken upon himself, and knowing it was only a matter of hours until we were due on stage. He had enough delusions of grandeur, so I would never have admitted it to him, but the fact was that the group couldn't function without him: he was the lead guitarist, the lead vocalist, and the egomaniac front-man. Without him we would be in serious trouble.

In answer to a question from Dave, Otto could inform us that we could expect a big crowd that evening. "It'll be packed tonight," he told us, "and with plenty of young frauleins eager to see the new group from England. You will do very well, believe me!" he assured us.

I couldn't share his enthusiasm, for I had a sense of fore-boding as we climbed the stairs to our rooms, afraid of what state we would find Joey in; Otto's mention of banging and cursing seemed somewhat ominous. Then we heard his harsh voice ringing out with *I'll Be There*, the current hit by the Four Tops, and the stringent chords from his Telecaster guitar, and I thought, *Now what?* We opened the door to be met by Joey's mad grin, and a convivial "Evening wankers!"

Then we stopped in our tracks and stared into the room in speechless amazement. Stuart was the first to find his voice. "Bloody hell!" he exclaimed incredulously, looking around him. "Has the boss had the cleaners in?" he asked. "This place was like a bombsite this morning!"

Putting down his guitar and lighting a cigarette, Joey squint-ed slightly as the smoke got in his eye, and looked smug. "No cleaners, lads," he told us. "I did it all by m'self." He was really enjoying his moment, watching our reactions, and obviously pleased at our response to his hard work and initiative. "I even tidied up your pit of squalor, Biffo," he told me, not even try-ing to hide the disgust he felt for that particular operation.

We were all mightily impressed by his efforts on our behalf. Joey positively glowed with self-satisfied pride, as he ushered us towards the bathroom to show us what he called his piece de resistance. Remembering only too well what it had looked liked that morning, we could hardly believe what we now saw: the toilet was clean, the chain replaced and the water even flushed, and we had a supply of toilet rolls; the sink was pristine without a green stain in sight, the taps sparkled, with one new for the hot water, and a new stopper for the sink; a clean new mirror adorned the wall, under which, a shelf had appeared, with all of David's pills and potions on it. Dave spent some time admiring himself in the new mirror, and seemed pleased with both the mirror and the reflection he saw there.

The look on our faces must have been a joy to behold. Stuart's moon-face was alive with relief and pleasure. "I can't fucking believe it!" he oozed, almost wetting himself. "Who did it?"

"I did," Joey said, looking smug and grinning at our reaction. "I told you I had things to do, that I was a man on a mission. I thought I'd better do summat about it to stop you buggers moaning like debs standing in cow-shit, so I bought what we needed and did the job." Then to encourage a little more praise for his endeavours, he asked, "Do you like it?"

We were genuinely impressed and eternally grateful. "Too darn right, Joe!" we echoed. "Well done, mate!"

Stu eventually came out of his reverie for a moment. "By the way, Joe, did you remember to pick up the bread and milk?"

The grin faded from Joey's face. "Well, no," he muttered, "I completely forgot about that. Sorry lads." Then he brightened again, as he fumbled in the pocket of his fur-lined parka. "I did buy something else though," he said, and held up a medal for us to see. "Look at this. It's a genuine World War II German Iron Cross," he enthused, "and it only cost twenty marks!"

We turned on him with menace in our eyes, and saw him wither before our glares. "We gave you money to buy bread and milk, not a frigging Iron Cross, you daft sod!" Stuart snarled at him, the angelic expression that had so recently been painted on his face, now replaced by a scowl of wrath.

Poor old Joey, I thought, one minute praised to high heaven for being a saint, and the next pilloried for being a mindless sinner. I decided we would have to stop all our moaning, and just make allowances for his sometimes erratic behaviour. For all his faults, he wasn't such a bad bloke, and his heart was in the right place. The trouble was finding where he kept his brains …

First Night
Nerves

It was closing on six forty-five when we presented ourselves in the dancehall ready to start when the doors opened at seven. We were washed, shaved, and given the amount of after-shave and anti-perspirant we had smothered ourselves with, we must have smelt like a whore's handbag, whatever that smells like.

The owner came up to grace us with his presence. "Good evening," he greeted us, "are you ready for your first night?" We all nodded eagerly in the affirmative – what else could we do? Then he gave us our instructions. "I want you to start playing as soon as we have everyone inside. You play for forty-five minutes then take a ten minute break, and keep doing that until eleven o'clock when you play through to the finale at midnight. Is that understood?"

"Crystal clear!" Joey confirmed.

"And please remember that I do not allow beer drinking or smoking" – he pronounced it trinkink or smokink, making what he said seem somehow sinister. Of course, we already knew this, but thought it wise not to interrupt him in full oratory; after all this was the gent who would hopefully be paying us for our efforts.

"I take it we can have a beer and a fag when we're on our break?" Stuart piped up, just to get that matter out of the way.

With German efficiency, he drew our attention to a table by the bar, and told us, "You will trink and smoke at that table!" It sounded like an order, and I wondered what would happen if we didn't *trink and smoke* when we sat there, as though that would ever happen … He gave us a brisk bow and left us, with a new command, "Have a nice evening, and play well!"

The doors opened and the place quickly filled up. I looked out at the mass of people crowding around in the semi-darkness, and called out "Looks like a full house tonight, lads," then counted in the first number with four taps of my sticks, and we kicked into *I Should Have Known Better*, a good danceable little ditty by The Beatles, and watched as the dance-floor immediately filled up with dancers. Stuart's Lennon-like vocals were spot on, while Joey played a blinder, not only on his guitar, but also on the harmonica that he had in a cradle hanging around his neck. People were smiling, dancing, singing with the song, and clapping to the beat, and everyone seemed to be enjoying themselves immensely, especially Joey who always thrived on being the centre of attention. He was right in the middle of the spotlight, and loving every moment of it, milking it for all it was worth. We were going down a bomb, and loving it.

A group of attractive young frauleins gyrated in front of the stage, laughing and smiling, and obviously giving us the come-on. I reckoned these must be the ones who, according to Johan, liked to fraternise with the English groups that played at the venue. Dave, on the bass, seemed to be singled out for particular attention, which was hardly surprising; the image he projected was so cool he could have got frostbite. With his long blonde hair swinging around his innocent face, and the flashing smile he blessed the assembled masses with, he was undoubtedly the group's babe-magnet, and just seemed to take it for granted. He had a grin across his vaguely handsome features akin to that of the famed Cheshire Cat, as he effortlessly fingered the strings on his bass as though they were a lover on foreplay. I could almost hear his brain ticking over as he debated which of the inviting women dancing before him he should choose – knowing him, he might take them all, I thought.

Joey was at the microphone. "For the final number of the first session," he announced, already in a sweat and giddy with delight at the way things were going, "we're going to play a new song for us," and he raised his voice even higher, as he introduced it, *Reach Out, I'll Be There!*

I screwed my eyes shut and said a silent prayer as I began to count us in, for we had only practiced this song once, just before we left England, and then we had cocked it up good style, so I feared the worst, thinking this is when we screw the evening up after a brilliant start. As it happened, my misgivings were unfounded, and we played it really well and got ecstatic applause for our trouble. It was enough to make Joey bow, the chuff!

As we came off the stage, I heard Stuart mutter, "Did you see the soft sod bowing to the crowd? The bastard will be blowing kisses, next!"

"Oh, leave him alone," I said, "he's happy, so let him enjoy his moment, especially after the rollicking you gave him for forgetting the bread and milk. Let him be happy, he deserves it." I know I was happy, after a really good first set, and a full house of enthusiastic revellers rooting for us.

Someone who was even happier was Dave, who was surrounded by giggling girls fawning all over him as he made his way to our designated table. "Just look at the smug git," Stu snarled, clearly rankled by his popularity, "he's frigging loving it, isn't he!" *And who wouldn't?* I thought to myself, but said nothing.

Four beers were already in place by the time we reached our table, and we took a long grateful mouthful, needing it badly after our stint on the stage. The place was loud with the noise of hundreds of excited voices chattering away and the air was heavy with cigarette smoke hanging like a cloud over us. There were smiles and laughter everywhere we looked. "Well," said Joey, obviously well pleased with himself, "so far so good! What d'ya thing lads?"

"Yeah," said Stuart in agreement, "it's going great at the moment. Let's hope it lasts!" He turned towards Dave, "What do you think, Dave?" he asked, but no answer was forthcoming because our eminent bass player and group stud de luxe had a fraulein wrapped around his neck, and whatever she was whispering in his ear, it certainly brought a smile to his face.

"I think we'll take that for a yes," I decided, and took a new mouthful of my brew.

Stu had something on his mind that couldn't wait. "'Ere Joe," he said, "at the end of the next session, will you do me a favour?"

"If I can, mate." Joey would do anything for anyone at anytime, that was just how he was, "Whatever you want," he said, and meant it. "What is it?"

"I don't want to see you bowing and scraping to these fucking Krauts like some kind of subservient waiter," Stu told him, "'cos if you do, I swear I'll deck you, okay!"

"Oh aye!" sneered Joey, looking down his nose at Stuart, "you and who's army?" Joey was a nice bloke with a temperament that could be far from nice, but it usually blew over as quickly as it came. He was also a pretty tough cookie who had never turned his back on trouble. As it was, Stu was of the same ilk, and could rumble with the best of them despite his cherubic features; it probably had something to do with his Scouse heritage.

The situation was still at an early stage, but I saw that it could soon develop to the next level, and quickly broke in before another potentially fateful word could be spoken. "Come on, fellahs, knock it off, will you. We don't want to blow our cool on the first night, now do we?" I reasoned with them calmly. "Anyway," I said, "we don't want to be scrapping

71

among ourselves, because I've got a sneaking feeling we might already have a spot of bother on our hands later on." I nodded my head to indicate a largish gang who were sombrely staring at us, and had been giving us the evil eye for the past ten minutes or so.

They were probably peeved because the local lasses were paying more attention to the travelling minstrels from the UK, than to them, and who could blame them? But jealousy on the part of a gang with a Saturday-night hard-on and nowhere to take it, and nicely tanked up too, usually meant trouble for someone, and we were the only candidates.

"Fuck 'em!" said Joey, who didn't give a shit anyway, "they're not going to start owt in here, with those bouncers on the door."

Personally, I wasn't too sure about that, but I had faith enough in our leader to hope he was right, and if he wasn't, I was going to make damned sure that he was between me and the storm troopers when they came to blitz us!

We played really well that night, feeling inspired by the feedback from the enthusiastic audience. We were all on a high, loving every minute of it, and put everything we had into each new song we played. By the time we were ready to go on for our last set my wrists were aching from the drumming, and my knees and ankles could hardly keep me upright after pedalling away at the hi-hat and the bass drum all night. I was also sweating profusely from my exertions, and really tired, but I still felt elated because we had gone down so well with the German punters. That is, apart from the scowling gang that had remained threateningly impassive in a corner throughout the evening, giving us the evil eye. But, as Joey had so tactfully suggested earlier; Fuck 'em!

It came as some relief to hear Joey announce the last song of the evening; it was to be another Beatles favourite, *Day Trip-*

per. We finished off to a round of enthusiastic applause and raised our hands to say *Thank you from the Charters of Chester*, and felt really pleased and excited about the reception we had been given and the rousing send off when we had finished. I looked at Joey and swore he was toying with the idea of bowing again just to get back at Stuart, but the withering look Stu gave him deterred him from doing it, and he just gave the crowd a final wave instead.

Joey unplugged his guitar. "Pheww," he blew the air out, tired but smiling from ear to ear at our success. "I need a beer and a fag," he said, "Come on lads, I'm gasping!" We hardly needed to be persuaded, and scrambled with him to our designated place by the bar, where we settled in to bring our adrenaline level back to normal. Dave had pulled a girl – surprise, surprise – and she was clinging to him like a limpet-mine. She was a small, attractive girl, called Doris, with a winning smile and an outgoing personality, but it was probably whatever she had whispered in his ear earlier that had attracted him to her more than anything else. Rather more surprisingly, it turned out that Stu had also pulled a sweet, fair-haired girl called Trudi, who seemed more than enamoured by him. It must have been his personality that did it, because a Greek god he was not!

I was feeling tired and had no illusions about a similar success, so decided to go to bed. Anyway, I was broke, so there was little point in remaining in the bar. But Joey wasn't having it. "You can't leave me on me own, you swine," he whined, clearly muffed by the fact that the Greenfield Stud had drawn in a willing Fraulein before him, which was certainly a massive blow to his ego. It didn't help matters that our moonfaced Liverpudlian lover had also got in ahead of him. Our star performer, Mr. Personality himself, was still on his own, while the bass and the rhythm were already strumming the chords;

it must have hurt like hell! He looked so crushed that even I felt sorry for him, but, being Joey, the lunatic smile was soon back on his face, and he was raring to go. "Hang about, and we'll have a few beers," he said, "I'll buy them."

He knew me well, did Joey. "Aye, okay," I agreed, brightening at the prospect. Just then Dave bent over to whisper in my ear, and inform me that he was going to bed. He slipped me six marks, and suggested that I waited a couple of hours before finding my way to our quarters. A nod is as good as a wink, but he didn't have to do either, because my new-found wealth no longer made it imperative that I leave the cosy confines of the bar for my bed, so Dave and his willing fraulein could have the place for themselves without any disturbance from me. What, with Joey's offer of free beer, and the six marks jingling happily away in my pocket, I was ready to make a night of it!

"Look at 'em," Joe said, as they wandered away from us, "she's all over him. Is she on heat or what?" He sounded like a grumpy old man, and no wonder.

"You're only jealous," I informed him, knowing well that he was, and enjoying pointing it out to him, hoping, in some perverted way, it would make him even more miserable.

But it didn't. On the contrary, instead of making him more despondent, he grinned from ear to ear. "Too damned right I am!" retorted Red Nose, with his lunatic laugh rattling away at the back of his throat like a foghorn.

True to his word, Joey popped off to buy the booze. By the time he returned with the beer, he was back to being peeved by the fact that Stuart had weighed anchor for the night, while he was still without a woman to soothe his aching brow, and he made no attempt to hide his disappointment. He was still preoccupied with this injustice when Trudi brought some of her friends over and introduced them as Elke and Maria, but he hardly noticed them.

"D'ya know what Biffo," he told, me shaking his head and looking puzzled, "here we are, two single fellahs from a group who have just pulled our guts out to entertain these people, and there's not a sign of interest or appreciation from a single bird!" He was so engrossed in his own self-pity and general resentment against the injustices of the world, that he didn't even notice that the girl called Maria was trying hard to catch his attention, and showing no lack of interest in him, bulbous red nose, and all. Ever the sensitive soul, Joey carried on as though she wasn't there. "It makes me sick to think that Golden Balls has tapped off with that Doris, and Stuart's already sorted out for the night. I mean, they're both fucking married!"

At this, Trudi pulled away from Stu, seemingly shocked by this revelation, while he in turn gave Joey a look to stiffen him. "Is it true, Stuart?" Trudi asked him, all wide-eyed and waiting. "Are you married?" To which he only nodded his head and smiled sheepishly, seeing his leg-over for the night about to pass into the realms of things-that-might-have-been. But Trudi only shrugged her shoulders, threw her head back and laughed. "What your frau doesn't know, cannot hurt her, yes?" and then proceeded to eat his face with a vengeance, as though this new knowledge made him even more attractive to her. I heard our Liverpudlian pirate give a moan, if it was of pleasure or pain I'll never know, but if he didn't before, then he now knew for a certainty that the night would offer delight in the form of a bit of delectable German rumpy-pumpy.

Joey had hardly noticed this little intermezzo, and was back at staring miserably at his beer in silence, and seemed to be completely unaware of the delectable wares sharing his table and cooing for his company. Tiring of trying for some response, Maria finally lost interest in him, and got up to go. As she left the table, she sneered at Joe, "I guessed all along that you were a single man. It stuck out a mile." And then she was gone, without Joey really having registered that she had been there at all, before she was gone.

With only a casual glance towards the door, as she passed through it, he murmured, "She loves me really, you know." The grin was back on his face.

"In your dreams, mate!" I told him. "In your dreams."

Thankfully, Joey bought another round, because my glass was empty, and I wanted my six marks to stay in my pocket. It was as well that the others had left the bar, and didn't have to listen to the rest of his self-pitying moaning, because it was even making me feel despondent, and I'm an authority on the subject!

Despite the fact that it was one-thirty in the morning, the place was still heaving with people, and the crazy woman was still feeding the juke-box to play that Sandie Shaw record over and over again. After having heard it none-stop for the past couple of nights, I had to admit it was beginning to grow on me, despite the fact that I had no idea what the Barefoot Contessa was warbling on about.

I saw Joe standing at the bar with a full glass in each hand, in animated conversation with a dowdy, older woman, and thought that he might still find some nourishment for the night, although with mutton rather than lamb.

Laughing, Joey plonked the beer down on the table in front of me, and toasted me, and I thanked him. "Cheers!" I said, and took the froth off the top of the glass. I looked at him askance. "Far be it for me to question your dubious taste in women Joe, but that one must have been a new low, even for you! But then, it did look like she was up for it, so you're on there!"

"You're kidding!" he spluttered. "I wasn't chatting her up; she was trying to chat me up, you daft sod!"

I laughed at the thought of anyone wanting to chat up our love-sick troubadour, red nose and all. "She must have been bloody desperate, then!" I told him, with no pity in my soul.

"That's quite possible," he informed me, "because it turns out that she's the local prostitute, and she seems to have had a slow night, and was desperate for a punter." His eyebrows knitted together as he creased his brow. "I couldn't get over how cheap she was." I couldn't decide if the indecision showing on his face was due to the fact that he had just blown a bargain or saved his money and his reputation. "You've heard the phrase, Willing for a Shilling, but she was on offer for one bloody mark!"

I quickly calculated the exchange rate, and came to the conclusion that this was less than a shilling. If that bought an exchange of compliments with that lady, I wondered what the six marks in my pocket could buy.

"At that price, I'll have to bear her in mind for future reference," Joey chuckled, "'cos if I don't get a bird by tomorrow night, I'll be getting bloody desperate!"

"You'd have to be, mate," I told him, casting a glance at her, "'cos she's hardly a beauty!"

"No problem," Joe retorted, "I'll bring a paper bag to put over her head."

"And they say that romance is dead!" I said, and sighed, smiling sweetly at him.

Just then, Johan Strauss, the toilet attendant, came over and perked us up by telling us, "The owner was very pleased with your performance tonight, and is very enthusiastic about you."

Well, that was enough to get Joey going. He sat up straight in his chair, smiling like a kid with a lolly on a stick, "Yeah, we were pretty good, weren't we!" he agreed enthusiastically. "And I was bloody brilliant tonight, and the frauleins were all over me!"

Johan made a point of studying the empty seats around us. "But where are they now?" he asked, and smiled. "I only see your drummer here with you, but no girls."

Joey noted the put-down, and placed the blame elsewhere without a blink of his eye. "It's Biffo, here," he told him. "He cramps my style."

Johan the Toilet Man was in a philosophical mood. "Better to be silent and be thought a fool, than to speak out and remove all doubt," he said, looking profound as he said it.

Out of the corner of my eye, I saw Joey with a dark look on his ruddy face, silently mouthing the word "twat!" but he let it go with that, and stayed silent.

Before the situation could become too awkward, Stuart thankfully arrived with Trudi grimly hanging on to his arm, blushing a deep shade of red. "Do me a favour and give me the key to the van, Joe," he said, holding out his hand, palm up, and obviously anxious to get it and be on his way.

"What do you want the keys to the van for?" Joey asked, enjoying the moment, as he saw Stuart's impatience and discomfort, and relishing the power he now held over him,. "Are you going for a ride?" he asked innocently.

"Just give me the keys!" Stuart told him, with a measure of irritation and a lot of desperation in his voice.

Joey finally took pity and rummaged through his pocket for the key. "Why don't you just go upstairs to your bed?" he enquired, which was quite a sensible thought.

"Because the Stud's already up there with that Doris bird!" Stuart almost screamed it at him, in sheer frustration. Then he lowered himself towards Joey's grinning face, nose to bulbous nose and eyeball to eyeball, and snarled, "Just give me the bleeding van keys, will you!"

Joey casually tossed them on the table. "There you are mate," he said sweetly, "all you had to do was ask me nicely!"

then we watched as Stuart rushed out of the bar with Trudi hanging on desperately.

Joey was grinning, but I knew that he was hurt and disappointed by the fact that the others had someone to keep them warm for the night, while he was on his own. "Maybe you'll pull a bird tomorrow, Joe," I said, trying to comfort him, because I could see he was upset.

His eyes stared somewhere into the distance as he replied, "Yeah, we'll see …"

Johan had been quiet during this amusing little incident, observing what happened through shrewd eyes. "What about you, Biffo," he asked, "aren't you going to find a fraulein too?"

I thought, *aye, aye, is Johan one of those, and fancies his chances?* but cast it from my mind as being very improbable, for I had seen him eyeing the ladies himself on more than one occasion. "No, mate," I told him. "You see, I can't get a girl because I have no confidence."

"Yeah," Joey piped in with his croaky voice, "and he's ugly too!"

Just then, I noticed Otto the barman talking to a young blonde girl who was sitting on a stool at the bar. He was stroking the back of her hand and smiling at her. I was intrigued enough to keep watching, if only to see what her reaction would be. She half-turned towards me, and my heart skipped a beat as I recognised her as the girl who had caught my interest in the cafè earlier that day. Johan had followed my gaze, and noticed my interest. "She is a pretty fraulein, isn't she?" he commented.

I couldn't argue with that. In fact I thought she was stunning. "Yes, very pretty," I agreed, and turned away just as she casually looked in our direction. Although it hardly seemed likely, I asked Johan if she was Otto's girlfriend. He guffawed and shook his head in reply, then told me that she was Otto's niece and not his lover, which was a relief to hear. He told me her name was Henni.

Joey had been very quiet for some time, and only idly followed our conversation, now burped out, "Henry? That's a terrible name for a girl," then fell back into morose silence.

In the space of the few seconds my attention had been claimed by my companions as we discussed her, the girl had gone, and my moment was over. Feeling that the night had no more to offer, I rose unsteadily to my feet, and bade Joey and Johan a goodnight, and trudged wearily up the stairs to our quarters to get some much-needed sleep. I stopped by the door at the sound of girlish squeals of delight followed by grunting and panting from within, all accompanied by the squeaking of bedsprings in labour.

I quickly closed the door behind me, offered an embarrassed apology as I passed the copulating couple on the bed, and dashed into my depressing room, closing the door behind me in a fruitless attempt to keep their noise out. They kept me awake for another frustrating hour or so, completely unabashed by the fact that they were keeping me from my beauty-sleep, and how they were doing it. In spite of my increasing irritation, I have to admit that I was mightily impressed by Dave's stamina and staying power; they must have been at it for three hours or more, and I certainly didn't notice any break for a cup of tea and a chat in the hour or so I had to listen to them panting away. Dave had been right – he really didn't need any powdered rhino horn. He was horny enough without!

The Golden Vision
Speaks

I awoke the following morning to the sound of heavy traffic rumbling by on the road outside, and gradually became aware of voices from the room next door. I could hear Doris laughing and talking above the others, which confirmed the fact that she had spent the night with her dim but dashing blonde lover. Through the paper-thin partition between us, I could hear grumbling and grousing, which was followed by a short silence before the door was slammed shut and footsteps scuttled down the wooden staircase outside our quarters. Curiosity got the better of me, so I decided to find out what was happening, and gingerly opened the door, to be greeted by the sight of a rather bedraggled Joey, who looked for the world like he had been dragged through a hedge backwards.

"Who was that?" I asked, nodding my head towards the door. "Was it Dave?"

"Aye," he confirmed, "with that Doris bird."

"So she has been here all night then," I stated.

"Oh, give that man a balloon!" Joey cried sarcastically and grinned. "Of course she's been here all night, you daft bugger! With our blonde-haired bass player plucking her strings all night," he added, unnecessarily – I mean, I had noticed! "I didn't see them when I came in," he continued, "because I'd had a bit too much to drink and just crashed out right on my bed." I could believe it, looking at the state of him. "Then I woke up to see Dave reclining on his pillow, smoking a fag, and her standing buck naked in front of me in the process of picking up her clothes. I thought I was bloody dreaming; I mean, it's not every day you wake up with a dolly-bird juggling her tits and flashing a smile at you!" He seemed disconcerted by the memory.

"So what was all the shouting about?" I asked.

He looked sheepish, which was not a pretty sight considering the huge red nose that covered half his face, and, to my amazement, he told me, "Well, I just suggested that he could have woken me up and we could have had a threesome, kind of thing."

"You said what!?" I exclaimed in disbelief. Even for Joey, this was a new low. I knew he was feeling desperate, but there are certain things you just don't intrude upon; such as pride and feelings; aye, and your mate's still-warm lover. "And I can guess what he told you," I said. I was already thinking that this was a sure-fire way to break up the group, and I certainly didn't want that to happen again.

"Yeah, he wasn't too happy," he admitted. Then I saw his eyes light up, and he smirked, "But I did get the impression that she was up for it," he said, and I could see his brain already working on the possibilities.

"Yeah, sure," I sneered, "and it's good to see that your ego's made a full recovery from last night's debacle, because then nobody would have you, you ugly bugger!"

We allowed the debate to rest as we each pondered the information just given. I finally broke the silence by wondering where Stuart was. "I've got no idea." Joey didn't seem to care either. "But he hasn't slept in his bed. Perhaps he's spent the night with that Trudi bird."

"What, in the van?" I couldn't believe it; it must have been freezing cold outside.

Moments later, the man himself arrived, rubbing his hands together to get some life into them. His nose was purple and he was shivering with cold. It turned out that he had spent the night in the van, by necessity and certainly not choice. After having enjoyed themselves together in the back, Trudi had eventually gone home, and Stu had been ready for some much-needed rest. But when he came to the door, it was bolted and everyone had gone home. "So I had to go back and sleep in the frigging van," he told us between chattering teeth. "It was freezing cold in there." He shuddered at the memory. "I thought hypothermia was setting in!"

"It serves you right, you randy sod!" Joey told him, with no pity for his misfortunes, then immediately regretted having said it, when Stuart stuck his head forward and reminded him that he owed him five marks for the bet.

"Me too," said Dave, as he came back through the door. "In fact, you should make it ten for what you suggested about Doris." He sneered at poor Joey who was cringing at his downfall, feeling his ego diminishing by the second. "What's up with you Joey?" Dave asked disdainfully. "Can't you get your own bird? Have you lost your touch?"

For a man like Joey, these were wounding words indeed, and he cringed at the sound of them. "I was only joking about that, mate, honest," he tried, but nobody believed him. "I'm sorry, but I don't know what came over me," he apologised, and I could see that he meant it.

Listening to this discourse with some distaste, Stuart airily observed, "So I gather that you didn't have any luck last night then?"

"Not a bloody nibble, mate," Joey grudgingly admitted, finally crumbling before the onslaught.

I can never stand to see a grown man cry, and although Joey wasn't even close, and probably didn't even know how to, I felt he needed some support to build him up again, so I told him, "That's not strictly true, Joe, because that Maria was giving you the eye last night enough to eat you, but you were too wrapped up in your own self-pity to notice."

At this, Joey perked up, showing interest and curiosity. "You never told me that," he reprimanded me, obviously wanting to get more details. But I wasn't in the mood to give them, and decided to let the bugger live in ignorance, which was a state to which he should by now be pretty well accustomed. However, I thought it might be amusing to remind him of his options, so I told the other two band-minstrels, "Joey was actually lying when he said that no woman had tried to chat him up last night, because old Hilda at the bar wanted him so badly that she was offering him one mark for the use of his ugly body." I paused to let it sink in, and added, "But the bloody cheap-skate wanted two!"

"One mark," Stuart exclaimed derisively, "he aint worth that much! Bloody hell, he should be paying her to take the scabby bastard on!" which was all charming stuff intended to boost the morale of the despondent would-be lover with nobody to love.

It actually did buck him up, and Joey was again smiling all over his creased and well-worn face. "Well, if I don't get lucky tonight, I'll have to take myself in hand," he told us, and chuckled to himself.

"That's a bit sad," Stu pointed out, "'cos then you've got nobody to talk to!" and laughed at his little witticism. But the way Joey talked he wouldn't be without conversation, even if it was only with himself.

"He can talk to J. Arthur," Dave put in, surprising me once again by the fact that he could not only follow what was being discussed, but actually understand it, and even come with the odd humorous point of his own making – that bloke wasn't as daft as I thought he was. Or was he …?

The topic was changed to more pressing matters, as Dave enquired about breakfast. "We could have had cornflakes, but somebody," he stared daggers at Joey, "somebody forgot to buy milk!" An audible sigh was heard from the culprit, followed by a low mutter that might, or might not, have resembled an apology. "So what have we got, then?" Dave asked.

Joey brightened up, and began to list our alternatives. "Apart from the cornflakes, which we don't have any milk for, there are two tins of beans, which we can't warm up without the primus, a packet of crisps, a large bar of Kit-Kat, and, let's see," he rummaged around in a drawer, "yeah, and a packet of corn plasters."

"Then it's the café!" Stuart concluded, and we all piled out through the door, glad to be able to close it behind us, and get a wider perspective of life's possibilities than what those two small rooms and toilet could offer.

The café wasn't as welcoming to me as it had been the previous day, because a certain young lady was absent. Although I hadn't exchanged a single word with her, I realised that I had been looking forward to seeing her again, and now I felt surprisingly disappointed, and despite the hunger that was gnawing away at my empty stomach, the coffee and roll did little to help. I thought about my mother's bacon butties, and felt even hungrier; I would have given my right arm for one just then, but the fact was that I only had five marks to my name, and could hardly afford the coffee. Times were hard, but they were about to get a damn sight harder.

The next three days of our tour were undoubtedly the worst of them all. We had nothing to do in the daytime, and all the day to do it in. I was definitely at my lowest. I had no money, no cigarettes, other than those I begged from the others, and my only intake of food during the day was a bowl of pea soup at the café around the corner. I spent most of my time either asleep in my bed or lying on top of it forlornly counting the cracks in the ceiling, feeling homesick and miserable. It's not supposed to be like this, I thought to myself, I'm supposed to be enjoying myself. I was in a black and bottomless pit of depression. If someone had come to shoot me in the head, I would have thanked them profusely for putting me out of my misery.

The worst part was when we played in the dancehall in the evenings. I was just going through the motions, not really caring, and threatening to throw myself out of the window if we had to play *Winchester Cathedral* or *Wild Thing* once more. But the real killer was that the place was now only a quarter full, with the audience only giving us polite applause, which was a far cry and hefty let-down from the heady excitement of our opening night.

I think we were all beginning to feel it. We'd wake up in the morning, scratch our bollocks, fart, then roll over and go back to sleep. When we did eventually stir ourselves, and actually get up, we would promptly sit down again on the edge of the bed, as we desperately searched for a decent sized stump of a cigarette we had put out hours earlier. There was no spark and little conversation between us, and paranoia was settling in with a vengeance.

This was hardly sex, drugs and rock'n'roll, and the sorry spectacle we represented would hardly have stirred an iota of excitement or interest among whoever might otherwise have lived under the false conception that life on the road for a rock'n'roll group was a buzz from morning to night. On the contrary, they would probably have felt pity or disgust had they seen us.

I was definitely ready to pack my gear and go. The contract we had for the duration now only felt like a millstone around my neck, weighing me down at the prospect of having to live through this for another five weeks. I wondered if the others were as depressed as I was. Looking at them, it was hard to tell. Perhaps they too, were only going through the motions and putting on a brave face, just for the sake of appearances.

Lying on my bed one afternoon, feeling particularly sick, lonely and depressed, I decided that enough was enough and I was leaving for home. I sat up on the edge of the bed and began to rehearse how I was going to tell the others of my decision, knowing that I would be letting them down, but no longer caring. I almost shuddered at the thought of the abuse they would throw at me, and rolled back on the bed with eyes shut, trying to build myself up to face them.

I don't know how long I lay there. It might have been five minutes and it might have been five hours, for in our present situation, and my own state of mind, time no longer held any significance. Then a knock on the outside door brought me back to my senses.

I heard Stu call out "Come in! The door's not locked!" There was hardly any point in locking it, for who in their right mind would want to come inside?

Then I heard a hearty German accent greeting them, "Good evening, gentlemen!" it said, loud and booming, "I hope you are well, despite the weather?" I wondered what the weather was, for I hadn't been outside the building for a couple of days. The voice boomed out again, full of enthusiasm and good humour, both of which had been lacking in our small community for the past few days, "The time has come that I hate, and you love," it said, " because today I have to pay you for your excellent musical services. In short, it's payday!"

"Thanks Herr Schmidt," I heard Stuart say, "it's come just in time for one or two of us, I can tell you." Then I heard the door bang shut as our paymaster left, and the rising sound of voices in the next room exchanging excited chatter, obviously relieved at finally having money again.

It took a few minutes to penetrate my head, coming through slowly, before it eventually got through to me.

Money?

Money! My mind screamed as though suddenly coming alive. It was as though the grey skies had miraculously parted, the rain clouds scudding away to be replaced by glorious sunshine. I could almost hear heavenly choirs singing Hallelujahs. Money! Glorious money! Everything seemed to fall into place again. I realised that it was money, or rather the complete lack of it, that had caused my depression. But now I could actually eat again. I could drink! I could be happy, and not go hungry! All my self-pitying thoughts of leaving to go back home were forgotten, erased in a moment. Gone. I had money!

I popped my head around the door, and Stuart tossed me an envelope with a happy smile on his face, "Here you are Biffo," he said, "three hundred marks. That should put a smile on your miserable face!"

And it did. Three hundred marks was about twenty-five quid. I felt rich! "I'm going to enjoy myself tonight," I promised myself, for after a few desperate days of total depression, I was now a changed man, and raring to go. "Look out Schleswig, here I come!" I shouted at the cracked walls that had so recently been staring at my miserable carcase in silent disgust. I was so elated, I even had a wash and a shave!

That evening, the excitement and euphoria returned, and the place was packed full again, probably more because it was Friday, than because we happened to be on, although I do believe that many did come just to hear us. The happy crowd was enthusiastically dancing, talking, shouting, laughing, and generally having a great time, and so were we. Doris and her crowd of friends had found their place at the front of the stage, winking and waving and smiling at us, and making eyes at Stuart and squealing as he plucked his bass and shook his long golden locks at them.

But if anyone was on a roll, it was definitely Joey, who was playing a blinder. He had shrugged off the lethargy of the last few days, and was giving it everything he had, which was a lot. He was egomania personified, milking the applause, which was tremendous, and the female adulation, like the star he undoubtedly was, and might have been. After all the bickering we had endured during the previous days, it was invigorating to see him in such good form. His enthusiasm and zest for life was like a much-needed tonic to us all, and especially to me, as I enthusiastically hammered the daylights out of my drums. Why, I even played *Winchester Cathedral* with some degree of enthusiasm!

Joey's evening was about to get even better, because Herr Schmidt came over to him in the first break, having heard that he had fixed up our lodgings, thanked him profusely, and thrust a wad of money into his hand to compensate for his endeavours and outlays.

Such was the shock of this completely unexpected windfall that, before he knew it, Joey had called the waitress over and ordered a round for us all, including the girls who had settled at our table. One of these was Maria, the girl he had chosen to ignore on our first night. She was all over our benevolent benefactor, laughing with him, and whispering in his ear. She had obviously been taking a lesson from her friend Trudi, because he was putty in her hands as she caressed and cuddled him. The look on his face was a picture, with his eyes positively sparkling and the grin going from one ear to the other, and then on a bit. What it was, I could only guess, but I heard her mutter "Grosse!" in an impressed tone of voice, as she clambered all over him, and the smile on her face as she said it, was like a cat's; I could almost hear her purr.

So Joe, Dave and Stu were all set up for the night, and good luck to them I thought. Although a number of other attractive girls congregated around us, none showed any particular interest in me, not that I blamed them. I didn't want to hang about as the group's wall-flower alibi for celibacy, so I decided to find the bar and remain there until I was middling mindless and ready to be carried to my bed.

During the course of the next few hours, after my inhibitions had been suitably anesthetised by beer, I managed to broach the subject of Henni with her uncle Otto, wondering if she ever came to the dancehall to hear the groups. I had spent some energy looking around in the hope of seeing her, but had been disappointed. The fact that she was on my mind from time to time, bothered me, for I hadn't even spoken to her, and had no idea what her response would be if she was to know that such an ugly wastrel had become attracted to her. With any sense, she'd run a mile!

Otto understood, not that that could have been too difficult looking at my pathetic, dejected and love-smitten face. "Yes, she goes to the dance quite often," he told me. "In fact, I know that she is coming tomorrow to hear you play." Well, this was good news, and I perked up considerably at the prospect of seeing her face again, although I knew that I didn't have a hope in hell of anything more. Otto looked at me with an astute expression on his face. "Why do you ask?" Before I could stutter some kind of reply, he continued, "I hope you do not have any ideas of misbehaving with my Henni!" He looked at me grimly, but I don't think he meant to be too hard on me, although I would have if I had been in his place.

"No," I assured him, stuttering my response, "I wouldn't dream of it!"

I was in great spirits the next day, walking around with a stupid grin on my face and whistling to myself at the prospect of the evening's session, and what it might entail. I now had money in my pocket, a full belly, the knowledge that the girl of my dreams would be coming to hear us play that night, and a feeling that life was definitely beginning to look up for me. I found myself la-la-ing to a Beatles song as I shaved, *If I fell in love with you, would you promise to be true and help me la-la-la*, then Stuart's voice cut into my reverie by shouting to me, "Kill that frigging cat!" which somehow spoiled my moment.

When I had shaved, he wondered what was wrong with me. "You're usually as miserable as sin before we go on, but tonight you're full of beans, and yodelling," he said. "What's up, are you on a promise for tonight, or what?"

"'Course not!" I said, shaking my head at such an idea, "but thanks for asking."

The dancehall was absolutely heaving as we started the night with the Kinks' classic *You Really Got Me* which had everyone raving. Joey's guitar solo was probably the best rendition he had ever done, accompanied by his maniacal laughter, loving every moment as he strutted his stuff before the crowd. I was really buzzing, putting my heart and soul into every beat I played, hoping to impress a certain someone who might hopefully be somewhere out there in the semi-darkness watching.

I still hadn't seen her when we took our first break and fought our way to our table for a well-earned drink, but I did see Otto working the bar like a man demented. In spite of the crush of thirsty revellers, he was actually smiling, which was somehow unusual for him, as he happily bantered away with the waitresses while filling their orders. His body language spoke volumes, and he was obviously completely at ease with his life and the pressure he was under, keeping the booze flowing to fill the gullets of the overfilled dancehall.

Being aware, as I was, of his concern for his niece and the possibility of her being apprehended by some of the uncouth and rowdy inmates, I felt somewhat deflated when I saw his smile and relaxed demure, for that could mean that she was not coming after all, and he knew it. That would explain why he was so happy and relaxed.

The break was over only too soon, and we were back on stage. Half-way through the set, we slowed the tempo for a couple of songs, and Joey, with his nose positively pulsating in the glare of the spotlights, launched into *Yesterday,* which was one of his favourites. Personally I loathed the song. I never really liked it when Paul McCartney warbled his way through it, but Joey's painful rendition really put my teeth on edge, because, try as he might, he just couldn't sound sincere, and with his limited vocal range, the high notes were way out of his reach. His whole body was all aquiver as he valiantly tried to get up there, but he would have needed a ladder to even get close. It was as though someone had stuck a feather up his bum to watch him standing on his toes and straining but never really getting to wherever he was going, which was basically up. It was fun to watch, but murder to listen to.

But the real reason that I disliked the song was that I had to use brushes, which I never liked and never quite got the hang of. I much preferred to use the sticks, and then preferably with the heavy side out, to make as much of a racket as I could. So I stared at the ceiling in boredom as I played, and prayed that Joey would get a hernia as he strained himself fit to burst, but to no avail.

In the middle of the song, when I was beginning to look forward to getting it over with, I cast a glance into the crowd and suddenly caught my breath as I saw her. My miserable heart gave a skip of delight and came to life, and I could feel a smile spreading over my face. The joy and relief I felt was short-lived as I saw that she was dancing with someone, and that they both seemed to be completely at ease in each others company. I felt a twinge of jealousy that quickly turned to renewed despondency.

During our next break I was beginning to feel quite deflated. I felt like the inner tube of a pushbike with a slow puncture, getting flatter and flatter by the second. Despite this, some perverse masochistic malfunction inside my head, forced me to look around me to see where she was. As it happened, she was sitting at a table quite close to my own. Unfortunately, her date was with her, and they were obviously enjoying each others company, sitting snug and close as they smiled and chatted earnestly together, completely at ease being together. He offered her a cigarette which she declined with a smile that I would have died for.

I averted my eyes, feeling despondent and frankly, somewhat lonely. I knew that I had no reason to think that she might be interested in me, and the fact that I had been so exhilarated by the knowledge that she would be coming to see us had no basis in any indication from her that she even knew that I existed. It was purely a result of my infatuation for her after seeing her for a few minutes in the café – I mean, we hadn't even exchanged a single word, apart from ordering coffee from her, so why should I have had such futile hopes and aspirations for the evening? After all, she didn't know me from Adam, and how was she to know I was like a love-sick puppy for her. I cursed myself for hoping that she might have wanted to have anything to do with me. It was stupidity on my part, for why should she? For her, I didn't even exist!

By the time we had finished the last number for the evening, I was ready for a drink to steady my nerves and alleviate some of the self-pity I had built up during the past couple of hours, and I rushed straight down to the bar, which quickly filled up around me as I waited my turn, deep in thought. Before my drink arrived, a big red hooter came at me through the crowd, and Joey called out to me, wondering why I had left in such a hurry, "You missed out, mate," he informed me. "Some girl came up and asked about you, but we didn't know where you'd gone, so she buggered off again." He smiled his Dirty Joey smile, "You were on there, mate!"

I stiffened. "What girl?" I asked, somewhere between hope and despair, and almost bursting for the answer.

He put on a show of exaggerated concentration. Thinking hard, he placed a finger to his bottom lip as though for inspiration, and enjoyed watching me fume as he slowly drawled out, "Now, let me see," he thought about it, then decided, "She was a pretty girl, and, she had fair hair, and, yes, somehow she seemed familiar like I'd seen her before somewhere, but for the life of me, I just can't place her." The bugger!

I went to the table and was joined by Stuart and the tantalising Trudi. She was a good looking girl with a wicked sense of humour, which she would have needed to be with Stu who had a really off-the-wall style of finding fun in almost everything. He shouted across to Joey, who was still patiently waiting at the bar, "Hey, waiter! Two more beers over here, and make it snappy" Joey turned, grinned and stuck two fingers in the air. "There you are, Trudi," Stu said, cackling away, "two beers coming up!"

Three of the four musketeers were gathered, while D'Artagnan was upstairs thrusting away with his well polished rapier, which was what he did best. I decided that I needed more information to build on what Joey had told me, and asked if it was right that a girl had been asking about me. "Yeah," he confirmed, "I think it was that waitress from the café across the road." My heart stopped, and I couldn't stop my eyes from jerking through the crowd like a lost puppy desperately looking for its mother. But this sudden hope was quickly dashed as I remembered that she was with someone else, so I sighed deeply, and sank back into my normal state of apathy.

Johan the Toilet Man joined us, and reminded us that we had the next day off, and wondered what we were going to do then. Joey knew us better than we knew ourselves, and decided for us, as usual. "We need to get out of this place and get some wind under our wings," he declared. "We can go somewhere for a run in the van," he told us. Old Joey wasn't as daft as he looked, because we did need to get away before our squalid existence smothered us completely.

But then my attention was drawn to the door where Henni had suddenly appeared with her boyfriend by her side. For the umpteenth time that evening my heart stopped beating, and hope and despair fought inside my befuddled head. I watched as they found two empty stools at the bar and conversed light-heartedly. Despite the man by her side, it was as though her radiance illuminated the whole room. She was smiling and laughing, and the smiles and laughter lit up her face and her exquisite features. The faces around me seemed to blur out of focus as I gazed at her in awe, and the noise and general conversation seemed muffled and distant. I allowed myself a wry smile, and felt my head filling with emptiness.

Then I was brutally brought back to reality by Joey's voice barking at me, "Eh, Biffo! See that girl at the bar?" As though I hadn't. "That's the one who was asking about you."

Trudi put her face into mine to smile and inform me, "That's Henni." I already knew that, but wasn't telling. Trudi gave me a knowing look. "She's a pretty girl, isn't she?" I nodded in agreement, but said nothing, feeling that was the best course of action to avoid the hackling I would otherwise be up for if Stu and Joey caught the scent of my infatuation and began to howl.

So I changed the subject. "Where are we going tomorrow, then?" I asked, suddenly all ears.

Joey decided he wanted to go to Berlin to see what it was like on the other side of the wall. "We can have a look at the barbed wire, guards, watch-towers, and all the rest of it," he enthused. "And have a gander at all the squalor and that."

"We don't have to go to Berlin to see squalor, mate," Stuart pointed out, "just take a look at our quarters, and in particular, your bed. We've got all the squalor we need here!"

Johan calmly suggested that this was not a brilliant idea. "The guards are used to seeing scruffy people trying to get out of there, not scruffy people trying to get in."

"What d'ya mean, scruffy?" Joey pretended to be affronted. "I'll have you know that we have style. Why, t'other day the good people of Schleswig couldn't keep their eyes off us!"

Johan continued unperturbed. "There and back, is seven hundred kilometres, and frankly, my friend, with the state of your van, I don't know if it would make it."

"Yeah," Stuart agreed with him, it's only the rust and grime that keeps it together!"

Now Joey was really affronted. You could laugh at him, mock his girl, kill his cat, and probably even steal his money without him taking it too hard, but his van was something else. "There's nowt wrong with that van!" he insisted, in a voice so high-pitched that it proved that he actually could have reached the upper notes on *Yesterday*. "It cost me forty-five quid!" he informed us, as though this was a declaration of its quality, which it probably was, although not in the way he thought.

"It got us here, didn't it!"

I decided to try to bring some reason into the conversation, if only to bring Joey's voice- level back to normal. "They're only joking with you Joe," I told him, then gave him time to calm down. "But you have to admit that there was a bit of a rattling coming over here, and something's definitely knocking in the engine, and there are some alarming clunking noises coming from the gearbox." I watched him wither before me as I spoke, and the look in his face made me regret having mentioned these minor details, because I suddenly found that I was becoming somewhat despondent myself at the prospect of the van actually managing to get us back home again.

Just then, I felt an elbow dig into my side as Joey brought my attention to the fact that we had a visitor, and I looked up to be confronted by Henni's smiling face looking back at me. "So here you are," she said to me in faltering English. "Have you been hiding from me? I was looking for you, but nobody knew where you were." She paused and gave me an inquisitive look. "Where were you?" She seemed genuinely interested.

I could feel myself getting hot under the collar and the colour coming to my face, and felt even more flustered than usual. "Oh, yes?" I stuttered, trying my best to sound cool, and failing miserably. "Well, you've found me now, so what can I do for you?" Now how's that for giving a first impression to the woman of your dreams?

She sat down uninvited but more than welcome, on a chair next to me and leaned across the table as she supported her face on the back of her hands. The smile was still there, and it was pleasant. "I just wanted to tell you that you are a fantastic drummer," she said, without a hint of sarcasm. "You were the driving force behind the group. Like a train pounding away." By now I must have been as red as Joey's nose. "And you are such a good singer," she continued. Out of the corner of my eye, I saw Joey's mouth sag at this. She looked intently at me with her big blue eyes, and breathlessly told me, "I thought you were wonderful tonight."

Now, being used to it, I can handle scorn with indifference, but praise has never been scattered over my head, so I reacted in the only way I knew how, and stuttered, stammered, ummed and arred, feeling tongue-tied and acutely embarrassed.

I heard Joey behind me, sarcastically asking, "What the hell have you been feeding her on, Biffo?" but we both ignored him.

I felt like a rabbit caught in the headlights of a car as I looked at her face. She was even more beautiful close up than from a distance, with the flawless complexion of a porcelain doll. I could smell her perfume and see how her eyes studied my face as though she wanted to discover every detail for memory.

Then I noticed her boyfriend standing behind her, watching us with a smile on his face, and I quickly pulled myself together. "Er.." I began, making a heady start to the conversation, "Er … and did your boyfriend like us as well?"

She laughed. It was a sweet laugh. "Yes, he did. But he is not my boyfriend. Pieter is my brother." It turned out the brother was on leave from the army and was due back at barracks the next day, so he had come along to have a final send-off before returning to base.

My relief must have shown; I could see it in her eyes. She knew she had made a conquest, but then, with her looks, she must have been used to that. She got up to leave, and I felt a sudden urge to beg her to stay, but being me, I remained silent and didn't do anything to stop her. Quite unexpectedly, she placed an arm around my neck and planted a quick kiss on my cheek. "I'll see you tomorrow night," she trilled.

I remembered that we weren't playing then, and almost panicked. "Actually we're not playing tomorrow," I almost wailed at her.

"But you will be here?" she asked.

Wild horses couldn't have kept me away. "Yes, definitely," I assured her, "in the evening."

She smiled again. Was it relief? "Then I'll see you tomorrow," she said, and walked to the door where she turned and blew me a kiss and called back, "Gute nacht, Biffo!" leaving me in a state of shock and all atremble.

I looked at the others around the table. They had all been following this quite surprising turn of events with some interest. "What the fuck was that all about?" I asked, feeling quite bewildered.

Stuart leaned towards me with a twinkle in his eye and a grin on his face, "You're definitely in there mate, if you can control your nerves and play your cards right!" he told me.

"Play his bloody cards right?" Joe sneered. "The bugger even stutters when he's playing bleeding snap!" No heart, that man ...

Johan gave me a knowing smile and tapped the side of his nose as though it was some kind of secret signal, "Confidence is all it takes," he told me. "A little confidence is all you need." He nodded his head up and down as though to confirm the fact and make me believe it.

Trudi rolled her eyes at me, and said, "Henni is a pretty girl!"

I was on the proverbial cloud nine. She had actually talked to me, and even given me a kiss. She had complimented me and wanted to see me again tomorrow. As unbelievable as it was, Henni seemed to fancy me!

What else could I do? I called to Otto at the bar, "Five beers over here, please!" and the smile on my face wasn't at the prospect of a foaming new beer, but at the thought of what the next day might bring with it.

A little later I decided I was ready for some sleep and got up to go. Stuart decided that he was also ready for bed. "I'm going too," he informed us, then helped Trudi up from her seat. "Come on Trudi, are you ready?"

"Ready for what?" said Joey looking aghast at him and fearing the worst. Stu put his arm around Trudi and looked down at Joey to inform him that she was staying the night with him. "Says who?" said Joey indignantly.

Stu told him who. "Me!" He grinned, but there was a certain threat in the tone of his voice. "Why, have you got any objections?"

"Well, yeah, I have," Joey whined. "It's going to be bloody frustrating if you two are going to be lying there within six feet of my pit, isn't it? How am I supposed to sleep, eh?" Joey just didn't like others enjoying themselves when he wasn't. "It aint right," he moaned, "it's just not fair."

"You'll just have to take some sleeping pills," Stuart suggested sarcastically. Then bent towards Joey and snarled, "And I'll bloody chin you if you even suggest sharing her favours!"

As I lay in my bed, I smiled contentedly at the thought of Henni, and the fact that she actually liked me and I was going to see her again the next night. Life was looking up!

In the enveloping darkness of my room I eventually fell asleep to the rhythmic lullaby of bed springs creaking away on the other side of the wall, where Stu and Trudi played the melody while poor old Joey was just a singer without a song.

Ein Freier
Tag

It's the bells that made me deaf, you know, is a line from Victor Hugo's *Hunchback of Notre Dame*, and I had every sympathy with old Quasimodo when I was awakened by the continuous pealing of bells from the nearby church. They were making enough row to wake the dead and kill off the dying. They were certainly making my life a misery. I recalled that Joey had promised to take us all for a spin in the van to have a look at the local scenery, to give us some much-needed inspiration and a spot of clean air in our lungs. I found my watch and tried to focus my eyes on it. It was ten-thirty. Ten-thirty! We were supposed to be off before that! I lunged for my clothes praying that they hadn't left without me, and rushed through the door to the other room, then came to an abrupt halt at the sight of Trudi sitting on the edge of Stuart's bed wearing only panties and a black bra with the strap hanging provocatively loose down one arm; very sexy, I thought, nice legs too! Then I pulled myself together and became my usual dithering self. "Sorry about bursting in on you like this," I stuttered, and tried to avert my eyes from the vision before me, if only to spare her modesty.

Apparently, that was unnecessary, as she seemed completely unperturbed by my sudden appearance. She smiled at me, and chirped a happy "Guten morgen!" as though she was quite accustomed to having big hairy strangers popping in to watch her dress, which might, or might not, be far off the mark.

We were alone in the room, which gave me some degree of anxiety, not least because she was bending forward with one leg pulled up as she nonchalantly painted her toenails a deep red, as she sat on the bed. If I hadn't been feeling horny before, I wasn't far off then, I can assure you. The sun's rays shone through the gap in the curtains to light her golden hair, and she looked absolutely stunning.

To take my mind off the delightful temptation before me, I asked, "Where's Stuart?" not sure if I was pleased or concerned by the fact that he was absent. The flushing of the toilet told its tale, and I realised that I was actually relieved to hear it.

Stu joined us with a face full of tissue paper to stem the tide of blood from his morning shave. "You really should buy a new razor blade, Stu," I told him, "because that one must have been used by Sweeney Todd, and with a lot less blood-letting, at that." He gave me a sarcastic smile that made two of the tissues loosen and fall off his face.

"Anyway," I said, cutting to the chase, "I thought we were going for a trip today, so, where's Dave and Joe?"

"I've got no idea where Dave is," Stuart informed me. "He's probably off somewhere with Doris." He didn't seem concerned. "But we'll go for a drive once this bugger manages to get his arse in gear," he said, and nodded towards the other bed, as he removed the remaining tissues from his wounded face.

I hadn't noticed that Joey was there because he was as dead as a dodo. He was lying face-up with only his great shiny nose peeking out from under the blanket. There wasn't a sound or any movement coming from him. "Is he alive?" I asked, joking, yet not quite certain. How anyone could sleep through the racket from the church bells was beyond me. I looked closer, and couldn't even see any indication of breath coming from the bundle on the bed. I turned to Stuart. "Are you sure he's not dead?" I asked, actually beginning to worry.

"Positive," he assured me, and cackled his early morning laugh. "The ginger bastard rolled over just a few minutes ago, farted, and rolled back again, the disgusting sod!" He pulled on his t-shirt. "Give the bugger a kick," he told me, "or we'll never get going."

I looked across at Joey and thought I saw an eyelid flicker, and a definite twitch around his mouth. He was still alive. Without any warning, he sat bolt upright in his bed, grinning like the idiot he was, and exclaimed, "Guten morgen campers!" It was as though he had had electrodes attached to his goolies and someone had just turned on the switch, it was that sudden. It took us all by surprise, not least Trudi, who actually screamed, not that I blame her, for the garish ginger apparition that appeared not six feet from her, had come from nowhere, and was now grinning so much that his eyes had disappeared behind tight slits. In fact his whole face was a mass of creased lines with his great big shiny red nose sticking out of it like a lighthouse. No wonder Trudi screamed, for he would have put the fear of God into any unsuspecting female, and even gave me quite a start.

She quickly calmed down when she realised that it was human after all, but the shock still made her hands tremble as she lit a cigarette. "I thought you didn't smoke," I said.

"I don't," she replied, "but I need one now."

Joey finally finished his ablutions and looked almost human by the time he pulled on the fur-hooded parka coat that made him look like Nanook of the North. "Right, then," he exclaimed, rubbing his hands together in anticipation, "let's go."

But we got no further than the van door before he decided that we needed some breakfast. It turned out that the café was closed because it was Sunday, but Trudi told us that we could eat at a petrol station further down the road. "Where's that, then?" enquired Nanook from inside his fur.

Trudi informed him. "It's by the boats on the other side of the roundabout."

"Ah, the roundabout!" I said, as though it was a fond memory brought back from oblivion. "You must remember the roundabout, Joe. After all, you went round the bloody thing about twenty times when we came to this place!"

It was freezing cold outside, and the engine took a few turns before it started. Stuart and his lady-friend cuddled up together in the back, possibly for warmth. As we pulled from the curb, I noticed something on the floor. It was frozen stiff to the rubber mat, but I wrenched it loose and picked it up. I was amazed to see that it was a pair of panties. They were rigid with frost, and stood out from my hand like a crumpled LP record. "Yours, I presume?" I said, as I handed them back to the young lovers sitting there.

Trudi blushed a deep red and covered her face with her hands in embarrassment, but Stu was completely unperturbed. He took them, opened the window, cracked them against the door so bits of frost fell off them, and threw them out. "We wondered where they were," he said nonchalantly, and closed the window again.

Joey laughed. "It must have been a bit draughty walking home without them!"

As we strode into the eatery, which to all intents and purposes was a transport café, we attracted some rather unfriendly stares from some of the lorry-drivers within. One in particular seemed to get quite excited at Joey's rather bizarre appearance, eyeing him with a puzzled expression on his face.

We found a table and were immediately confronted by a swarthy gent with a four-day growth of beard and a grease-stained overall, smoking a cigarette out of the corner of his mouth with about an inch and a half of ash dangling at the end of it. "Bitte?" he said, in an uninterested tone of voice, and gave us a look that stated that he considered it below his station to have to serve such dregs of humanity.

"Guten morgen, mein herr! Konnen wir vier kaffee und vier wursten mit brot haben, bitte!"

Joey was impressed. "Bloody hell, Trudi, you don't half speak good German!" he exclaimed.

"That's because she is German, you dozy sod!" Stuart shook his head in pity. "Moron!" he murmured, more for his own satisfaction than Joey's enlightenment.

I wondered why Trudi hadn't ordered in English, and got a long explanation that I found quite interesting. She held up her hand with an inch between her finger and her thumb, to show how little some Germans knew of English. "Kleine," she said. "Not enough to engage in conversation. Do you understand?"

"Jawohl!" I said, teasing her.

A smile creased her face. "Sprechen Sie Deustch?"

"Nein," I said, shaking my head and chuckling, "You'll have to give me lessons."

"Maybe I will," she replied, and set off on another giggling fit.

Clearly not happy at watching our little tête a tête, Stuart piped up with a disgruntled, "And just what's so bloody funny?"

"Nothing," I told him, "we were just having a chat, as one does."

"About what exactly?" he continued, pressing on regardless.

"This and that, you know. Just chatting. Like, what's the price of fish in Bremerhaven, and that kind of thing. Just chatting..."

"What about the price of fish in Bemerhaven?" Joe asked, desperately trying to figure out what was going on.

"Joey," I said.

"What?"

"Just shut the fuck up, and eat your wursten, will you!"

With breakfast nicely in place, we finally took off on our jaunt with full bellies and in a good mood and happy frame of mind.

The city of Schleswig was left behind as we headed into the unknown through a landscape of fields and woodland that stretched as far as the eye could see, and somehow eased the pressure of confinement that had slowly been suffocating us during the past week or so.

The good-humoured banter between us was of the usual infantile style, intermingled with smiles and laughter. I think we were probably all equally surprised to realise that we were actually enjoying ourselves!

Then Joey sniffed the air with his big red nose. "What's that smell?" he asked.

"What smell?" My nose was bunged up and I wouldn't have smelt a haddock if it had been held in my face, while Stu came with the expected suggestions to what might have caused it.

A couple of minutes passed with Joey strangely silent and concentrated. "What is that fucking' smell?" he repeated. "It's driving me up the wall." He slammed on the brakes to bring us to a stop, and we heard a hub-cap detach itself from the wheel and watched as it skittered off to disappear into a ditch fifty yards further down the road.

Joey was dismayed. "Shit!" he howled, "they're five quid a piece they are!" Then he jumped out of the van to check for damage, swearing under his breath and contemplating the economic consequences of his loss, while Stu and I enjoyed his distress.

Whatever it was, the smell stayed with us as we drove on, minus one hub-cap, and even Joey seemed to get used to it. He relaxed and accepted it, for there really wasn't much else he could do.

After enjoying the scenery for a couple of hours, and relaxing in the warmth of the van, we decided to stop at a small pub we saw closing in on us. It was a half-timbered building bearing a sign that stated *Weinstuben* on it. "Is that a pub?" Joey asked just to be certain, then pulled off the road and parked the van by the entrance.

It was a warm and cosy place, with a log fire burning fit to put me to sleep. With a glass of frothy German beer at hand, it almost did. After a while Stu noticed a snooker table and suggested a game. Joey was in, already half-way there. "I'll give you game," he said, "and we'll make it one mark a frame just to make it interesting."

Trudi took the opportunity to go to the ladies room, so I was left alone, peacefully gazing into the dancing flames from the fire, content and relaxed and letting my mind drift. Who would have thought that I would find myself supping beer in a strange place called Eckenforde, by the Baltic Sea; that I would be playing for hordes of Germans who obviously loved what we were doing from up on that stage? It was a lifetime away from my own local and my old life. And it was certainly a far cry from the Blacon British Legion Club where I had made my debut during the break between the bingo sessions with Johnny Byrnes and The Dateliners all those years ago. It had been our first professional gig, if you could call it that. For our pains the secretary had given us a ten bob note. "Here you are lads," he said as he handed it over, "nip to the bar and get yourselves a drink." And our fee for the evening immediately disappeared back into the bar till from where it had just been taken.

I smiled at the memories and was in the process of allowing new ones to enter my mind when my thoughts were suddenly interrupted by Trudi's return. She patted me on the head as she sat down. "A pfennig for your thoughts, Biffo?" She sat down beside me and crossed her legs provocatively, showing acres of thigh that I could hardly keep my eyes away from. She couldn't help but notice. "You like my legs?" she asked with a wicked smile on her face.

What could I say? "Yes, very nice," I mumbled, and brought the glass to fill my face and hide my embarrassment. Actually, her legs were not all I liked. I loved the blonde hair that tumbled down to her shoulders, her blue eyes that positively sparkled, and her cute, slightly turned up nose. Everything about her was appealing; her sensuous lips and engaging smile, and the way her face lit up when she laughed, which she seemed to do all the time. "Yes, Trudi," I admitted, "I do like your legs."

It could have been the effect of the beer, or the warm and comfortable surroundings I found myself in, but right then, Trudi was certainly looking very attractive indeed, and I was beginning to fancy her rotten. I lit a cigarette simply to have my mind occupied with something else, and allowed the smoke to drain from my nostrils in an attempt to look cool, but this illusion was quickly shattered when the smoke made me sneeze loudly.

We sat without speaking for a couple of minutes until we both felt uncomfortable in the silence. She seemed to have run out of things to say, or was possibly embarrassed by my compliments, while I was trying to figure out what had made me give them in the first place.

The laughter and bickering from Joey and Stuart, still noisily playing snooker, attracted her attention. "They are a noisy pair," she commented, and smiled. "They are always laughing and joking, ja?"

"They're both good mates, but they just like to have a few laughs taking the mickey out of each other," I explained. "But it's all just harmless fun."

"And David is also good fun," she said, "and very friendly and popular with the girls." As if I didn't know!

"Yes, all the girls fall for Dave," I told her. "He can choose anyone he wants. I'm only surprised that he didn't pick you, because you're a very attractive lass, if you don't mind me saying so."

She gave me a knowing look, and shook her head. "Do you think so?"

I could have kicked myself for what I heard myself saying, but the excitement of having said it and realising that this little repartee might go even further, spurred me on. "Of course, I do. I wouldn't have said it if I didn't," I told her. "You're a beautiful girl."

She almost blushed, and demurely lowered her lashes for a moment. "Thank you," she said, then brought the conversation back on the rails. "David is very handsome, but he is not for me. He is too preoccupied with how he looks, and very vain about his appearance. Not like Joe and Stuart. You know, Stu is very funny and has a lot of charisma, and I like to be with him."

"Then he's a lucky bloke," I mumbled, and meant it.

She gave me an appraising look that lasted too long for my comfort. "You are not like them though, are you?" she asked, without really expecting a reply. "You are more quiet and serious," she decided. "But you have no girl. Do you not like girls?"

Well that was one that I didn't want left hanging about. "Of course I do!" I told her, mildly affronted at the very suggestion. "The thing is, I haven't got the confidence to chase women, and I got hurt a bit when my girlfriend dumped me. After that, I decided that I wouldn't get involved again. That way, I couldn't be rejected. So I keep my distance for self-preservation, and not because I don't want a good-hearted woman in my arms."

I didn't realise it at the time, but the expression on her face and the light in her eyes showed the effect my words were having on her. Suddenly I seemed to be interesting. A challenge. If only I had understood how such openhearted confession could effect the weaker sex, I would have been mouthing away for years, and getting well recompensed for my trouble. That kind of candid confession seemed to bring out the maternal instinct in the most hardened female soul, bringing succour with it, like Florence Nightingale holding the lamp to show the way.

"You have an honest face," she told me, which was a surprising statement. "And I love your deep brown eyes" which really made me squirm and grab for a new cigarette. "They are just like a puppy dog." So that was why she had patted me on the head! I thought she might be about to throw a stick for me to fetch. "Do you have a girlfriend at home?" she solicitously enquired of me.

I informed her that I did have before, but that she had given me the elbow in January. At this news, she almost fell off her chair. "January!" she gasped, open-mouthed. "Why, that is a long time to be without a girl!" She was right about that. "And it is a very long time with no rumpy-pumpy!" She was bang-on there too.

I laughed at her openness. "Yeah, I suppose you're right," I admitted, "but you get used to it. It's like giving up fags – hard to begin with, but easier as time goes by."

She shook her head in disbelief, and some degree of pity. "That is sad," she said, "that is very sad."

I thought that things were beginning to become just a little bit too personal, so I grabbed my glass for comfort. Just then, Stu and Joe thankfully came back after having finished their game. "Who won?" I asked them, all interest.

"This ginger bugger beat me five games to one, and I owe him four marks. But he was cheating," Stuart moaned, obviously not too happy about being beaten. Joey pocketed Stu's money with a smirk of triumph, and we pulled on our coats and headed out into the cold to continue our sight-seeing.

As we drove off, I heard Stuart enquiring about my lit-tle conversation with Trudi, wondering what we had been laughing and joking about earlier. The more she told him, the more he asked, and the more I realised that he was both suspicious and jealous. Tiring of listening to his interroga-tion I turned around to him. "For Christ's sake, leave the girl alone, Stuart. If you really want to know, we were plot-ting how we could all be rid of you, and make the world a better place so me and Trudi could ride into the sunset on a white stallion to live a life of debauchery without you bothering us with your fucking stupid questions!" I finished on a high note.

That slowed him down for a while, and he remained quiet, probably deciding whether or not to believe it. Joey laughed fit to burst, while I sat with a self-satisfied smirk on my face, quite pleased with my little tirade, and reliving it word for word. I eventually relented, and informed him in a less harsh voice, "We were only being sociable, when you two idiots were playing with your balls," I told him. "We were only chat-ting, and if you want to know, Trudi was telling me that you were a nice bloke, very funny, and with a lot of charisma, and that she likes you very much!"

Just then Trudi calls for Joey to take a left turn he was about to miss, and he wrenched the steering wheel hard left in a squeal of screaming tyres that had us falling about inside the van, then we heard the familiar metallic clatter of yet another hub-cap detaching itself to skitter merrily down the road and disappear. "Getting to be an expensive day, eh Joe?" I chided him, pulling myself back into my seat.

Hunched over the steering wheel, he grimaced. "Too fuckin' right, Biffo!" He sighed. "Who's daft idea was it come on this friggin' Sunday drive, anyway?"

"Yours, you dozy bugger!" Stu and I sang out in chorus, chortling away at his misfortune.

Unknown to us, a police car had been witness to our rather erratic driving and decided to follow us as we drove off again. Joey became aware of the fact when he saw flashing blue lights in the mirror closing on us quickly, and then we heard the siren screaming away and putting the fear of God into us. "What the fuck's up now!" Joey whined.

We duly pulled to a stop and two policemen strode menacingly towards us. "Name and nationality, bitte?" they briskly demanded of Ginger Joe, whose creased features stared back at them through the open window.

Joey calmly told them. "Donald!" he stated in crisp English. "Donald Duck!" He let this information sink in, before continuing. "My companions and I are all English, whilst the giggling young lady in the back is from Schleswig, and is, as such, German. Her name is Trudi."

I sank further down into my seat and buried my head in my hands, thinking for God's sake, Joey, shut up before you get us all arrested! Completely unfazed by Joey's response, the senior official opened his mouth again. "Right, Herr Duck, would you please get out of the vehicle." I could hear Stuart chuckling away in the back seat, ready to burst, but I doubted that Trudi was finding the incident quite as amusing.

I cast a careful glance at the other policeman and saw an inkling of a smile on his face, as Joey showed his papers to the other officer. Then I heard Joey start up again, and I grimaced and wondered where I could hide. "What appears to be the problem, officer?" he enquired, going into his *pretending to be drunk routine*. "Lisjen ociffers," he said, rolling his piggy eyes and staggering slightly, "I'm not ash drunk as many thinkle peep I am, honest!" The two officers could no longer contain themselves, and they both cracked up laughing at Joey's lunatic antics. Joey turned to us and gave us a wink and a thumbs-up.

It took them a minute or two to compose themselves, before sanity again returned to the situation, bizarre as it was.

"Herr Duck, or may I call you Donald?" said the senior officer, which immediately set the younger one off in another uncontrollable fit of laughter. The senior man studied him for a moment, managing to keep his face straight, then continued. "Donald, would you please keep an eye on your speedometer when you drive around here, and slow down when you turn corners. Is that okay, Herr Duck?"

The other officer then bent his head into the van to enquire where the blonde haired bass player was. "The one who attracts all the frauleins like flies to cow-shit," he said. It was then that I recognised him as being one of the gang who had been giving us the evil eye for attracting all the women the other night. I noticed that the smile had left his face, and he was no longer laughing, and I thought that the night might still not be over, and suddenly had visions of damp cellars and truncheons running around my head.

"Oh," Joey butted in, as he always did, but totally unaware of the situation I had sensed, "Dave's probably giving Doris what's-her-name a right good seeing to right now!" and beamed all over his stupid red face. I didn't think this was the news the policeman most wanted to hear, and Joey's flippant answer did nothing to improve the look on his sullen face.

We were saved from whatever fate would otherwise have befallen us, by the sound of the radio in the police car calling them up. Apparently, or should I say, thankfully, there had been an accident in Eckenforde, and the two policemen got in their car and we watched with some relief as it sped away into the distance.

Donald The Ginger Haired Duck put the van in gear, and brought us back out on the road, and soon had us driving at some considerable speed, apparently having forgotten the policeman's warning. We had only driven a couple of miles when the road split. Joey didn't hesitate for a moment, and roared full throttle to the left. A frantic cry from Trudi in the back-seat informing him that he had taken the wrong road made the maniac slam on the brakes so the van swerved from side to side, with a squeal of burning rubber on tarmac and completely out of control. I braced myself and prepared to die, but the van came to a standstill with no other damage than my badly frayed nerves.

"So we're on the wrong road, are we?" We were engulfed by the smoke and stench from the burnt tyres, and had just missed the bus to eternity by about half a second, but Joey was as calm as could be. "Then we'll just have to get back on the right one," he said, and drove off again. None of us said a word; we were still speechless from the shock. I thought that we must surely have used up our quota of misfortunes for the day, and that the rest of the trip back to base would be uneventful. But I was wrong.

A sudden loud bang almost made me wet myself from the shock, and resulted in our ginger- haired driver wrestling with the wheel with a demented look on his face, as he fought to stop the van from slewing sideways into the roadside ditch. He finally managed to end up half way over the grass verge where we came to a stop with a might thud that had my head half way through the roof.

Trudi was screaming to wake the dead, I was trembling with the shock and blabbering away as though I was talking in tongues, there wasn't a sound to be heard from Stuart, which told more than a thousand words, and apart from his shiny red nose, Joey's face was completely drained of colour.

"Is everybody okay?" Joey's voice was almost a whisper.

Stuart regained his voice. "What happened?" The shock was still in his tonsils.

"What happened?" Joey was beginning to regain some colour and his voice was back to basics. "It's a fucking puncture," he said, then got out of the van. He found the offending tyre and began to kick it violently. "Shit! Shit! Shit!" he cursed with each new kick, then gave an extra kick for good measure, accompanied by a heartfelt, "fucking bleeding shit!" which came almost as an afterthought. Just then, Joey was not a happy bunny.

He lit a cigarette while he considered the situation and what had to be done. It was obvious that we would have to change the tyre or the wheel, but that would certainly not be easy, because we would first have to get the van off the grassy bank, and that was going to be more than difficult in the dark.

"Have you got a spare tyre?" Stu enquired.

But Joey had already found salvation in the form of a petrol station we could just make out further down the road. "Right, you shower! Out with you!" he ordered, then proceeded to manoeuvre the van off the bank. We then watched as he carefully drove the van towards the garage, with the deflated tyre making a schwulchy slapping sound, while the three of us trudged forlornly in its wake. By the time we arrived, Joe had already jacked the van up and was in the process of putting the spare in place. "Fuck!" he exclaimed, quite exasperated, "this one's flat as well!"

Trudi saved the situation. After a few words with someone in the garage, the offending tyre was taken away and came back a few minutes later, bouncy and full of pep, and ready to roll. Joey immediately began to struggle with the nuts and bolts of the operation, and was definitely becoming more wrought and tired by the second. He yelled at us. "Are you two shit-brains gonna help me here, or do I have to do everything meself!" So I bent down by his side, and watched as he struggled on, feeling that a little moral support was the least I could offer, but it didn't seem to help. "Bugger off out of my way, you miserable sod!" he snapped at me. "You're a waste of frigging space, Biffo! You're a totally useless prick!" he snarled at me.

I took the hint and decided that others would have to offer him succour in his moment of grief. I turned to Trudi and gave her a smile. "He likes me really," I assured her. Then I suggested that Stuart offer some assistance. "'Ere Stu, give him a hand before the ginger bugger explodes."

I ambled over to sit on a low wall, and lit a cigarette as I surveyed the comical performance acted out before me. I shouted out encouragement to Joey, as he struggled with a nut, "A bit more downward pressure on it, mate, that's what you need!" A cursory *Fuck off!* told me that my valuable advice wasn't required, so I left them to it as I puffed away, quite content to watch their toil.

I was joined by Trudi. She patted my shoulder as she sat down beside me, then gave me a peck on the cheek. "What's all this about?" I asked, somewhat taken aback. "Stuart will deck me if he sees you doing that!"

She was unperturbed. "Why would he do that?" she asked, giving me a broad smile. "It was just a friendly kiss. We are friends, yes? Can't I give a friend a friendly kiss?" She slipped her arm through mine and put her head on my shoulder, and pulled closer to me. "It's getting chilly now," she said. Personally I was getting quite hot under the collar.

I found myself chatting away with the delectable Trudi, quite at ease with her snuggling against me, and enjoying both the conversation and the warmth of her body pressing against me. Our cosy chat was rudely interrupted by the strident sound of Joey's crackling voice shouting, "Jesus, sodding hell!" as he threw the wheel-brace to the ground, leaving the metallic sound to echo around the garage. This was immediately followed by a retaining nut that rolled across the floor with Stuart in hot pursuit to capture it before it fell down a grid.

"This is more entertaining than watching a friggin' pantomime!" I guffawed.

Trudi wondered how I intended to spend the evening, since we had the night off. I didn't have that many options open to me, so I told her that I would probably end up in Otto's bar, having numerous beers and getting plastered, which was more or less what I had in mind.

She gave me a demure smile, and reminded me that Henni has said she would be coming in that evening.

"I'd almost forgotten about her," I admitted, and was surprised to realise it was true. "With spending the whole day in your very pleasant company, I haven't had a chance to think about her."

She gave me another of her enigmatic smiles. "Danke!" she said rather coyly. "You are always giving me compliments, Biffo. I think you are a nice guy."

I took a quick glance in the direction of the two moaning mechanics to make sure that Stu was keeping busy. If he saw us this close and laughing things might get ugly. But they were still valiantly striving to get the wheel in place, so we continued our little tête a tête undisturbed, until Joey's bark interrupted us. "Get your arses over here," he shouted, "or we're sodding off without you!" So we scurried towards the van. Trudi's arm was still linked through mine, and I remember thinking that was not a sensible way to approach her oil-greased lover. As I clambered into the van, Stuart gave me a cursory glance, but said nothing. I saw Joey had a handkerchief wrapped around his hand with blood seeping through it. I pointed at it. "What happened?" I asked with some concern.

"What happened!" he yelled. "When you were sittin' on your arse doing nowt as usual, I slipped with that friggin' wheel-brace and took all the skin off me knuckles!" The voice came back to the normal grating sound that emanated from his mouth. "It didn't half hurt," he whined. "I'm surprised you didn't hear me yellin'."

I laughed. "Believe me, Joe. We did!"

I carefully examined his hand as it rested on the steering-wheel, showing genuine concern as I studied it. "Is it serious, Joe?" I asked him, looking worried. "I mean, we really do have a right to know. Is it …?" I swallowed. "Is it …?" I braced myself, ready to hear the worst. "Is it your J. Arthur hand?"

Stuart fell about on the back seat in pleats of laughter. Even Joey grinned. "Go forth and multiply!" he told me, but the grin stayed on his face as he drove on into the darkness.

We finally arrived back in Schleswig. I knew we were back because I recognised the roundabout, and wondered how many turns Joey would take before deciding where he was going, but for once, he got it right first time. Trudi gave Stu a kiss when we dropped her off, then waved and blew me a kiss as she walked away from the van. He noticed. "What the fuck was that all about?" he asked suspiciously.

"How would I know?" I retorted. "But your little lady is a right friendly girl, isn't she!"

I could see the seeds of suspicion that had been planted earlier in the day were already growing big enough to cast shadows. I didn't like it, but then again, I found it exciting, as though Trudi and I were elicit lovers playing a game with Stu behind his back, just waiting to get discovered. I knew that everything between us had been quite above board, but the fact that I was suddenly the man in the middle as far as he was concerned, gave me a thrill.

Dave was sitting alone and forlorn at a table in the bar when we finally arrived, and we were greeted with a sour, "Where the fuck have you lot been all day? I've been stuck here on me own for bloody hours!" he moaned.

"You never bother about where we are when you're hanging out with that Doris bird," I pointed out. "So where is she? Worn the poor cow out, have you?"

He gradually relaxed in the knowledge that we were finally back, and managed a smile. "It's a long story," he said. "I'll tell you about it later." Then he remembered that he was supposed to be the hurt party, and went on, "It would have been nice if you could have left a note, when you were going off somewhere. At least, then I wouldn't have to worry about you." As if!

"We did leave a note for you, you dozy bugger!" Stu informed him. "Trudi wrote it and put it on your pillow!"

"I know," Dave confirmed the fact. "I found it."

"Well, there you are, then you knew where we were!"

"No I didn't," he protested. "That note was in bloody German!"

Joey sat with a face smeared black with grease, nursing his injured hand and feeling sorry for himself, and gloomily informed Dave of our days outing. "It's been a bloody pain in the arse, mate," he told him. "I've lost two friggin' hub-caps, I've been stopped by the police, we got a major blow-out that almost killed us and means we have to buy a new tyre, and I've ripped me bloody hand apart." He was hoping for pity, but didn't get any.

"Anything else interesting happen?"

"Only that we found out that you're a marked man, mate!"

I told him in a serious voice. "We ran into some policeman who was very interested in your whereabouts, so I'd watch my back if I was you."

Dave got a worried look on his face. "Shit!" he said. "That must be the one Doris has warned me about. She says he's the jealous sort, and fancies her rotten. He's a vicious bastard who beats up on his rivals." The worry on his face dug deeper with each word.

"Well, that certainly explains a lot, eh?" We all turned to Stuart, waiting for more. "It was obvious that the bugger's got it in for Dave, here. So now he'll be coming in again to hear him play and straighten his ugly mug for him afterwards."

Dave's face fell, and the colour drained from it. "D'ya think so?" he wailed with his eyes almost popping out of his head at the thought.

"Naw," said Stu. "Nothing could improve that ugly mug of yours!"

Day Off
– Sunday
Evening

Following an enjoyable hour spent in the bar relaxing and re-living the events of the day, I returned to our rooms to have a wash and shave and to change my clothes. I even decided that a dash or two of Old Spice was in order in case Henni actually did turn up later on – well, you do have to make a little effort don't you, and I was beginning to smell a bit niffy after a week or so living in such dismal conditions.

I was sitting on the edge of the creaky old bed when I became aware of Stuart leaning on the doorframe to my room, staring intently at me. His face was devoid of its usual friendly smile and the eyes had lost their sparkle. I feared the worst. He closed the door behind him. "I'd like a word with you about this afternoon," he said. "Do you understand?" I understood only too well. "I'm not fucking blind, you know. So I want to know, what's goin' on?"

"Going on?" I said. "What do you mean, going on?" clutching at straws to get time to think.

"Don't piss about, mate! You know bloody well what I'm talking about. You and Trudi!"

"Me and Trudi? What about me and Trudi?"

"Every time I looked around today, the pair of you were being very friendly, whispering and giggling. I saw you on that wall at the garage, all chummy and close, with her arm around you and planting a kiss on your ugly mush."

I decided that attack was the better part of defence, so I went for his throat. "What a load of bollocks! It's all in your perverted frigging imagination, you soft git!"

"Oh yeah?" He sneered at me. "Then why was she blowing bloody kisses at you when she got out of the van?"

"I've already told you," I told him again, "I don't bloody know!" I saw that he didn't believe me. "Bloody hell, Stu, you're a right insecure bastard, aren't you!" I relented. "Anyway, Trudi's not my type," I lied, "I wouldn't touch her with a barge-pole."

The smile came back on his face where it belonged, and he chuckled. "You lying bastard!"

Happily, I was off the hook, and quite relieved as we joined the others in the bar downstairs. It was already filling up with other drunks and dysfunctionals like ourselves, including the crazy woman who was already putting more cash on the juke-box to play old Sandie's record over again. Johan was there too, as usual. I sometimes wondered when he had time to check the toilets, for he seemed to be a permanent fixture in the bar. When he heard we had been to Eckenforde that day, he told me that he had once worked there for a week. "It was at the sprat smoking factory," he informed me. "I couldn't take more than one week working there, because I just could not stand the smell."

From sprat-smoking to shitehousemeister, and preferring the latter to the first, was a new one on me. He really had moved up in the world and found his true vocation in life. I chuckled at the thought, but had the decency to remain silent.

Instead I expressed some wonder at the fact that this venue was quite a happy and cosy place to play and drink. It wasn't how I had expected the Star Palast circuit to be. I recalled Lonnie's warning about the owner being a gangster.

"He is," Johan said, without a hint of exaggeration in his voice. "Manfred is a gangster and runs his empire quite ruthlessly from his base in Kiel," he told me. "Herr Müller is revered by some, but feared by many more. Anyone who falls foul of him will feel his wrath, and for some it can have very serious repercussions …" His voice trailed off.

I was now enthralled by what I was hearing. "What, you mean like ending up in a concrete overcoat with the sprats in the Baltic?"

He nodded his head. "Something like that, yes."

"So we don't annoy him, right?"

He only stared back into my face without replying, but that look spoke a thousand words, and was quite enough for me.

It turned out that our present venue was not part of the Star Palast circuit as such, but a place where Manfred Müller tested his new groups to see if they were good enough for the circuit proper. If a group wasn't up to it, they would be unceremoniously shipped back home. The fact that we were still on German soil seemed to indicate that we had passed the test.

I wondered where we would be sent when we were finished with our stint in Schleswig. After all we were there for six weeks, and had five weeks of our contract left. "You might be here for another week. Then you will either be sent to Lüneburg, Flensburg or possibly to the Start Palast in Kiel which is the biggest and most important in Manfred Müller's empire," Johan informed me. But he guessed that we would finish our tour in Kiel.

I noticed that Doris had arrived and was already wrapped around her hero, whispering sweet nothings in his ear, and to Joey's obvious relief, Maria had found her way back to him and was giving him her undivided attention. I wondered if she was short-sighted, for as nice a bloke as Joey certainly was, I couldn't understand what she found appealing about him. A lived-in ruddy face with a nose throbbing away like a Belisha beacon, topped with a mop of unruly ginger hair, couldn't have been anyone's idea of handsome, but there she was, eating him alive. I decided that it must be his extreme tackle, which was a veritable legend among the women back home – at least, those with faulty eyesight.

Just then the doors opened and in walked Trudi, almost taking my breath away at the sight of her. She was completely dressed in black, from her boots to her neck and everything in between, and her long blonde hair fell over her shoulders in sharp contrast. The whole room stared at her as she walked to our table and sat down. She gave Stuart a kiss, and me one of her trade-mark smiles.

Of course, Joey had to spoil the moment as usual, and re-marked "What's all the black gear for, then? Are you off to a funeral?"

Stuart laughed and joined in. "Or maybe she's joined the local SS!"

The girl was obviously ill at ease with these comments. She had probably spent the last few hours getting nicely dolled up for the occasion, only to be put down as soon as she appeared. I felt sorry for her, and tried to cheer her up. "Don't listen to them," I told her, "I think you look absolutely stunning," and got a grateful smile for my trouble.

The night wore on with the beer flowing and animated conversation intermingled with raucous laughter ringing about us. We were all enjoying ourselves. All that is, except Trudi. The smile had long-since left her face, and she sat in silence biting her bottom lip and staring into the distance. She must have noticed that I was looking at her, and gave me a weak smile. "So you're back from wherever you've been, then," I said, giving her a smile to cheer her up. "A good trip was it?" She sighed, but didn't reply. I thought I saw a tear in the corner of her eye, but then my attention was caught by some antic from Joey.

I looked at my watch, and wondered if Henni was actually going to turn up as promised. It was getting late, but there was still plenty of time. I hoped she would. Just then, unhappy Trudi said something to Maria in German, and they both got up and headed for the toilets. I don't think either Stu or Joey noticed. Dave certainly didn't with Doris' tongue half-way down his throat. Stuart was telling Joey a joke which I didn't bother to listen to, then Joey cracked into uncontrollable laughter that had him rocking so much that he fell off his chair and crashed to the floor, taking a couple of glasses with him. Naturally this attracted some attention, but it was the sight of Joey's ginger top and bulbous red nose just showing above the table-top from his position on the floor, that had us all laughing loudly. "Piss off you bastards!" he howled, "I could have done myself an injury!"

In the midst of our laughter, the two girls had reappeared. I noticed that Trudi was looking considerably brighter, but looking at the redness around her eyes it was obvious that she had been crying, and I felt for her. But then my attention was drawn away from the damsel in distress, as the doors swung open, and Henni came towards me with a smile so warm it could have melted an iceberg. I got up to greet her – it must have been love – and got a kiss on the cheek in return.

Dave managed to untangle himself from the mass of woman in heat that clung to him, to enquire, "Who's this then?" as he gave Henni the once-over and flashed his teeth at her. "No wonder you fancy her," he said aloud, "she's a little cracker, isn't she?"

Joey had been strangely quiet for what, a whole minute, and decided to put in his three pennies worth. "'Ere! I'm ready to bet any comers that Biffo 'ere doesn't get his leg over with her! Anyone want to bet?"

I was absolutely horrified, and felt acutely embarrassed by his outburst. I really could have killed him on the spot. Instead I turned to Henni to apologise. "Sorry about that, but the ginger idiot has had a fraught day and one too many sherberts."

She smiled back at me. "Don't worry. I've heard a lot worse." I could have kissed her with relief. In fact I could have kissed her without relief too, for she was really attractive. The others lost interest and left us to ourselves. I noticed that everything seemed to go into a blur around us again, and my mind and emotions were entirely focused on the vision before me. It was almost unbelievable that I was gazing into the eyes of such a beautiful girl, who was smiling and giving me her undivided attention as though I really meant something to her. For someone who had made an art form out of low self-esteem and self-pity this was heaven, and time passed in total bliss.

After some time, I noticed that Dave had taken his leave, with Doris, not surprisingly, also missing. I didn't need to be a member of Mensa to know where they had gone. Joey was gyrating like a pudding on the dance-floor, with Maria laughing at his antics. I had never seen him dance before. Seeing him now, I understood why, because he looked like the rear-end of a pantomime horse, and might as well have been for the lack of grace and coordination he showed. But he was making up for his lack of talent with exaggerated exuberance.

Stuart on the other hand, seemed withdrawn. He had a distant look on his face, and was deep in his own thoughts. A small humourless smile was fixed on his face. I put this down to the fact that he had gone from beers to vodka, which was his favourite tipple. I thought that boded no good, but the rate he was packing back the shorts would certainly get him skunk-drunk in quick time. He noticed me looking at him and raised his glass to me. "Cheers Biffo!" he said. "And thanks!" For what, I had no idea. Then he rambled over to the bar and joined a group of rowdy young people standing there.

Trudi looked aghast as he remained with them, leaving her to herself. She looked as though she was about to cry, then left the table and headed for the toilets again, biting her lower lip as she made her way there. I had no idea what had happened, but something must have been said or done, and I felt genuinely sorry for the lass, and perhaps a little guilty.

My attention was brought back into sharp focus with the words, "Hello, remember me?" I apologised to Henni, and explained what I had just witnessed. "Perhaps they have had an argument," she suggested, looking unconcerned. There had certainly been a cold atmosphere between them for the past couple of hours. "Perhaps that is why your friend is drinking so heavily at the bar?" she wondered, and I looked up to see she was right, and Peter was really putting it down, with gusto!

It wasn't too hard to forget these details, as we began to get to know each other, discovering that we were enjoying each others company, talking and laughing, with enough innuendo to make even a dumb-skull like me realise that we were flirting. The more we talked the more I fell hopelessly in love, but the unbelievable was actually happening, and I could feel it – she was showing a similar attraction towards me. It was completely unlike me in every way, but I found myself swooning away with the kind of stuff that would have made me sick to hear others say. "When I first saw you, you took my breath away," I told her, leaning close and staring into her baby-blue eyes. "I've never seen such a beautiful girl in my life!"

I was shocked and surprised at what I heard coming out of my mouth, and expected her to laugh me in the face, but her eyes widened, as did the smile on her face, and she leaned across the table and kissed me full on the lips. "That is the sweetest compliment I have ever had," she trilled. "Thank you."

It was then that Trudi found it opportune to return to our table. She was still clearly unhappy. I gave her a quick smile, but she averted her eyes. I decided that the time was ripe for a refill, if only to get away from whatever problems were lying dormant on Trudi's side of the table. "Would you like another drink, Henni?" I asked, but she didn't. Apparently, one was enough, which seemed somewhat out of character for the place. Anyway, she explained, she would soon have to go, because her father was coming to pick her up.

She must have seen the disappointment written on my face, because she hurriedly explained, "I have to get up early to take exams at the college, otherwise I would stay. I have exams all week, but I will come back here next Friday." Then she brightened. "It is my birthday, and I will be celebrating with all my friends." Then a worried look crossed her brow. "I will see you then? You will be here?" she asked uncertainly.

"Definitely," I assured her, "you couldn't keep me away!" and gave her a warm smile.

I noticed the cold chill as the door opened, and looked up to see a stranger enter and walk towards us. He was obviously Henni's father. "Pappa, this is Biffo, who I have told you about," she said, introducing us. He bowed his head slightly, shook my hand, and gave me a Guten Abend. I swear blind, if he had clicked his heels together like a true Nazi, I wouldn't have been surprised.

Henni gave me a smile and a quick peck on the cheek. "See you on Friday!" she called to me as they reached the door, then they passed through it, and were gone, leaving me alone with my thoughts, feeling like a tyre with a slow puncture.

I was brutally shaken back to reality by Joey's raspy voice in my ear. "You dozy bugger," her sneered, "you'll never learn, will you!" He was grinning like the inane maniac he was. "I've just been watching your pathetic performance, with all the bowing and scraping for her old fellah," he chuckled. "You do it every time, don't you!" I was going to ask what I was doing all the time, but he beat me to it. "As soon as a bird gives you a smile, you put her on a friggin' pedestal, and what happens then, you chuff?" He still didn't wait for a response. "When you've put them up there, you let them shit on you from a great height, that's what!" He smirked. "Just like that Anne bird at home!" I cringed at the mention of her name, and almost cried for mercy.

"Ah! But …" I stuttered, trying to find a valid reply to his taunting jibes, but nothing came out, so Joey went for the jugular.

"Don't give me any of your limp-wristed, arty-farty excuses," he sneered. "You know it's true, so face up to the fact that she used you. She shit on you from a great height!" Then Uncle Joe gave his errant pupil the Facts of Life According to Joe, as though they had been written in stone and carried on his shoulder from the top of the mountain. "Treat 'em mean, and keep 'em keen!" Having offered me these words of wisdom, he gave me a wink, and a pat on the back, as though to say that now that I had been told the secret, I was ready to face the world. Thank God, he then wandered off to bother someone else.

His cutting remarks pranced around in my mind, and I began to feel depressed. The evening had begun so well, and had developed to a fantastic level, only to end in the course of minutes, leaving me alone and disappointed. It only took Joey's momentary presence to crush the disappointment into drops of total depression. I never had Joey down as an advisor on affairs of the heart, but perhaps he was right on this particular point. Perhaps I shouldn't allow myself to fall too hard, and show it? Anne had certainly given me the knocks when I did, and I still had the bruises to prove it.

My moment of despondency didn't last too long however. As I looked up, I saw a long-missed smile on Trudi's face, that shone a beacon of light into the gloom surrounding me. She changed places to sit next to me. "Do you mind if I sit here?" she asked, and put her arm around my shoulder. I cast a nervous glance in Stuart's direction to see what he was up to, but there was no cause for concern, for he was holding court with his new-found admirers. He was the centre of attraction as he played his guitar and sang an unending collection of pub songs from back home. He was in a boisterous mood, and his eyes were twinkling merrily as he entertained the mob. This happy state of affairs was no doubt brought on by the fact that he was now drinking vodka straight from the bottle between each new song – and there were many songs! Stu was as high as a kite and enjoying himself silly. The rapturous applause from his audience only spurred him on to new songs and more booze. I could see that the bottle was almost empty, but Stuart's cup of happiness was running over. It was good to see him happy again, but looking at the evidence of his vodka-intake, I wondered at what cost it would be.

Seeing no immediate danger of a Scouse Kiss splitting my nose, I let Trudi's arm rest where it was. "Are you okay?" I asked her, wanting to show that I knew she was unhappy, and prepared to share her burden with her.

She looked at me intently with sad and searching eyes, as she spoke. "Why is he like this tonight?" she asked miserably. "I gave him a kiss on the cheek when I came, but there was no reaction from him at all. He seems aloof, and he has ignored me all night. Why is he being so cold and indifferent to me, Biffo," she snivelled, "has he said anything to you?"

Well he had, and he hadn't, so I decided not to take that road, and just shook my head. But she kept prodding, so in the end I told her of Stuart's comments regarding our little tête à tête on the wall at the garage, and the fact that she had blown me a kiss when she had left the van.

She stared across at Stu, who by now was totally oblivious to the fact that she and I were very close and in intimate conversation. "So that is what this is all about," she said, and smiled, "jealousy."

"Has he got any reason to be jealous?" I asked, and waited for a reply that didn't come. "After all we're only friends, aren't we? We are friends, right?"

"Yes." She nodded her head but kept her eyes on me. "Very good friends, too!" She gave me a smile. "I like you very much, and like to be with you." By now I was beginning to fidget nervously. "You know, Biffo, you are a very nice guy." As an afterthought, she added, "And I love your deep brown puppy eyes," which almost had me squirming.

I ummed and arred before I managed to form a sentence. "That's very flattering. Thank you." Then I decided that I had to get her off my back, because I could definitely feel her about to climb on board. So I began to run myself down. After years of practice, it wasn't too difficult. "I'm just a self-centred bastard with a chip on my shoulder," I told her. "I'm anti-social and can be a real pain in the arse, and I'm so depressing to be with, that even I get depressed being with me, and I'm depressed most of the time. To top it all, I'm the king of losers. So basically, I'm not worth bothering about. Any girl with any sense, should keep her distance," I warned her. Having said it, though, I felt depressed at the realisation that it was all true. "Anyway, Trudi," I continued, "you shouldn't take Stuart's behaviour to heart. Mark my words, he'll be back to his usual jovial self by tomorrow."

Trudi made no comment. Instead, she changed the subject. "Did you enjoy your evening with Henni tonight?" she asked. "She is a very pretty girl." Why did she keep saying that?

"Definitely!" I assured her with some exuberance. Then I admitted that it hadn't quite been up to my expectations. "It wasn't exactly an evening though," I looked at my watch to show what I meant, "I mean I've spent longer waiting for a bus!"

Trudi laughed, possibly for the first time that evening. "I like someone who can make me laugh," she informed me. "Laughter is infectious, is it not?"

I thought about the remark Stu had made about girls falling for blokes who could make them laugh. Perhaps he had a valid point. Although, come to think of it, in my own personal experience, girls had a tendency to laugh at me rather than with me. But that's another kettle of fish.

I may have been slow, but I was getting the distinct impression that we had crossed a line, and were about to cross another, and this realisation made me nervous and very uncertain. Trudi was a very attractive girl and was certainly coming on to me. Even I noticed that. And my own attraction to her was becoming evident. I crossed my legs to hide the evidence. Then again, Stuart was my mate, and although he was still busy with his entourage, I couldn't go behind his back. And then there was Henni! God, but this was becoming complicated, and damned frustrating!

"It's Henni's birthday next Friday," she said. "With all the joking about you not having a woman, perhaps you will get lucky then." She winked at me and smiled provocatively.

"Yeah, if you believe in Santa Claus and the Tooth Fairies," I replied. "I know that just won't happen, believe me." Then, to try to get away from my embarrassment, because this was beginning to become very personal, I informed her, "Anyway, by next Friday, we'll probably have been moved somewhere else."

This news certainly wiped the smile from her lovely face. "No, you can't leave!" she said, with desperation in her voice. It quite took me back.

"You know as well as I do, that all the groups come and go," I told her. "Well, we've come," I said, and tried a bit of levity, "that is, all except me." But my little joke didn't work, so I continued unabashed, "And now we have to go. That's just the way it is."

Now she was really down in the mouth. Thankfully, Joe turned up, so I turned my attention on him. "You realise we're gonna have to carry that drunk bugger up to his bed," I told him, nodding my head in the direction of the Liverpool Lush, "It's that, or have him break his neck falling down the stairs."

Joey wasn't worried, but then nothing ever worried him. "He'll be alright," he stated, "I've seen him in a worse state than this many times before," and he grinned.

"We'll still have to help him," I insisted.

"It's his own fault he's ended up in that condition. Nobody forced the bugger." Joey was unrepentant, but I knew I could rely on him. You could always rely on Joey if you really needed him.

Just then Maria shouted across to Trudi to inform her that they were going to have to take a taxi home because it was raining, and began to slip on her coat. As Trudi moved by me I caught the scent of her perfume. It was intoxicating. She was so close I could feel the warmth of her body, and I felt the glow rising in me again, but now she was in the process of leaving, and I felt like I had the plague and everyone was running from me – first Henni, and now Trudi. "Will you be back tomorrow?" I almost pleaded.

She shrugged her shoulder. "Maybe," she replied. Then she gave me a wan smile. "Will I be missed if I don't?" she asked, and looked across to Stuart who was totally oblivious to the fact that his girl was about to leave, and to anything else by the look of him.

I felt really sorry for her. I felt pretty depressed myself, so if the pity in my voice was for her or for myself I don't know.

"Well, I know that I'll miss you," I said, and meant it. This moment was interrupted by someone shouting that the taxi had arrived, and Trudi just had time to give me a quick peck on the cheek before she ran to catch up with Maria, and they disappeared through the bar door and into the night.

I was hunched over my beer, feeling miserable, which was my wont, when I caught sight of Joey grinning at me. "What are you grinning at you ginger git?" I demanded.

"You, you dozy sod," he sniggered. "Who the fuck d'ya think I'm smirking at!"

"Why? What's up now?"

"Well, mate, I've known you for quite some time, and seen you do some bloody daft things, but you've certainly surpassed yourself tonight!"

"Stop talking in frigging riddles, will you, and just tell me what you're talking about," I demanded impatiently.

"You really are one of life's losers, aren't you," he told me in a gentle voice. "Who but you would let two birds give you the kiss-off in the same night, eh?" He shook his head in exasperation and rolled is eyes to show what he thought about that. "I mean, they were both ready and willing, slobbering all over you, but you just let them walk away. Now is that daft, or is that stupid? You tell me."

I acknowledged that he was right, and almost kicked myself. I racked my brain for a witty response, but decided it wasn't worth the bother, and simply told him, "Just shut up, Joey!" Surprisingly, he did.

The bar was thinning rapidly, and there were probably only a dozen people left inside when we heard Stuart's slurred voice ring out "Will someone take this fuckin' guitar off me, now!" Joey had no sooner rescued the guitar, before Stu gave one loud burp, farted noisily, and promptly fell off his stool to crumple in a heap on the floor.

"I told you he was bladdered!" I exclaimed to Joey, irritated by his lack of interest when I had touched on the subject earlier.

Looking down at Stuart snoring merrily away on the floor and dead to the world, Joey sniggered, "Well, it's the only thing you have been right about today!"

It was an exhausting struggle, but we finally managed to manhandle the dead weight up the stairs and dump it on the bed. We tried to get his clothes off, but gave up trying once we had managed his boots. "Leave the drunk bastard as he is, Joe, or this will be the death of me," I told him, breathing heavily and ready to drop.

"The death of you may happen before you reckon, mate," he said, with a grin the size of Greenwich, "because I've more than a sneaking feeling that old Stuart's more than pissed off at you chatting up his bird. That's probably why he got blotto tonight."

"That's all it was," I insisted, "talking. Just talking! You know that. You were there."

"True enough. I know that, and you know that. The thing is – does he know that?"

I looked at the lifeless corpse snoring away on the bed, and had to chuckle. "Well he certainly doesn't now!" I said. Then the storm clouds that threatened on tomorrow's horizon brought the worry to my voice. "So you reckon I should tread carefully with him tomorrow, then?"

"Yeah!" replied Joey. "I would if I was you. I definitely would. I think it would be for the best, don't you?"

I did.

Just Another
Manic Monday

I awoke to the sound of agitated voices and Joey's maniacal laughter roaring away in the other bedroom, and wondered what he was laughing at, and more importantly, who he was with. It surely couldn't be Stuart, who must still be dead to the world after having consumed most of the vodka in Schleswig. So who could it be? I wondered, and allowed my befuddled early-morning brain cells to speculate on the question. Who? I thought, and shook my head to think. No, it couldn't be... Who? I thought again, and still didn't find the answer. Who could it be? Who? I was beginning to sound like an owl. I just couldn't understand who it could be. Stu would still be dead; we had left him in his yellow and black t-shirt, looking for all intents and purposes, like a dead wasp. And it couldn't be either Maria or Trudi who had both gone home last night. Dave was out for the night with the delectable Doris, so who could it be?

Having spent the first minutes of my day in such heady intellectual deliberations to no avail, my curiosity finally took the better of me, and I heaved my aching body in an upright position and entered the other room to get the answer to the universal question that had ensnared mankind throughout the centuries, and me with it for several moments: Who?

I was confronted by the sight of Joey lying on his back convulsed in laughter, with his legs flailing wildly about in the air, a scene not unlike that of a fly having been zapped with a can of fly-spray and now in its death-throes. The scene was so comical, and Joey's hysterical laughter so infectious, that I joined in the chorus, laughing with him and at him without really knowing why. A movement to my side gave me a start, and I turned to see Dave forlornly sitting on his bed, staring disconsolately at the floor.

"Bloody hell, Dave," I gasped, "you made me jump!" I had been so engulfed in Joey's hysterics that I hadn't noticed him.

"It'll probably be the only frigging jump you'll be getting in Schleswig," Joey cackled, "so you'd better make the most of it!"

He was probably right, but I decided to ignore him, and instead turned my attention to the sad figure slouched on the bed. "What are you doing here?" I asked, genuinely surprised. "I thought you were spending the night with Doris."

"And so he did!" Joey gasped as he tried to catch his breath between bouts of laughter that were now interspersed with loud hiccups that punctuated the laughter, and only made him laugh even louder.

"Well," Dave sighed audibly, "let's just say that things didn't exactly go to plan." He found a cigarette and lit it. "I'll tell you all about it." This set Joey off on a new burst of hysterics, as he had obviously already been told the tale, and knew what was coming.

As Dave turned towards me I saw a beauty of a black eye, and a deep gash across the bridge of his nose. "What the hell happened to you?" I asked, and a wicked smile crossed my face. "You didn't fall off the wardrobe when you were playing Tarzan to her Jane in one of your kinky sexual games?"

"I should be so lucky," he moaned. then winced in pain as he gave me a quick smile, immediately regretted.

By now my curiosity was bursting. "So what the hell did happen?" I asked eagerly, hoping for some juicy details, and ready to be entertained. I was already wide awake and enjoying myself. This was definitely the best start of the day I had had for a long time.

"Well, you know I've been spending my nights in Doris's comfortable bed at her parents' house when they've been away in Hamburg. It was great, and a damn sight better than being stuck in this hole, with you lot." He nodded his head to indicate our penthouse lodgings. "But early this morning, my luck ran out," he said, and lowered his head in self-pity, apparently oblivious to Joe's renewed hysterics. "I almost shit myself when I heard someone come into the house, and her father shouting out from the bottom of the stairs." He grimaced at the memory. "It couldn't have come at a more inappropriate moment. We were in a sweat and working hard and getting there, and then her dad called for her and came up the stairs, probably attracted to the light from her bedroom." He shuddered noticeably. "I was in a blind panic, and jumped out of the bed to find my clothes."

My attentive interest was momentarily interrupted by guttural sounds coming from Joey as he squirmed on his bed almost choking himself laughing. I left him to his death-throes and returned my attention to Dave.

"The door swung open and I was confronted by a big bloke. He must have been six foot twelve, with arms like Popeye on spinach. He stopped up like he'd been struck by lightning, and just stared at me with bulging eyes. You wouldn't believe the look on his face! Then he looked down at me chopper sticking out like a gun barrel, but falling fast under his steely glare."

Joey was now reduced to hiccups and gasping for air. I was silent and open-mouthed, and impatient to hear more. "Go on, then," I said. "What happened then?"

Dave looked uncomfortable. "The bastard lunged at me and smacked me in the face a couple of times, and then hit me in my stomach so I doubled over in agony and fell on the floor." His hand went to his face and he let his fingers carefully caress his wounds. "Then the sadistic bastard kicked me in the goolies." He shuddered, and used his free hand to cover the aforementioned anatomy as though to confirm that it was still intact and protect whatever was left from further abuse. "I honestly thought my cock was sticking out through the top of my bleeding head!"

By now, Joey had fallen off the bed and was rolling on the floor holding his sides, and ready to burst. I was trying hard to suppress my own mirth in case it stopped the story, which I definitely wanted to hear to the bitter end, but it was hard work. Knowing that Dave would be more interested in sympathy and interest rather than gloating ridicule, I asked, "And just what was Doris doing when all this was going on?" and tried to hide the pleasure his pain was giving me.

"She was screaming and shouting, *Don't kill him! I love him! Leave him alone! Don't kill him!* and stuff like that. But the more she screamed and the more hysterical she became, the more enraged he became, and as I scrambled around trying to pick up my clothes the sadistic sod kicked me straight up the arse so I stumbled forward and fell arse over tit all the way down the stairs. I felt every bleeding riser. It's a wonder I never broke my neck. It was all over in a flash." I could see it before me, in full technicolour, and relished what I saw. There was no way I could still keep a straight face, so I stopped trying, and burst out laughing instead.

But there was more. "Anyway, my fall was broken when I landed on the family dog. It was a frigging German Shepherd called Adolf, and it was not a happy puppy, what with the screaming from upstairs and me falling all over it, so the bleeding thing decides to join in the general mayhem, barking and snarling. It jumped up yowling as I dropped on it, and the bloody thing went berserk and grabbed my ankle. That hurt like bloody hell, and I was so desperate that I started to punch the bugger on the nose, but that only made it come back at me for another go. And, d'ya know, as I lay there trying to defend myself from the frigging dog, Doris's mother comes at me screaming and stomped me on the face, the bloody cow!"

By now I had joined Joey, and we were both helplessly in the grips of hysteria, our laughter now so high-pitched we could have been in the eunuchs' choir. I noticed that Dave had stopped his narrative and was looking positively disgruntled at our lack of sympathy. Fearing that he might refuse to finish the story, I managed to pull myself sufficiently together to show a minimum of sympathy between my juvenile giggling, and begged him to continue.

He seemed to consider my request to and fro before deciding to give me the benefit of the doubt, and continued. "By then I was staggering about like a drunk, with my whole body in excruciating pain. Then I felt a sickening thump on the back of my head, and there's her old man standing over me with one of my own bloody boots in his hand ready to hit me again. Instead he gave me another kick and started screaming at me again like a man possessed, ranting away like a frigging lunatic. I managed to stagger out of the door to get away from him, defeated and bloody, then that fucking Alsation, Adolf, decided to join in the fun again, and sank its teeth into my arse and chased me down the road snarling and barking and taking bits out of me as I ran. The bastard!"

By this time, Joey and I were both beside ourselves, rocking with laughter and with tears rolling down our faces. I had to wait quite some time before my hysterics subsided enough for me to enquire about what happened next.

"Next!" Dave exclaimed indignantly. "Next was trying to get my bloody arse back here as quickly as possible, because I didn't have a stitch on, did I!"

I couldn't believe it. "Naked?" I gasped. I had to repeat it, just to reassure myself that I had heard what I had heard. "Naked!"

"As the day I was born, mate!" he confirmed. "Apart from the pain that went from my head to my ankle, I was freezing cold and getting soaked. I had to dodge down dark alleys and into hedges and hide in shadows whenever I saw anyone coming. I felt like frigging Orson Welles in The Third Man!"

"So what happened to your clothes?" I asked, and felt a smirk coming on again.

"In Doris's bedroom," he replied. After thinking about it, he decided that this was not necessarily so. "Well, most of them were, anyway. The rest, including my boots," and he shook his head sadly as he mourned there loss, "were left strewn down the stairs and the hall, and probably outside the house," he moaned.

"He could at least have let you get your clothes on before kicking you out into the snow," I told him, deciding that he needed some moral support.

"Haven't you been listening, you stupid bastard?" he exclaimed, suddenly getting riled. "The bugger was trying to fucking kill me!" His shoulders sagged again, and he paused before he continued. "The worst part was that dog, Adolf. In all the chaos and pain, I was praying that he wouldn't rip off my crown jewels. I'm telling you, the very thought even makes me sick now!" and a tremble shook his aching body.

Joey was now laughing so much I honestly thought he was going to have a heart attack, but I left him to it, and concentrated on Dave, wondering how he had managed to get back into the building.

"I hid in the bushes next to the cafè across the road, waiting for the last few customers to tumble out, and then I dashed across the road just as Otto was finally locking up, and rushed in. I was shivering and blue with cold. Otto's eyes almost popped out of his head as he stared at me, bollock naked, shrivelled and blue, demanding a double whisky to warm me up and steady my nerves. I told him I'd have to owe him for it, because I had nowt on me."

I couldn't be sure if Dave had just made a joke for the fun of it, or if the joke was on him, but then you never could tell with that blonde bugger, and I could never quite decide if he was simple or just a daydreaming mind-wanderer, or if he really was a smart lad who only pretended to be one or the other to create an even greater aura of mysticism to build his myth upon.

"I had to use both hands to hold the glass, because I was trembling like Little Nelly on her wedding night, but I downed the drink in one go, and then crept up here to find some warmth under my blanket." He looked from me to Joey and back. "I could hear you two snoring, and when I looked at Stu, here," he nodded towards the corpse, "I honestly thought he was dead, but then the bugger farted, so I knew he wasn't." He sighed, and tried a brave smile. "The last think I remember before I fell asleep, was thinking that nobody's ever going to believe me when I tell them."

"I'll tell you what, Dave," Joey chuckled as he dabbed the tears from his eyes, finally having gained control of himself now that the show was over, "that's the best laugh I've had, mate! And we've no option but to believe you considering your injuries and bruising." He noticed Dave's feet, and raised his eyebrows at what he saw there, obviously impressed. "And these teeth marks on your ankle don't lie, do they?" A more worried tone took his voice, as he squinted at the wounds. "They're still bleeding too," he said, then concluded with the observation that Dave should be off to the doctor to get a tetanus jab, just to be on the safe side. Whether this sudden concern was for the patient himself, or for the band, that might suddenly find itself without its bass player and babe-magnet, was of no consequence. But at a guess I'd have to say that the band came first for our erstwhile leader.

"Looking at all those pills and potions he's brought with him, he's more than likely covered for every ailment including bubonic plague," I chuckled.

"Aye, that's right," Dave commented, "everything except a roll of plaster tape to shut your frigging gob up!"

Changing the subject, I asked, "What are you going to do about your clobber?" I mean, he didn't have all that much with him for a start, and what he was going to do without what he had left behind, was a mystery to me. "Are you going back for it?"

Dave gave me a withering look. "You really haven't been listening have you," he hissed. "Between the parents and that frigging wolf, I was almost killed last night, and you expect me to go back to knock on the door to ask if Doris can come out to play, and by the way, can I please have my clobber back, Mister!" He sneered at me. "You're bloody daft!"

I could see his point. I tried to make light of the situation by indicating that Doris might bring his clothes with her when she came around that evening, but he wasn't in the mood for idle chatter. "And pigs can fly!" he snorted. "Anyway, they've probably already burnt the stuff." He tried to raise himself from the bed and winced with the pain, bringing his hand to hold against his side. "Shit, that's bloody sore!" he gasped. He eased his body into a better position. "I think I must have broken a couple of ribs when I went crashing down those stairs."

He should have found some sympathy among his brethren, but there was none to be found. Despite the trials and tribulations he had endured, and the pain he was obviously bearing as bravely as he could, we could only enjoy the picture of what he had gone through, and be grateful to him for offering so much for our entertainment. We were still appreciatively chuckling away as he began to dab iodine on

Adolf's teeth-marks, accompanied by numerous expletives as the iodine found its own mark and stung him into blabbering submission.

"In all your miserable self-pity, I think you should offer a thought for your little lady," I pointed out. "Bearing in mind what her parents did to you for de-flowering their daughter, I wonder what they did to her?"

"Deflowering!" Joey snorted derisively. "Deflowering!" he repeated with scorn in his voice and on his face, which was ugly enough without it. "I bet Doris has had more pricks than a second-hand dartboard! If she was any looser, she'd fall apart!" He laughed, and shook his head at the very thought.

"Oi, you two!" Dave interrupted, somewhat peeved at Joey's observation. "You're talking about the girl I love!" There wasn't even a suggestion of a smile on his face when he said it, so the dozy bugger probably meant it. "If I thought I could get away with it, I'd take her home with me, because she'd turn a few heads at The Dog and Duck, I can tell you!"

"I don't suppose your missus would be too impressed though," I pointed out, and smiled at the image of our blonde haired hero returning with the spoils of war, and introducing them to his fair lady – *Hey look what I've found, darling!*

"Yes, there is that, I suppose," he acknowledged, and gave me a grin. "I brought a puppy home one night," he told us. "I'd bought it for a fiver from some bloke in the pub. But the missus wouldn't even let me bring it into the house."

"There you are then!" Joey grinned at him. "It's obvious that your missus has an aversion against mongrels that go for a fiver!"

"Sod off you ginger git!" Dave snarled at him, but the twinkle in his eyes showed that he took Joey's observation for the good-humoured bantering that it was.

I was suddenly puzzled by the fact that all the noise and laughter we had produced hadn't affected Stuart at all. He was still lying on his bed like a beached whale, dead to the world and ready for the birds to start pecking at the blubber. "Give him a dig, Joey, and see if he's still alive," I suggested, and Joey obliged with a dig at his ribs and two fingers to pinch his nose tight.

The bulk finally moved slightly and slowly opened its eyes to stare blankly at us, and a croaky voice from hell came from somewhere deep in its throat, "Bloody hell, I'm frigging dying!" it gasped.

"Considering what you put away last night, I'm not bloody surprised!" Joey told him. "You supped a whole bottle of vodka, you alcoholic drunk!"

Stuart groaned loudly, gave an even louder fart, and mumbled, "Vodka? What vodka? I don't remember anything!"

Looking at the sad sight before us, it was difficult to envisage the strutting rocker he was on stage, roaring out the songs with raw gusto and making the girls squeal. Now he was just alcoholic blubber in a dirty yellow and black t-shirt that gave allusions to a queen bee. "That reminds me about the time when I was a nipper and walked into the shop down the road," Joey piped in. "My nose barely reached the counter, and the old woman behind it asked what she could get me." He chuckled to himself. "Without a flicker of emotion, I asked for one dead wasp. She was really taken aback, and told me that she didn't sell dead wasps," Joey sniggered. "Yes you do," I told her, "because you've got one in the window!" He nodded towards Stu. "And now we've got one here," he said, and shook his head in disgust or pity, "only this one's still breathing, just!"

Joey and I went for some breakfast at the café leaving Stuart to reacquaint himself with the world of the living, and

Dave to dress his wounds. "Ein bockwurst mit brot, kasse mit brot, und zwei kaffe mit milch, bitte," I ordered as the waitress stood before us with her pencil hovering over a pad, ready to write down our order. Joey was mightily impressed by my prowess in the local lingo, and I have to admit that I was quite pleased with how quickly I had picked up the odd few words myself. Although certainly quite restricted, I did already have the rudiments of vocabulary necessary for a primitive conversation. I explained that I had picked things up from talking with locals like Johan and Trudi, which was quite true.

"Yeah, you have been spending some time with her, haven't you," Joey observed. "Every time I looked around the last few days, I'd see you two laughing and joking. It's hardly surprising that he got pissy-eyed drunk last night." I indignantly repeated my earlier assertion that we had only been chatting. "Aye, I know," Joey conceded, "but Stuart's a bit possessive, and doesn't like anyone infringing on what's his."

"What's his!" I exclaimed. "He doesn't own her, you know. She's just a nice lass who happens to be his girlfriend while we're here in Schleswig. Anyway, if he's so concerned about her, tell me why he left her to herself and ignored her all last night. She was really upset about that!"

Changing the subject, Joey wondered if we might be getting a visit from Doris's avenging father that night. "I can just see him coming up on the stage with a carving knife and castrating old Dave in the middle of a song."

"It would be a bit more dramatic than your rendition of *Yesterday*, and that particular song should definitely get the chop," I pointed out. "Maybe he should do you as well then you might reach the high notes!"

"You never did like that song did you? The trouble with you, is that you've got no taste!"

"The trouble with me, mate," I pointed out, "is that I have!"

Joey decided to change the subject. "You fancy Trudi, don't you?" The question took me by surprise.

"No!" I emphatically denied, and began to squirm in my seat.

"Go on, admit it," he badgered me, "you fancy her rotten!" His eyes held mine, watching for a reaction. "I mean, just look at how frigging protective you were towards her yesterday when Stu was giving her grief! You were all over her!"

I could hardly deny the fact. After all, we had been pretty close, and getting even closer all through the previous day and night. "Okay, you nosey bugger," I finally agreed, "I like her and enjoy her company, but there's no law against that!"

He eyed me astutely. "What about that other one? That Henry, who you've been sniffing around. What about her?"

"Her name's Henni, you berk!" I corrected him.

"Yeah, well, whatever. I thought you were drooling for her? She'll be back on Friday. It's her birthday or something, isn't it?"

"Joe, the answer to your questions are, yes and yes. Okay?" Then I pointed out what was obvious to me, if nobody else. "Anyway, she's miles out of my league, and by the time we get to Friday, we'll probably have been sent somewhere else, maybe Lüneburg."

Joe sat up, suddenly alert and interested, and no longer concerned with my love-life or lack of it. "Who told you that?" he enquired.

"Johan told me last night, but he's not sure when we'll be sent off."

"That bog cleaner is a veritable font of knowledge, isn't he!" Joey said, sarcastically, apparently a little irritated by the fact that he hadn't been the first to be informed.

Just then we saw Dave limping slowly across the street, obviously in some pain. He came in and carefully eased his aching body down on a seat by the table. Replying to our query, he could confirm that Stuart was still in his bed praying for death to take him.

Joe carefully observed our wounded warrior as he ate his breakfast. "The birds won't be ogling you for your looks tonight, mate," he told him. The spoonful of cornflakes stopped in mid-air and a worried frown creased Dave's battered face, and I could almost see the shock beginning to take him. "Have you seen yourself in the mirror today?" Joe continued. "That black eye is a beauty. You look like a fucking Panda. You'll have to get yourself some sunglasses to cover it up before we're on tonight."

Dave gingerly touched his face and winced, then fell into a morose silence as he slowly munched his cornflakes. He finally gave a sigh and stared dismally into the bowl. "I wonder if I'm ever going to see Doris again after what happened?"

"Look on the bright side, mate!" Joey always looked on the bright side. "Given the tender state of your tackle, it might be a good idea to give it a bit of a rest." Probably never having known a night without exercising his pride and joy, Dave looked doubtful, but said nothing.

We decided to check on the fourth member of our erstwhile group, to make sure that he was still breathing. The door stood ajar when we approached our lodgings. "You dozy bugger, you didn't lock the door, Dave!" Joey admonished him, already fearing the worst. We apprehensively opened the door and saw that Stu was still dead to the world and snoring loudly. We could also see that the place had been ransacked. "Fucking hell," Joey screamed out, "we've been burgled!" He grabbed Stuart and shook him like a rag doll to get him awake.

"Wha! Wha! What!" mumbled Stu as he tried to figure out where he was and what was happening to him, and why.

"We've been robbed!" Joey screamed at him. "And you, you pissy arsed idiot have slept through it all, and let them do it!"

As the realisation of what had happened struck me, my heart began to beat like a bass drum and my mouth became dry. I felt terrible, but if I felt this way, Dave certainly couldn't have been any happier knowing that it was his carelessness that had caused our present problems. I rushed into my room, fearing the worst. Like the first room, it had been turned over, and it was not a pleasant sight to see. My only thought was for my camera, for I had little else of value with me. I always carried my money and passport on me, so at least they were safe. I went down on my hands and knees and reached far under the bed to see if the Chelsea boots that I used on stage were still there, for I had placed the camera in one of these for safe-keeping. My searching hand found a boot and drew it out, and I felt the camera inside it even before I had it clear of the bed. I breathed a huge sigh of relief, and sat down heavily on the bed to calm my ragged nerves. I heard the animated voices of the others as they checked their own possessions to see what was missing, with Joey still cursing Stu.

"Fucking hell, the bastards have taken my leather jacket!" Stu's voice howled in despair, and sent me crashing through the door to see him with his face buried in his hands, as he cursed himself, with Dave and Joe looking on open-mouthed. I truly felt for him, for I knew that leather jacket meant a lot to him. He wore it with pride, feeling that it gave him a certain swagger, a certain persona of being someone to be aware of. The shock of the robbery had certainly brought Stu out of his lethargic hangover, and he now sat on the bed, glowering at Dave as though he was about to kill him there and then.

Then an evil smile crossed his face as he told Dave, "You're gonna be bloody sorry when Yozzer gets to hear about this, because it was his frigging jacket!" His voice rose at the end of this little information.

I noticed how Dave's face muscles tightened at this news. "Who's this Yozzer?" I asked.

"Yozzer is a scary hard case who happens to be a friend of mine and that gormless chuff over there." He nodded towards Dave, who had become paler by the second. "And he's going to go frigging mental when he hears about this, isn't he Dave?" Dave grimaced. "Especially when I tell him whose fault it was!" He scowled at him. "Be afraid Golden Balls," he warned, "be very afraid!" Dave sat down on the bed with his head in his hands and sighed audibly, probably thinking that he hadn't deserved this on top of all his previous problems.

Joey had been quiet up to this point, seething in simmering silence at Dave's stupidity. Apparently deciding to become Action Man again, he stubbed out his cigarette and took control. "Right, we've got to do something about this!" he declared. "We have to report it to the police!"

"What's the point?" Stu stated sarcastically. "Whoever it was will be miles away by now. Besides, it wasn't even a break-in because that thick-head over there left the door open so they could just walk in and help themselves – to Yozzer's leather jacket!" He leaned towards Dave and angrily shouted the last words into his face.

Desperately trying to defend himself, Dave replied, "It wouldn't have been taken at all if you hadn't been lying there in a drunken stupor like a beached whale!" I have to admit, he did have a point there.

We eventually ascertained where the cop-shop was situated, and headed off to report the heinous crime, with Dave limping after us and feeling miserable. As usual, Joey took it upon himself to be our spokesman, and gave a policeman all the grizzly details of the ghastly crime while the rest of us shuffled about feeling awkward and out of place. Suddenly a side-door opened and a younger policeman came through it. He stopped up when he saw us. "Ah!" he exclaimed, "the English group from the dancehall!" He noticed Dave, and smirked as he peered into his battered face. "Retribution at last, I see!" he guffawed. Dave muttered something under his breath but said nothing, sensible bloke.

"Well that was a complete waste of time, wasn't it?" Stuart stated as we came back into the street. "They'll do nowt about it. I mean, how are they going to find one leather jacket here in Germany? I mean, everybody's got one!" Knowing Stu was right, Joey acknowledged the fact with a shrug of his shoulder and a nod of his head, as we toddled on in silence through the snow flakes that had begun to fall, feeling miserable and fed up.

The cold seemed to have done wonders for Stuart, for he was gradually coming back to life, and it was first then that he noticed the state of Daves's battered face and his heavy limp, and enquired with some concern about their origins. Joey grinned at the prospect of hearing the story again, and decided to tell it himself, so we went into the nearest bar and despatched Dave to the counter to get the necessaries, while Joe began the tale. He sometimes had to stop as he convulsed himself in laughter, knowing what was coming, and Stuart was wreathed in smiles and wobbling like a jelly as he chortled away wiping tears of laughter from his eyes.

Dave stayed quiet during this entertainment and nonchalantly smoked a cigarette, trying to look cool and collected, as though remaining aloof from it all, and failing on all counts.

Stu finally gained his composure and turned to Dave. "Not your favourite dogs these German Shepherds then, Dave? Fascist bastards aren't they!" Surprisingly, even Dave smiled, and I thought that he might be coming to terms with the fact that, in retrospect at least, his earlier encounter with the family pet really was funny.

"Well," Stu said, looking from one face to the next and smiling benevolently, "with me being completely out of my mind drunk last night, is there anything else I should be told about?" I cringed, and prayed that Joey wouldn't put his big mouth where it didn't belong.

"Do you remember playing the guitar at the bar?" Joe asked.

"Did I..?" He seemed surprised. He frowned as he thought about it. "Well, vaguely ..." He thought about it again. "I think ..." He gave it another thought. "Was I any good?"

"No way!" Joey chuckled at him. "You were crap, like you always are!"

"Do you remember falling off the chair?" I wondered.

"Falling off the chair?" Stuart was amazed. "What chair?"

"The one you were sitting on, you daft sod!"

Stuart was silent as he absorbed this information. Then a new thought entered his head, and he asked, "How the hell did I get to bed anyway?"

"With great difficulty!" Joey guffawed. "Me and Biffo had to carry your fat carcass up the stairs, and almost died doing it!"

He was appreciative of our efforts. "Thanks fellahs. I owe you one!" Then he dived into the depths of his mind again to rummage around in the murky details swirling around there before emerging to the surface with yet another question. "What happened to Trudi?" he wondered.

Grinning wickedly, Joey answered, "Ask Biffo. He'll tell you!" he smirked. "He'll fill you in with all the details!" If I'd had a gun I think I would have shot him there and then, right in his grinning idiot face, but I didn't so had to make the best of it.

"She got pissed off with you ignoring her all night and getting hammered, so she went home," I told him. "She was very distraught, and spent most of the night in the ladies room crying her eyes out at your indifference, you uncaring sod!"

I saw how his eyes narrowed as he stared into my face. "And how do you know all this then, where you chatting her up again?" he asked suspiciously. "I seem to remember you pair being heads on and whispering together like lost lovers all yesterday." I squirmed just a little, but enough for him to notice. "So who did she go home with," he asked, "was it you?"

Joey replied before I could. "She went home with Maria in a taxi," he told him, and I nodded my head to confirm the fact, although it didn't seem to ease the devious doubts in Stuart's suspicious mind.

Thankfully Dave chose that moment to down the last of his drink and get up to announce that he was leaving to find somewhere he could buy sunglasses, and wobbled off into the snow. He was back again within minutes, wearing his purchase with some pride. "What do you think, lads?" he asked enthusiastically. So we told him in no uncertain terms of our collective opinion, which was less than positive. He was completely unfazed. "I think they make me look cool and mysterious," he intoned, obviously pleased with himself. "Like Stu Sutcliffe in The Beatles."

"Didn't he die when he was over here, from a haemorrhage or something?" Joey wondered.

Stuart chuckled, and gave Dave a withering look "And Golden Balls here, is going to die from a beating in The Dog and Duck, when Yozzer gets his hands on him!"

"Unless Adolf gets him first," I pointed out, and we all laughed.

Dave was nonetheless still disappointed by our reaction to his purchase. "I don't care what you buggers say, I think these shades are frigging brilliant, and the girls are going to love me in these tonight, you just wait and see!" At least, he seemed convinced. "They're going to be swooning all over me!" and the very thought seemed to make his mind wander to pastures unknown.

"That's alright," Stuart quipped, "as long as you don't bring your white stick on stage!" I was pleased to see him back to being his normal happy-go-lucky self. The twinkle in his eye and the ready smile were back in good style, and he had stopped sniping at me about Trudi, which was quite a relief.

We decided to spend the afternoon practicing new numbers, for we were repeating too many from our present repertoire as it was and needed some new material. I was definitely becoming increasingly embarrassed by Joey continually informing the audience that we had such and such a request for any particular song, just to have an excuse to play it again. The audience wasn't stupid and must have known that we were beginning to scrape the barrel for songs we knew, and I was becoming seriously tired of some of the stuff we were playing, not least of which was Joey's strangulated version of *Yesterday* which I particularly hated. "You know you can't sing the thing properly," I informed Joey, "so do us all a favour, and drop it, because it's driving me mental!"

Joey opened his mouth to speak, but I stopped him with a wave of my hand. "Don't say anything, Joe, I've heard it all before," I told him. "And I'm warning you, if you play that frigging thing tonight I'll get off my drums and walk off the stage!"

He made a face at me, and cooed, "Oooh!" then grinned at me. "Who's being a drama queen now, ducky?"

"I'm not kidding, Joe," I insisted. "If you play *Yesterday*, I'm walking off!"

Stuart took the opportunity to suggest that we had the practice session the next day instead, claiming that he still felt too delicate. "I couldn't handle all that stuff right now. I need a rest, a day off, you know what I mean."

"Bugger off, Stu," sneered Joe, "you had a day off yesterday!"

"Did I?" He thought about it. "For the life of me, I really can't remember!"

By popular vote it was decided to wait until the next day for our much-needed practice. Instead, Joey suggested that we went to a music store to stock up on guitar strings and such-like, so we headed towards the only such venue in the vicinity, where we were greeted by someone bearing a striking resemblance to Heinrich Himmler, with steel-rimmed glasses and all. He gave us a courteous bow as we entered the establishment, "Guten Abend, mein Herren," he offered, to which Joey informed him that we were English and only browsing. "Bitte, help yourselves, gentlemen," he welcomed, and showed with a gesture of his hand that we were free to find our own way around.

Dave soon found his way to the bass guitars and began to drool over them, while I found a stunning set of Ludwig drums set up with all the cymbals, and other equipment. It had fantastic finish and superbly crafted accessories, and in my mind I was already sitting proudly behind them with my sticks ready to strike. These were the Rolls Royce of drum-kits compared with the battered set I had had for four years and which was decidedly beginning to look a bit tired and jaded, much like myself, I suppose. The owner, noticing my obvious interest, handed me a brochure, but I could only sadly shake my head and inform him that it was regrettably too expensive. I finally drifted back towards Joe and Stu who were busy selecting guitar strings. They called to the owner and paid for their purchases, and we left with a pleasant *Auf Wiedersehen* to see us off.

We had hardly walked twenty yards from the store when Stuart and Joe started giggling like naughty schoolboys. Puzzled, Dave enquired what was tickling them, and this set off a new round of laughter. Stu eventually calmed down sufficiently to inform us that while we had been keeping the owner busy, they had themselves been busy helping themselves to a dozen or so sets of strings each, and they patted their pockets to show where they had hidden their ill-gotten gains. "It was like taking candy from a baby," Stu said, and they both started up again, laughing themselves silly at their dubious accomplishment, and showing no sign of remorse.

"You dozy buggers!" I shouted at them. "He'll know it was you, and he'll have the police on us!" I was mortified. How many English groups were playing in Schleswig at the time? The answer to that was that there was only one, and we were it. They'd only have to come to our show that night and take us off the stage and straight to the station. "Shit!" I exclaimed, quite distraught, "as if we haven't had enough trouble in the last couple of days!"

"Keep your hair on, Biffo," Stu chuckled, "he probably won't even notice that it's gone."

"That's not the point though is it," I hissed back at him, "it's still stealing, isn't it!" I may have had many warts, but I was never a thief. "Have you already forgotten how pissed off you were this morning when you found that we'd been robbed, and your bloody leather jacket had been nicked?" It should have been a point for afterthought, but it had no effect on the fledglings of crime, who kept chortling away at their own temerity.

"We didn't forget you, Biffo," said Joey, grinning like a tom-cat, and produced a pair of drumsticks from somewhere inside his clothes. "There you go, mate. Enjoy!" He sniggered at my crestfallen expression. "I distinctly remember him telling us to help ourselves."

It was already done, and all I could do was to worry about the possible consequences, which I did do for the rest of the day, being the worrying sort that I was. I swore under my breath on a number of occasions, cursing Stu and Joe for the thieving hoodlums they were, and the trouble they were likely to bring upon us, but the day passed without further incident, and it was finally time for us to play the part of rock musicians once more – at least, this kept us out of mischief as long as we were on stage.

At precisely seven o'clock I counted in the first song of the night with four taps on the rim of my snare drum, and we kicked in with Spencer Davies' *Keep on Running*, which immediately filled the dance-floor with gyrating bodies. Strangely, the delightful Doris was not among them, although I doubt if Dave had noticed, for he was already getting plenty of attention from other girls as he effortlessly fingered the fret-board, driving the song along on his heavy bass strings that throbbed right through the room. He was smiling, and no wonder. From behind the shades of his new sunglasses he could see the women drooling for him. He had been right; the sunglasses did give him an aura of cool and mysterious that had the girls fidgeting for him. Or perhaps it was just that the other girls had noticed Doris's absence and were intent on making the most of it. Whatever it was, Dave was revelling in the adulation and smiling from ear to ear as he plucked away at the strings.

I decided to get myself a pair of the same make first thing next day!

We settled down at our table for the first break. Joey was happy in Maria's company. She gave me a smile of acknowledgment to show she knew I existed, then returned her attention to her ginger lover. Stuart, meanwhile, whether or not aware that Trudi had not put in an appearance, or even caring for that matter, was getting the undivided attention of a girl called Astrid, and very obviously enjoying it.

Dave, the Star of the Show and Super Stud DeLuxe, was surrounded by his adoring fans. He was in his element with all the adulation from dozens of delectable women ready to throw themselves at his feet. Some of the newer ones were even asking him for his autograph. He was really enjoying his moment as the girls scrambled around trying to edge each other out of the way to thrust anything that could be written on before him to sign. I hadn't even known that the bugger could write his own name. But then again, it might not be his own name he was scribbling. One enterprising girl even proffered a pair of her knickers for him to sign. Guess once if the lecherous bastard enjoyed that! He looked across at me and gloated. "Now that's what I call a number one fan, Biffo!" he called, before he disappeared back into the throng.

Thankfully, the lights began to flash to bring us back on stage. Our repertoire was enough back home, but was quite inadequate for the five hour stints we had to do now, and we had long since stopped using a play-list, for I would have gone mental had I known what was coming next. Joey would just ad-lib and announce something, and we would pound our way through it. Half-way through the set, he announced that we were slowing things down to play a particular favourite for our drummer. "He likes it so much, that he's especially asked me to play it for him tonight," he told the microphone, then turned his eyes on me. "So just for you Biffo, here is your special request," he said sweetly, and then the bugger started warbling, "*Yesterday, all my troubles were so far away ...*"

I could hardly believe it! The bastard was taunting me, to see how I would react. I pushed myself away from the drum-kit, and walked off the stage and found a chair where I plonked myself down and stared daggers at him. He avoided looking at me, knowing that he would have broken down in laughter had he seen me fuming at him in frustrated anger.

To be honest, and to my own surprise, his rendition was probably the most sincere he had ever managed, and when he wrung every emotion from the line *Why'd she have to go, I don't know, she wouldn't say ...* even I had a lump in my throat.

When the song finished, he milked the applause from the audience before he announced, "What did I tell you folks. That song is such a favourite of our drummer that he had to leave the stage to fully appreciate the beautiful words and music of this fantastic classic." He pointed an arm towards me, "So take a bow, Biffo!"

I was so taken aback by this request, that I did just that, which produced a new round of applause from the audience, who may well have thought that this was all part of the act. I couldn't help smiling at Joey when I re-entered the stage, but still muttered, "You bloody ginger bastard!" as I passed him on my way back to the drums.

At our next break, I asked him what that had all been about, and he just chuckled, and told me, "I was just trying to bring a smile back to your miserable bloody face!" I had to smile, in spite of myself, because Joey had more neck than a giraffe. He would probably have the last word in Echo Valley!

Meanwhile Dave's night took a turn for the better, or the worse depending on your point of view, when Doris turned up carrying a parcel, which prompted Joey to enquire if the contents might be Adolf. She giggled and put her arm around

Dave's neck and gave him a kiss, then informed him that his clothes were inside the parcel.

There was however still no sign of Trudi. Stu was currently in the clutches of Astrid, and had no vested interest in enquiring about her whereabouts, as he had obviously already lined up a heated night with his new-found admirer.

So there it was; Joey with Maria, Dave with Doris, Stu with Astrid, and me on my own, as usual. The chords of the final song were still reverberating around the dancehall as I quickly left the stage and found my way downstairs to the bar, for there was certainly nothing to keep me where I was. I eased myself onto a stool and ordered a beer, which soon appeared before me. Just then, the man sitting next to me spoke up. "Let me pay for your beer, Herr Biffo!" he said, and shoved some coins across the counter. "My name is Gunther."

I raised the glass to my mouth and thanked him, "Vielen danke!"

A smile crossed his face and his piggy eyes twinkled as I accepted the drink. I didn't know him from Adam and had never spoken to him before, although I had seen him at the bar every night since we had arrived a week or so earlier, but why he should suddenly have the urge to indulge in conversation now was a puzzle to me. He didn't speak very good English so I didn't catch everything he said, and just nodded and smiled whenever he said anything I didn't understand, more out of courtesy than anything else.

I studied his features as he babbled away, and noticed that they were beginning to glisten with sweat. He had a square head, close-cropped blonde hair, the aforementioned piggy eyes, a nose that seemed to spread halfway across his typically Kraut face, and his mouth twitched at the edges as he spoke. He seemed to have no neck, so his head just seemed to sprout straight out of his thickset torso. Despite the weather outside, he was just dressed in a t-shirt and jeans, and his arms were like Popeye's, strong and powerful, and with something written in German tattooed on the left, and an anchor intertwined with a rope on the other.

He was speaking quite excitedly by then, giving me a sickly smile, as he dragged his stool closer. "I've been watching you for several nights, and you are always on your own. You are never with frauleins," he pointed out. By now I really should have heard the alarm bells ringing, but such was the state of my alcohol-fuddled brain, that I didn't hear them.

He bought me another drink and leaned so close I could feel his breath on my face and tried to back away from him. As puddled as I was, I was still capable of some sort of reasoned thought, and I watched with some interest as his piggy eyes developed a hang-dog drunken look. He was now sweating even more, and had begun to mumble to himself. He suddenly gripped my arm in a vice-like grip, and pointed to himself with his free hand as he informed me through slurred speech, "I am Gunther! Did I tell you that?" looking at me with mad staring eyes. "I am in the Navy. I am the ship's boxing champion! I am undefeated champion of the whole Baltic Fleet!" he exclaimed, and blew himself up with pride, while I wondered how I could best find a means of retreat. He dribbled on, repeating "Boxing champion" on and on. He put his face into mine, "Boxing champion! Do you understand?" he snarled the question at me.

"Oh, yeah, absolutely!" I replied, rather hesitantly. "Boxing champion, eh? You must be good!" I was by now getting quite nervous. The fact that he was a boxer might explain his broken nose and puffed up piggy eyes. He was ugly and nasty, and the mood was about to become a whole lot uglier and nastier. Without warning, he began to shout and scream abuse as he tried to drag me off my stool, but lost his balance in the attempt and fell heavily on the floor. He slowly staggered to his feet, cursing even louder, like an animal in pain.

There were plenty of people in the bar, so I wondered why nobody intervened to help me out of the situation, but before I could think of an answer, he came at me again. Just then Johan entered the bar. He quickly sized up the situation and came to my aid by trying to calm things down, but this only enraged the madman further, and he roughly pushed the old man away so he stumbled and fell among tables and chairs, sending glasses crashing to the floor.

Gunther now grabbed me by the throat in a vicious hold that choked me, and put his ugly face close to mine, and I thought I was going to die where I stood. Then Joey suddenly emerged from nowhere and dragged him off me, leaving me clutching my throat and gasping for air. He spun him around and dropped him with one vicious head-butt. Gunthers whole face seemed to explode in a sea of blood, and he hit the floor like a sack of spuds, screaming in agony. To ensure that once down, he'd be inclined to remain there, Joey gave him a vicious kick in the goolies, that had me wincing at the sight, and followed it up with another to the ribs, then, just for good measure, and probably the fun of it, he stomped on his face with such force that I'm sure the Champion of the Baltic Fleet must have lost at least three teeth. He was screaming in agony and writhing with the pain. Needless to say, he didn't get up again.

This little incident had only taken seconds, but all those who had previously chosen to ignore my plight were already gathered around us to gaze at the bloody mess lying on the floor. Joey seemed to consider the situation for a moment, before deciding to give him another kick just for spite.

Otto the barman was in an extremely agitated state, and rang for the police, shouting excitedly into the telephone. By the volume of his voice, they could have heard him without the phone.

After my breathing had returned to almost normal, I turned to Joey. "Thanks for that, mate!" I could have kissed the ugly bugger for saving me. "I thought the Kraut fucker was going to kill me!"

Joey surprised me by laughing aloud. "Yeah, he probably would an' all, eventually," he said, seeming to be totally unconcerned with what he had just been involved in.

"What do you mean, eventually?" I asked.

He gave me a playful punch on the shoulder. "You really are a naïve bugger, aren't you, Biffo!" he said, and gave me a sympathetic smile. "Didn't you figure it out? He's a frigging bum bandit, and you were meant to be his piece of navy cake for the night!"

I felt physically sick. "Are you sure?"

We were interrupted by the sound of sirens and flashing blue lights that shone through the windows from the street outside, and the police marched in, followed by a crew of paramedics to attend to the bloodied casualty on the floor. I recognised one of the cops as the one who had been overly pleased at discovering Dave's wounded face.

For the second time in twenty-four hours, we found ourselves making statements to the police. They also took statements from eye-witnesses, but what they chose to tell could be anyone's guess. It was Johan who clinched it for us by giving a graphic account of what happened. This seemed to appease the police, who decided that they had all they needed, and headed for the door. For some reason, I gave them a grateful smile as they passed by me. "Danke, und Guten Nacht," I offered weakly, glad to see them going.

"What the fuck did you say that for, you belly-crawling bugger!" Joe demanded.

"I was only being polite," I insisted. "It does no harm, and remember, you could have been arrested for assault and battery, so we need all the friends we can get, right!" After considering this statement for a moment, Joey grudgingly concurred and became a bit more thoughtful.

Just then the remains of Gunther, The Baltic Boxing Champion, were wheeled out on a stretcher by the paramedics. Joey leaned over him and hissed something derogatory at him in a vicious voice. It wouldn't have surprised me if he had given him another kick in the head as a further reminder of his evening out.

We found our way back to our regular table, where Johan joined us. Thankfully he wasn't hurt. I thanked him for whatever he had said to the police to get us off the hook, and he chuckled. "I lied a little," he admitted. "It was just a little lie. But I happen to loathe that man. How do you say? He is a pain in the arse?"

"Or at least, someone else's!" Joey sniggered. He turned to me. "Talking of which, a piece of advice to you Biffo, because I may not be around next time you get yourself into trouble." He put his hand on my shoulder and looked me in the eye. "Get yourself a girl," he continued. "Get the cellophane off that dick of yours and get yourself laid instead of mooching around like a bleeding poof. Believe me, mate, you're sending out all the wrong signals with your indifference to the girls, so get yourself a woman, will you. There're plenty enough to choose from, so just get a woman and get laid!"

Maria listened to this with a smile on her face, and gave me a wink when Joe had finished, as though confirming that he was right, and this was the course of action to take.

I hadn't known what to expect, but I certainly wasn't expecting such paternal advice from old Joe. I sighed. "It's been a funny old day, hasn't it!" I said. Thinking about it, it really had!

"Yeah," Joey agreed, "it's been a right manic Monday!"

Practice
Makes Perfect

As I awoke to yet another depressing day in my depressing room, I became aware of a brilliant light bathing the walls of my boudoir. It was as if I had died and gone to heaven, such was the ethereal glow. Breaking wind brought me back to earth with a bang, and I decided to find out where the light was coming from – when I was ready to get up, if I was going to get up at all, which was not a given option considering the cold room and the amount of beer still inside my system.

As I lay there, weighing the pros and cons of getting out of my warm bed to alleviate my curiosity about the light, I began to think back to the events of the previous night. Joey's advice had certainly been sensible. The only problem was to actually get a girl who was willing to share a bed with a lout like me. Then I thought of Henni. She was a rare beauty, but it would be a case of crawling over seven miles of broken glass for me to get to her. If I thought there might be a hope in hell at the end of such a journey, I might very well attempt it, but I knew it was a no-hoper – she was completely out of my class, and I knew it. But Trudi had certainly grown on me during the past few days. In fact, I fancied her rotten, even though she was with Stuart. We had become very friendly, but she had never indicated that anything else was in the offing, for she was Stu's girl, and seemed to adore the bugger.

I forced myself to roll out of the bed and my eyes caught Eric Burdon's woeful tale on the wall, and I thought, *I bet you didn't have any trouble getting the girls over here*, then concentrated my attention on discovering what the hell was causing the strange light that was blazing through my room. I staggered to the window and looked out to see crisp white snow that had magically transformed the outside world to a winter fairyland. I stared at it in awe. I had never seen anything so beautiful. I decided to find my camera and go out to claim the vision for posterity, and as a reminder for future reference that Schleswig had not just been too much beer and too little fanny.

I pulled on all the clothes I had with me, wrapping up like I was about to follow Scott to the Pole, and waddled into the next room. "Hey, lads, guess what?" I shouted, all excited and not caring about the early hour, then I pulled up with a start as I saw the ample torso of Astrid holding on to Stuart as they tried to find space in his bed. He had a smug self-satisfied expression his face.

"What..?" Stu asked, not particularly interested, but certainly enjoying my discomfort.

I took hold of myself again. "It's been snowing," I told him excitedly.

He sneered. "Is that all! Dressed like that, I thought you were doing something exciting like going out to throw a few snowballs or make a snowman."

"He'd better make a snow-woman instead," Joey piped up from underneath his blankets, "to have something to practice on, so he doesn't forget how to go about it!"

"Yeah, but then he'll get frostbite and the frigging thing'll snap off!" Dave chimed in.

I wondered where they had all come from. A moment earlier I had been happy as a lark and ready for a new adventure, and now I was suddenly surrounded by derision coming at me from every direction. I noticed how Astrid turned her head from the one to the other as they spoke, apparently trying to figure out what was going on, and what our early morning conference was all about. She obviously didn't have a clue about what we were going on about. I studied her features for a moment. A moment was enough. Her hair was bedraggled, her makeup smeared, and she generally looked like something the dog had dragged in. How Stu could drop Trudi for a dancehall scruffer like her was hard to understand.

In answer to Stuart's question, I informed them that I was going out to take some pictures in the snow so I could have something to show when I got back home. "It'll be a bit more interesting than the one I've got of Dave's bum bobbing up and down as he gave Doris a drumming," I told them.

"Oh aye, and what are you going to tell your folks when they see that, then?"

"I'll just tell them it's a shot of the full moon reflected on the waters of the Schlei."

Joey chuckled. "Your old man might believe you," he agreed.

"He'd know the difference," Stu told him cheerfully, "after all the times he's seen your arse bobbing up and down as you straddled Randy Mandy in the back of the van."

I left the lodgings with their heckling comments following me down the stairs, and found my way out into the morning cold, and began to trudge through the almost deserted streets, suddenly feeling a tremendous euphoria of freedom creeping into my bones. I wandered through the snow for a few hours taking the odd snap as I went, but finally the cold became too hard to handle and I found my way back to our little café where I found Joey sitting alone at a table with two steaming coffees laid out before him. It seemed he had seen me coming and had the decency to order one for the only survivor of Scott's ill-fated expedition.

According to Joe, Stu was still lying in Astrid's ample bosom, whereas Dave was having a lie-in to rest from yesterday's rigors, and sighing for Doris's soothing flesh. "He was moaning half the night," Joey said, "and putting me off my concentration on Maria."

"So you had Maria with you?" I was surprised. "What happened to her?" I enquired.

"Oh, we just had a quick leg-over, and then she buggered off home."

"No foreplay then," I ascertained.

"Foreplay? What the fucking hell is foreplay?"

I let it drop, and decided that one of us had a lot to learn.

"You know what Biffo?" he began, suddenly becoming serious, which was unlike him. "After having shacked up with that fat bird Astrid, Stuart's definitely out of the running with Trudi, so why don't you get in there, mate?"

"She's not interested in me like that," I told him. "We're just good friends, that's all."

He looked at me as though I was from Mars. "Sod it," he said, "please yourself!"

Joey decided to crawl off back to the warmth of his pit, but I was more inclined to continue my exploration of the town to get more snaps of the wintry wonderland, so we parted, reminding ourselves of the band practice later that afternoon, as we went our separate ways.

The snow crunched under my feet as I aimlessly wandered through the streets enjoying every new sight I saw, until I suddenly found myself approaching the music store that Joe and Stu had robbed the previous day. I quickly pulled my collar even higher to hide my face and walked by. Our little bar was just around the corner, so deciding that I was cold enough, I went inside to warm myself with a beer beside the fire.

Unfortunately someone was already sitting by our usual table. He was reading a newspaper, and there was something familiar about him that I couldn't quite place. I was trying to work this out when my thoughts were brought back to the present by a female voice addressing me.

I looked up to see Trudi's smiling face, and I smiled back at her, surprised, but more than pleased to see her. Her long hair was tied back in pig-tails and her face had no make-up, but her warmth and natural attractiveness shone though to me like a beacon in the night and I felt like a ship-wrecked sailor plucked from the waves of despair and despondency, suddenly alive and with something to live for. She was beautiful, and I realised that I had missed her.

After the initial preliminaries, I nodded towards the man behind the newspaper, and asked if she knew him. "Of course," she replied. "That's Heinz from the music store. Why do you ask?"

Why indeed? Without thinking, I slid further down in my seat and turned away from him hoping he wouldn't look our way. Trudi couldn't help but notice, no more than I could hide my furtive attempts at concealment, and anxiously enquired about my sudden afflictions. I decided to tell her, and became more concerned for her reaction to these revelations for each word I spoke, but to my surprise, she laughed openly when I had finished.

Just then, I noticed that the music man lowered his newspaper, folded it neatly, and stared directly at me through his steel-framed glasses. "Shit," I muttered. "he's spotted me!" I watched as he placed his newspaper on the table beside his coffee-cup, got up and pushed his chair against the table, adjusted his jacket, and strode purposefully towards me. It must have been Trudi's laughter that had alerted him to our table.

He stood over me, but looked at Trudi as he spoke. "Guten Tag Trudi. Wie gehtes Ihnen?" Her reply and the rest of their conversation were conducted entirely in their native language, as one does. As such, I had no idea what they were talking about. I just looked into the face of whoever was speaking, with a stupid expression on my own. The man's tone and demeanour seemed to change when he asked her a question and indicated by a movement of his hand that he was referring to me. He appeared to be getting more and more agitated, and whatever he was saying was spoken in a severe guttural voice. Throughout their conversation, I continued to grin like a lunatic, and nodded furiously whenever anything particularly bombastic seemed to be said, while Trudi throughout it all, seemed to try to placate him. She finally stood up and gave him a sweet smile, then put a comforting arm around his shoulder and pointed at me as she began to explain something to him in a quiet voice. Whatever she said it seemed to calm him down considerably, and his whole demeanour and body language relaxed, and the hint of a smile even appeared on his face. There was a twinkle in his eyes as they darted about behind the steel rimmed glasses. Then he bent forward and gave her a quick peck on the cheek, bowed slightly, and left.

I almost collapsed with relief to see him go, then panicked again as a thought struck me, "He's not going to get the police is he?" I asked with desperation in my voice.

"No, of course not," she assured me, and laughed easily. "He did think that it was you who had been in the store yesterday when someone stole from him, but I told him you had been with me all day, so it couldn't have been you." I loved her then!

I relaxed sufficiently to forget about this worrying episode, and we began to converse and enjoy each others company. I wondered why she hadn't come to the dancehall the previous night, and admitted that I had missed her. "I like to be with you," I told her, "because you put a smile on my face," which brought a smile to her own.

"But the point is," she said, "did Stuart miss me?" which was a valid point on which I had no wish to comment. "I stayed away to teach him a lesson after the way he treated me. He was very unkind, and he made me very unhappy," she pouted. She seemed to become morose at the memory of it all, then looked back into my face and asked, "Did he miss me? Did he ask about me?"

I chose that moment to become busy with a cigarette to avert my eyes from her expectant face. I decided that discretion was the better part of valour, so I gave her a smile and confirmed that he had. Then I remembered that Maria was her best friend, and had seen just how distraught Stu actually had been at her absence, slobbering all over his new-found flame. "Er," I began, "have you seen Maria today?"

"I will see her later this afternoon," she replied. "Why do you ask?"

"Oh, nothing..." I lied.

She gave me a long searching look, then began to pull on her coat to leave. We said our goodbyes and she gave me a quick peck on the cheek, "See you tonight, Biffo," she said, then walked out of sight, lost in the bustle of people going about their daily business.

I watched her as she walked away, and felt guilty for having deceived her. Stuart didn't deserve a girl like that, I thought. I felt sorry for her. Then I felt even sorrier for myself, for not having a girl like that. I liked Trudi. She was fun to be with, and I felt relaxed when I was with her. The fact that I also found her extremely attractive hardly made my interest less keen, but I knew that I had no chance with such a lovely lass. Anyway, she was Stuart's girl, no matter how badly he treated her. I sighed, and resignedly began to move through the streets again, but no longer with my mind on taking snapshots of the local scenery.

As I slowly climbed the stairs leading up to the dancehall I could hear Dave's rumbling bass lines resonating through the floorboards. This was accompanied by the sound of Joey jarringly tuning his Telecaster guitar. *Twang! Twang!* Up and down it went as he painfully tuned up every string. When he tuned his guitar it always set my teeth on edge and shred my nerves. He could never perform this relatively easy task quietly. Oh no! That was far too simple. Instead, he would always set the tone and volume to "Joey" level, which was sharp, thin, clipped and as loud as he could get it.

The Fender Telecaster was an excellent workhorse of a guitar, but it didn't have the deep resonance, the sharp top-end or the mellow wiry warmth of the middle range of tone settings of its more illustrious stable-mate, the Fender Stratocaster, which was a trend-setting instrument designed by Leo Fender, and revolutionary in every way. It was slavishly copied by other manufacturers, but never bettered by any. After all, you can't improve on perfection. It oozed class. To me it was the guitar that put the rock in rock'n'roll. If anything could truly be described as being ubiquitous, this had to be it. Every group worth their salt would have one in their midst, and even I, never known for waxing lyrical about inanimate objects, would get a buzz from merely holding one of these cherry-red works of art.

Although it would be a close run, if pushed, I would have to admit that the thought of caressing the neck and body of an attractive young female would just about shade it, but only just.

"Oh, there you are," Joey greeted me sarcastically. "I'm so pleased you could finally make it!" Then he scowled at me. "What time do you call this?"

I looked at my watch and called out, "Three minutes past two, and what time do you make it?"

He gave me a smile. "Balls!" he said to nobody in particular, and continued tuning his guitar.

Dave seemed to be in a world of his own as he aimlessly wandered around the dance-floor checking the resonance of the bass speakers as he idly thumbed the sonorous bass patterns, with a very long lead dangling from his bass and snaking back to the amplifier on stage. I noticed that the bruising around his eyes had begun to turn from black to a more purplish hue with just a hint of yellowing around the edges. He wasn't wearing his new sunglasses, but then why should he when there were no girls present to impress?

As always, Joey had to stick his big shiny nose into my business and demanded to know what I had been up to, so I told him of the incident with the music store proprietor. For once, he fell silent, and allowed a worried frown to crease his already well-creased features. I advised him to stay away from the general vicinity of the music store. "He wasn't sure about me, but with an ugly face like yours, he's bound to remember you if he sees you again," I told him.

Joe thought about it, and probably decided that I was right, for he changed the subject. "You didn't tell Trudi about Stuart and that Astrid slapper, did you?" he asked.

"No, I didn't, but I'll tell you who will," I replied. "Your girl, Maria, that's who. They're meeting up this afternoon, and when she tells her, the shit is really going to hit the fan!" Joey smiled at the thought, obviously delighted at the prospect of new fun and games to come, when Trudi got hold of her unfaithful lover.

I looked at my watch and saw it was now two-forty, and we had still not practiced a single note. "Speaking of Stu," I remarked, "where the bloody hell is the bugger? He can't still be in bed with that fat bird, surely?"

"Well he was when we left," Joey smirked.

"I can't believe it!" I fumed. "You give me a rollicking for being a couple of minutes late, while that fat git's nearly

174

three quarters of an hour late, and you don't even seem to care!"

He became uncomfortable under my onslaught, knowing that I had a valid point, but not wanting to accede to the fact. "Well, under the circumstances," he mumbled, "I thought I'd cut him a bit of slack, give him some leeway, sort of thing, like …"

"Leeway? Slack? What the fuck are you twittering on about?" I demanded.

"Well, he's in his pit with his bird, and you have to make the most of it when it's on offer, right?"

"On offer!" I almost choked. "He's been in that pit of his with her for well over twelve hours! I'm surprised they haven't got welded together by now with all the friction that's been worked up between them. He should be here now!" I insisted, feeling considerable irritation.

Joey tried to mollify me. "Yeah, but you've got to remember that Stu's a special part of the group, so we have to make some allowances." That had no mollifying affect whatsoever.

"Bollocks!" I sneered at him. "I admit that the bugger has a great voice and is a good guitarist, but he's no more special to the group than you, or Dave, or even me," I told him. "We're all an integral part of the group, and if any one of us drops out it won't frigging function!"

Joey was determined to have the last word. "Okay, but don't forget that I'm the star attraction in The Charters! I'm the one the audience warms to the most. I'm telling you, I'm fucking indispensable!" he smirked, and roared with laughter.

At this point, Stuart, with Astrid in tow, finally deemed to grace us with his presence. "Afternoon wankers!" he cheerfully greeted us. "What's all the shouting and bawling about? Don't you know that some of us were trying to us some kip back there!"

"Don't push your luck Stuart!" Joey warned, clearly rankled by the fact that he had brought Astrid with him to the practice.

"We've been hanging around here for an hour waiting for you to shift your arse. What's your excuse?" he asked, "Are you joined at the frigging hip or summat?"

"Aye!" Stu chuckled, "Or summat!"

"Right," said Joey, trying desperately to bring some semblance of order back to the proceedings, "I suggest we refresh our memories of some of the old rock and roll classics that we haven't done for a while."

"That's easy stuff," Stu pointed out as he tuned the Rickenbacher guitar he had also borrowed from friend Yozzer back home. I hoped it wouldn't take the same path as the leather jacket had taken.

"We'll do Chuck Berry stuff like *Memphis, Sweet Little Sixteen, Beethoven*, and Johnny Kidd stuff, and Jerry Lee Lewis' *Great Balls of Fire* and *Whole Lotta Shaking*, and stuff like that," Joey stated, getting more excited with each song he named. "It's dead easy, isn't it?"

"Yeah," Stu agreed, "but if you suggest we do any of Cliff's stuff, I'll frigging deck yer!"

"Stu mate," Joey chuckled, "we're desperate, but not that desperate!"

"There's only one problem with this cunning plan of yours Joe," Stu said. "All of this is twelve bar stuff that I could play in my sleep, but the problem is remembering the words, because I've forgotten most of them now."

Joey had the answer. "Just do what Biffo always does, and make them up as you go along."

"I do not," I protested from the back of the drum kit, "I'm word-perfect, and you know it!"

They all laughed derisively. It quite hurt my feelings.

"Bollocks!" Joey's knowledge of the English language may not have been tremendous, but he certainly managed to make his point. "Word-perfect, my arse! Why do you think we never do any back-up vocals when you're warbling away? You sing different words to the same song every night. You never, ever, sing the same words on any consecutive night!"

I fumbled for words to defend myself with, but gave up, knowing full well that all he had said was true; I did make the words up as I went along – but nobody seemed to notice, except Joey. I shouted out, "Right, then, *Sweet Little Sixteen*, after four!" and counted them in, then began to sing.

We went through the paces of a number of old rock classics, and they all worked well enough to buck us up and to make us look forward to presenting them for the crowd that night. If nothing else, they got the adrenaline going and some of the aggression we had accumulated during the past week out of our systems, and we all felt better for our little session.

Stuart yanked the jack plug out of his guitar and placed it carefully on his amplifier. "Right, you lot," he said, "I'm off!"

"Off?" Joey exclaimed, somewhat taken aback by the suddenness of Stuart's announcement. "Off where?"

"To the café for something to eat, because I'm effing starving!" He jerked his head at Astrid, who had been patiently sitting by herself for two hours, and she dutifully got up and followed him towards the exit.

Dave smiled sympathetically as they disappeared through the door. "That poor cow's been bored stiff for the past couple of hours," he said.

Quick as a flash, Joey quipped, "Probably like the past twelve hours in the sack with Stuart!"

Joe and Dave lingered on the stage chatting about the music we had just played. They were a strange pair, and completely different; Dave was a lover, not a fighter, whereas Joey was whatever he wanted to be. Dave was helpless in everything except playing the bass and tuning the women, whereas Joe could tackle any situation without a blink of the eye. Dave was handsome and vain, whereas Joey was just Joey, cocky and full of himself and a cock-eyed optimist taking it for granted that everything would work out in the end whatever he did. They were both great rock musicians who could get any toe tapping, but more importantly, they were great people who you could rely on with your life, if the stakes were down.

I left them to their deliberations and wandered off to the window at the end of the hall, to gaze out at the view of the river. The late afternoon sun was low in the sky and glistened off the water as the boats bobbed up and down at their moorings in the slight breeze. It was a nice scene, and far from what we were used to back home. This was my first expedition out of England, and my initial trepidations had been unfounded; in spite of the humble lodgings, the long hard nights, the equally long but boring days, and the fact that everyone was having their legs over except me, I was actually enjoying myself.

Only days ago I had been ready to crawl on my knees to get away, but I now found myself already sad at the thought that we would soon be leaving. I felt I had made some good friends during our short stay, and knew I would miss them when we were gone. Johan was a nice and interesting man with a lot of philosophical wisdom garnered through a long and hard life, and I enjoyed his company. When we first met him, we thought Otto must be retarded, but he turned out to be a jovial companion who couldn't do enough to make our stay as pleasant as possible. Doris and Maria were nice girls and fun to be with, but I was on the verge of falling in love with both Henni and Trudi, not just for their looks, but for the wonderful girls they were and the warmth and affection they gave me. I was going to miss them all.

Joey had been right when he had assured us that there would be an abundance of blonde, blue-eyed frauleins ready and waiting with their ample charms, and that it would just be a case of notching up the score on the bedposts. Sadly I hadn't got a single notch on mine, and, even if I had had reason to do so, it would have had to be made with a hacksaw, as my bed was made of cast-iron. But the chance of me getting a fraulein to share my bed wasn't worth betting on, so the hacksaw could remain at rest.

We had once asked Stuart what he and Astrid talked about, since she knew no English and he had no interest in anything German, apart from the women. He seemed surprised that we could ask such a meaningless question. "Actually, we don't do much talking," he told us, then added, as a matter of fact, "It's just sex, that's all." He was right of course; being healthy heterosexual's, the lads were just enjoying what was on offer, and the girls involved, being healthy heterosexuals themselves, were sharing the pleasure with them, with the added spice of pretending that we were some kind of super-star rockers, at least in Schleswig. So it was a win-win situation for everybody. Everybody, that is, except me.

Dave brought me back to the present. "What are we going to do tomorrow?" he asked as they gathered around me.

"What do you mean *do tomorrow*?" Joey sneered. "The same as every day – stay in bed until whenever, snuffle, snore, fart and scratch ourselves, then turn over and repeat the procedure."

"Actually, I was thinking about taking a run somewhere in the van, just to get away for a bit. We could do with a change of scenery." I thought Dave's proposal was close to brilliant, and nodded my head enthusiastically in agreement.

Joey was less enthusiastic. "Hang on," he told us, "while you shower sit in the back taking the grand tour, I have to do the driving. I've already lost two hub-caps taking you buggers for a jaunt, and I'm not ready to lose the others just to show you lot the sights. Anyway, we haven't got any petrol and no money to spare to get any, so it looks like your little trip is off, and it's back to Plan A."

"What Plan A?" I wondered.

"Lying in bed and snuffling, snoring and farting!"

I wiped the grin from his face by pointing out that he would have to drive back to the garage in Brodersby to pick up the spare wheel we had left there after the blow-out a few days earlier. I pointed out that we could hardly travel between venues without a spare, and this revelation seemed to spur him into action.

"Fucking hell, I'd forgotten about that!" he exclaimed. "That puts a whole new slant on it, doesn't it!" He sat down to contemplate the implications of this sudden knowledge. After a few moments, he lit up like a lighthouse, and called out, "Got it!" then jumped to his feet full of energy and eagerness, "Come on, you shower," he called as he moved towards the door, "I've got an idea that'll save us money," and he was off, with the rest of us hard on his heels, wondering what was going on.

We were led to the van, where Joey flung open the rear doors and produced a petrol can and a piece of plastic tubing. I looked at these with mounting concern as it dawned on me what his money-saving scheme was all about. I looked at him aghast, "Please tell me you're joking, Joe!" The expression on Dave's face probably mirrored my own.

"Stop being a pair of bleeding wimps!" Joey admonished, apparently enjoying our discomfort. "Where's your sense of bleeding adventure?" He had it all down pat, "Me and Biffo will take turns at siphoning the petrol, and Dave can keep look-out."

I could hardly believe my ears, and even less believe that I was actually creeping furtively about in the dark an hour before we were due on stage, siphoning petrol out of any vehicle that didn't have a locked petrol cap, scuttling back and forth to tank up the van. Here we were, the rock and roll heroes of Schleswig, British rock's representatives abroad, The Charters on tour, the rockers who made the women squeal to their music, sucking petrol from a tube in the shadows like dockside whores at three o'clock in the morning. My cheeks were hollow from the strain of sucking and I stank of petrol, but I have to admit that I became quite adept at it, although I did get a little carried away once or twice and got a mouthful of Shell's finest.

Back at our quarters, I sat on my bed and took out a cigarette to calm my nerves, but just managed to stop lighting it as I remembered that I was primed for take off as soon as the match neared my mouth. I decided that Joey actually must be as mad as I had often thought he might be, and that he would definitely end up getting us all arrested, before he was finished. Thus far we had been stopped for speeding and dangerous driving, we had crashed the van, the music man was looking for us for the theft of his goods, Joey had half killed a local and would normally be facing a charge of assault and battery, and now half the cars in the vicinity were without petrol to get them home. And we had only been there a week and a half!

Suddenly Stuart burst into the rooms. He wasn't happy about us disappearing without telling him we were going, and he hurled abuse at Joey, who strangely took it all in patient silence, then began to search the room, looking for something he couldn't find. This intrigued Stuart sufficiently to make him stop his tirade to ask what Joe was looking for. Joey looked up at him, and demanded, "I can't find her, so where the hell have you hidden her?"

Clearly agitated, Stu asked, "Where have I hidden who?"

"Bleeding Astrid, that's who! The two of you have been joined at the hip all day, so what have you done with her?"

They both chuckled, Stuart's irritation now replaced by a grin. He flung himself on his bed, and rested his head in his arms as he stared up at the ceiling, seeming to be find relaxation in some memory. After a moment, he looked around with a puzzled expression on his face, and asked, "Is it just me, or can anyone else smell petrol in here?"

As I mounted the stage and sat behind my drum-kit, I recalled the previous Tuesday which had been the start of my days of misery. But when I looked out at the crowd I could see that it was sizeably bigger than it had been then, and that cheered me up. We had twelve new songs for the crowd – if we could only manage to remember the lyrics.

Joe announced the first song of the evening. It was one of those we had dragged back from oblivion earlier that day, and it was my song. I thought about what the others had said about me forgetting the words and just making them up as I went along, and, although this had never bothered me before they had pointed this out to me, it now made me nervous.

I gave a rapid count-in, and we started up with the strident chord changes, and my crash cymbal working overtime as I gave the hi-hat cymbals a good off-beat thrashing. It was a really solid sound. With my heart in my mouth I started singing, *I'm gonna write a little letter, gonna mail it to my local DJ ... It's a rockin' little record I want my jockey to play ...*

I don't know where the recall of the words was coming from, but they just kept tumbling out of me. *Roll over Beethoven and tell Tchaikovsky the news ...* I kept going, before finally climaxing with *Roll over Beethoven! Roll over Beethoven! Roll over Beethoven! Dig those rhythm and blues ...*

It almost brought the house down and there was enthusiastic applause from both the listening audience and the gyrating crowd on the dance-floor. It was a fantastic feeling that lifted our collective spirits considerably, and made our begrudged band practice earlier that afternoon seem worthwhile.

Our usual groupies were in close attendance as we took our first break. Doris with Dave, Maria with Joe, and we could just about make out Stuart's cramped body writhing underneath Astrid's ample charms as she sat on his lap wrapped around him like a boa constrictor. He was so trapped that he had difficulty reaching for his beer, and we only saw a straining arm appear out of the tangle as it reached for the glass, before it disappeared again back into the foliage of flesh.

Strangely, Trudi had not put in an appearance. Although I missed having her there, I thought her absence might be for the better, considering Stuart's entanglement with his new-found flame. The cat-fight that might follow would have been an unseemly fiasco, for given her superior weight-advantage, Astrid would certainly have won with either two falls, a submission, or a knock-out. Possibly all three!

Wondering if Maria had told her of his double-dealing, I asked her, but she had said nothing. "She would have to see for herself," she explained. Then her mouth tightened as she added, "And she did!" She explained that they had come together, but that Trudi had left in tears when she had seen Stu being devoured by the fat one.

I felt deflated by this information, and felt sad for the girl; she was too good for this bugger, I thought, and deserved better. "That's a shame," I said honestly. "For, at least I was looking forward to seeing her." I was definitely disappointed because I enjoyed her company, and realised I really had been looking forward to seeing her again. Once more, I could feel the air going out of my tyre. From the elixir of applause and some degree of adulation as we had come off the stage, I was now back to my normal state of despondency.

After the next session, I decided to go to the downstairs bar and drink myself into whatever degree of oblivion my now meagre resources would allow. I stood at the bar feeling sorry for myself, when a voice rang out above the noise from the juke-box and the general row around me, "Hey, Biffo, it's me!" and I turned to see Trudi waving me to her from a table by the wall.

She was pleased to see me, and I assuredly was very happy to see her. Before I knew it, I had put my mouth in it to really spoil the moment before it had even properly begun. "I'm surprised to see you here, Fraulein Trudi, " I told her, because I was, "after Maria told me how you'd had a fit and gone home after seeing Stuart with that Godzilla wrapped around him like a leech!"

She looked at me askance and a frown formed on her face. "Fraulein Trudi!" she exclaimed. "Isn't that a bit formal? I thought we were friends. And why are you being so flippant? Don't you think I've been upset enough for one evening?"

I grovelled before her, apologising and pleading innocence, and hoping for fair weather to get me out of the storm I had just sailed into. "I'm sorry, but I've had a bit of a hard day myself," I excused, "but yes, we are definitely friends, and I want it to stay that way!"

I never got a chance to continue for the bar suddenly filled up with her friends who all gathered around her and excitedly chatted away with her in German. I couldn't understand a word they said, but it didn't take a genius to work out that Stuart was part of it. In their excitement they managed to shove me further out of their circle in order to get closer to Trudi to comfort her crushed feelings and probably smirk at the entertainment it offered.

Doris and Maria arrived on the scene. Being her best friend, Maria elbowed her way through the throng to be closest to her, and the two of them then commenced to gabble away nineteen to the dozen. Meanwhile, I was being edged further and further away from where I really wanted to be, and finally found myself at a completely different table. I was joined by Johan, who enquired about the fevered fuss going on around us. I gave him a quick run-down on the situation. "Oh, is that all," he said, seeming a little disappointed, "I thought it was something important." In retrospect, that was quite an astute observation.

Johan and I were then joined by Dave and Joe, who informed us with a wicked grin on his face that he wanted a ring-side seat, "Because any moment now, the shit is going to hit the fan when Stuart comes in with Astrid." Sure enough, before he had finished speaking, Stu swaggered in with Godzilla on his arm, and headed towards our table. He didn't get far before his passage was halted by a wall of irate girls pushing at him and hurling abuse.

Somewhat taken aback by the venom of their attack, he tried to call something to Trudi, but only got a reply that was hardly complimentary. The expression on Astrid 's face and her reaction confirmed that she had heard Trudi's remark and was less than happy about it, and she began to pull him away from the throng of angry females, and they both beat a hasty retreat to the other end of the room, with the sounds of catcalls and abuse helping them on their way, leaving Dave and Joe bursting their sides laughing at the display they had just witnessed.

With the other table still crowded I decided to remain where I was and have a chat with Johan the shit-house meister, as he was as good a companion as anyone. "Have you had a good day, today?" he asked.

"Let's just say that it's been interesting," I replied without going into too many details about what we had been up to.

"While you were performing on stage there was apparently a lot of police activity in the area," he informed me.

Oh, aye?" I said, showing no great interest. "What was it now, then, someone not paying for their round?"

"Apparently they have got a number of calls from irate motorists who claim that someone has siphoned the petrol out of the fuel tanks," he said, smiling knowingly to himself.

I almost choked on a mouthful of beer at hearing this little snippet of information, and panicked, as I was prone to do in such situations. "Do they know who did it?" I asked in a nervous voice. "Were there any witnesses?" I was already beginning to dither, and prepared to offer my wrists for the cuffs claiming *it's a fair cop, Guv!* and ready to do my penitence in the deepest dungeon they could find for me.

"There were witnesses," he confirmed, "and they gave a very good description of the criminals. In fact, I hear that the police will be coming here tomorrow morning to interrogate you all."

I jumped to my feet to find Joe and tell him, but Johan pulled me back by my sleeve, laughing as he told me, "I was only joking, honestly!"

I fell back into my seat like a sack being dumped there and tried to steady my nerves. "How did you know it was us?" I managed to ask, as I nervously pulled at my collar.

"I did not know," he replied, "but there is certainly a strong smell of petrol around the group members tonight!"

And they say the Germans have no sense of humour! The bugger had wrapped me up all nice and neat and served me for supper, and I helped him do it.

Tuesday had now turned into the early hours of Wednesday morning, and I was becoming tired and not a little maudlin.

I looked across at the other table where things now seemed to be back to normal, with the inhabitants there laughing and joking, and generally having a good time. Johan followed my gaze. "Who are you looking at, Biffo?" he asked.

"The blonde girl," I slurred, "Trudi." I couldn't take my eyes off her. "It might be the beer," I said, "but I think she's looking particularly attractive tonight."

"From where I'm sitting, she's attractive any night!" He looked back to me. "Have you ever told her? Does she know how you feel?"

I coughed uncomfortably, and shifted my feet, "Er, well, no, not really, well maybe," then finished up with the resounding conclusion, "I dunno, really …"

"Well, don't you think you should tell her, if you like her so much?" he chided. "How else is she to know how you feel about her? Extra-sensory perception, perhaps?" He lifted his eyebrows in question.

I looked across at her again, and saw her in close conversation with Maria. They were both smiling, and I noticed Maria indicated me with the flat of her outstretched palm. Then they both got up and pulled on their coats, as Trudi smiled and nodded her head at whatever Maria was telling her. Then she walked straight over to me, planted a kiss on my cheek, and said, "I'll see you tomorrow, Biffo. Auf wiedersehen!"

I sat there with a stupid grin on my face. "Aye, come up to see me, and make me smile."

She gave me a demure look and a cheeky grin. "You never know," she said, "I might just do that!" and then she was gone.

The Hour Glass
is Running out
of Sand

My eyes flickered slowly open to what was now Wednesday proper, and I heard the sound of raised voices with Joey sounding off again. "What d'ya expect, you dozy unthinking sod! D'ya expect her to say nowt about it when the pair of you are having it off right in front of her? Now that was really putting her face in it, wasn't it, you fat bastard!"

I could barely hear what Stuart was saying, but he was definitely moaning back at Joey for his uncompromising onslaught, which had clearly needled him enough to retort, "You just don't understand, do you? Can't you see, I'm a free bleeding spirit, and you know I'm weak when it comes to women. I take what I can get, when I can get it. Anyway, you ginger bugger, correct me if I'm wrong, but wasn't it you who waxed lyrical about all the frauleins eagerly waiting for us?"

I heard Joey cackling merrily away before he replied, "That's right, but not two at a time, in the same bleeding room. I've heard of shitting on your own doorstep, but you've trod in it too!" His voice became derisive, "Free spirit, my arse!"

Just then the toilet flushed and I realised that Dave had again had to spend the night in our humble abode, now being reduced to a grab-it-while-you-can lover like the others, since being expelled from Doris's palatial love-nest. "I thought we were going for a run today," he whined, "it'll be too late, if we don't get off now."

So we did the necessaries and finally stumbled out into fresh air. At the van, Dave asked me nicely enough to be allowed to sit in the front, for me to let him, so I climbed into the back seat with Stuart. "I feel lousy," he moaned. "Really down, I don't mind admitting!" He sighed audibly.

"I'm not too happy myself, either," I informed him, "so spare me any sad sorrow stories, because I'm not interested. I heard it all before, with you babbling on about free spirit and all the rest of it. The only free spirits you should be concerned about are the vodkas the punters at the Dog and Duck pass on to you for entertaining them with your guitar!"

Joey began to laugh. "Entertaining them? The punters only buy him drinks so they can get a bit of peace when he's downing them!

"They love me in there!" Stu insisted. "In fact, at the end of each evening they always have a whip round and give me the cash."

"Aye," Joey was still chuckling away, enjoying himself, "and what do you do with it? I'll tell you – you spend it on more vodka."

"So what!" Stu couldn't understand what the problem was. "What d'ya think I should spend it on?"

"Guitar lessons!" Joey shouted out, and almost drove us off the road, laughing.

"Watch it, mate!" said Stuart, clearly provoked at this lack of respect, for if there was anything at all he took seriously, it was his undoubted prowess on the guitar. "You're skating on very thin ice here, d'ya hear me?"

"I'm skating on thin ice!" Joey chided. "That's rich coming from you. You're already through it, you fat git. It's called drowning."

A period of quiet reigned for a while, only interrupted by Stu's constant sighs and the occasional thoughtful and wry expression that appeared on his face.

It didn't take a genius to see that he was none too happy, and I knew him well enough to know what was bothering him. I decided to find out, just to confirm my own suspicions. "What happened with you and Astrid last night, after all the other girls had strung you up for your two-timing she-nanigans?"

"She wanted to know what all the trouble was about," he mumbled. "Especially concerning the cutting barbs that Trudi threw at me." He turned towards me. "That's when she sussed out what was going on," he told me sadly, and gave another sigh. I stopped him. "Hang on a minute," I said, trying hard to suppress a smirk, "are you going to tell me that Astrid was blissfully unaware that you and Trudi were an item?"

He nodded his head. "That's right. With Trudi not turning up the other night, I thought I'd get away with it, but now she's given me the brush-off," he said, wallowing in self-pity.

"My heart bleeds for you Stu," I told him. "My heart really bleeds for you, you dozy fat pillock!"

Dave's voice broke in from the front seat. "Is there any chance that we can actually go now? Or are we going to stay here all day?"

Joey clicked the ignition key, the engine roared into life and we moved off, with Bulbous Nose demanding to know where to drive to get to the garage in Brodersby.

Fifteen minutes and several wrong turns later, the grinning idiot turned into the forecourt of the garage and parked. The van remained motionless as did our driver, which was completely unnatural for a live-wire jumping jack like Joe. After sitting motionless for five minutes, Dave slowly turned to Joe. "Well?" he said, and waited for a response.

This brought Joey back from wherever he had been. "Well, what?" he wondered.

"Are we going to sit here all day," Dave hissed at him, "or are you going in to find out what's happening with the spare!"

Joey ruefully rubbed his chin, and scratched at the three-day orange rubble on it. "I can't speak German," he decided, as if he had just discovered the fact. He turned back to me.

"You know a few words of the lingo, so you'll have to come in with me Biffo," he ordered.

"A few words, yes," I admitted. "Like how to order a coffee or a beer, or even a sausage in bread, but how's that going to help you get your spare wheel back?"

So we all trudged in together to be greeted by a mechanic who was wiping his hands on an oily rag and eyeing us suspiciously, which was hardly surprising judging by the way we came in looking like the Wild Bunch about to rob the local bank. Suddenly his face lit up at the sight of Joey's distinctive face, and he roared out over his shoulder, "Wolfgang! Lothar! They are here again!" and within seconds the aforementioned had slid out from wherever they were hidden, and they all proceeded to the van, where they stopped to stare at it in disbelief, kicking the tyres, peering inside and rocking it from side to side, while making guttural sounds to comment on one thing or another, and chuckling away like the circus had come to town.

Each found some particular defect that particularly amused him, and pointed it out to the others, then rolled about laughing, slapping each other on the back to stop from choking, before the next would find something and the volume of laughter would reach hysterics once again.

Joey became clearly rankled, and shouted out, "Oy, what the fuck is this – workers' playtime, or summat!"

This brought the trio's attention back to the fact that they had an audience, and an impatient one at that. The one who appeared to be the foreman came to us dabbing the tears from his eyes with a rather dirty rag, and still chuckling. He apologised, but pointed out that he just had to show the others what he had already told them about earlier. "I fixed your tyre the other day, and I told Lothar and Wolfgang about the state of your van, but they would not believe me. But now they have seen for themselves." He glanced at Lother's face and gave a short burst of mirth, before he regained control. "I cannot believe you have driven it all the way from England without everything falling apart," he shook his head in disbelief. "It must have been a miracle."

"Tell him about the hub-caps, Joe!" I whispered, and saw how he cringed.

The foreman had by now calmed sufficiently to speak without giggling. He looked at Joey, "I recognised you from the other evening," he explained. "You are, how do you say, quite distinctive, yes!"

The ginger man took this as a compliment, not even considering that it might be his especially ugly features that made him memorable, and began to grin.

"There you go, Joe," I offered conversationally, "if he recognised you, then it won't be difficult for the owner in the music store to recognise the thieving bastard that robbed him!"

I got a cursory, "Fuck off!" and a dig in the ribs as receipt for my delivery.

Joey decided he had had enough abuse for the moment, and demanded to know if his tyre was ready. It turned out that they hadn't even started on it because they were certain we would never come back for it, so Lothar was despatched to fix it there and then. After a few moments we heard him calling from inside, "Which one is it?"

The foreman thought for a moment then called back, "It's the one without the hub-cap!"

We wandered about outside while we waited, and finally settled on the wall I had shared with Trudi a few days earlier. Joey wasn't too happy about his pride and joy bearing the brunt of such merriment. "That van's great," he insisted. "It was a bloody good buy!"

"Well the doors haven't fallen off yet," I acknowledged.

"Not yet, but they will," Stuart stated.

"Unless the wheels fall off first," Dave pointed out.

"Listen you bastards," Joey snarled, bubbling over nicely, "I've half a mind to let you walk back to Schleswig if you don't stop taking the piss!"

"If you had half a mind, you'd walk back yourself rather than risk driving this thing!" Stuart retorted, and gave the van a kick for good measure.

Joey stubbed out the cigarette he had been smoking and stood up to stretch. "If I sit on this wall any longer I'll more than likely get piles!"

"Don't you mean haemorrhoids?" I asked.

"Aye, them and all," and he wondered off, rubbing his thighs back to life.

A few minutes later, the foreman came out, rolling our wheel before him. He stopped by the door and beckoned us towards him. "I'm afraid the tyre and inner tube were too badly damaged to repair," he told us, "so we have fitted brand new replacements." He held a piece of paper up for us to see. "Here is the bill."

Our jaws dropped when we saw what it cost. We each floundered about in our pockets looking for enough cash to cover it. As I counted out my few coins, my attention was drawn to a sleek dark blue BMW saloon that had pulled into the forecourt, and the faintly familiar figure in a smart dark suit that stepped out of it. He strode up to the suspicious gang gathered before him, and demanded to know of the foreman what was happening. On hearing the foreman's explanation, he calmly informed him that he would cover the cost of the tyre himself. "You see, Erik, I know these young men. I met them in Otto's bar when I picked up my daughter on Sunday. These are the English musicians my daughter has been telling me so much about." It was first then that I remembered him, and that he was Henni's father.

Turning to me, he shook my hand, saying, "Guten Tag, Biffo. How are you?"

Both surprised and pleased that he remembered me, I thanked him for paying the bill, and assured him that he had certainly got us out of a sizeable financial hole by doing so. He waved it away as nothing. "As it happens I own this garage," he told me. As an afterthought, he added, "And the BMW franchise for the area." He wasn't expecting any response to this news, and didn't get any. "Anyway," he continued, "it is the least I can do for the entertaining evening you provided for my son and daughter the other night. Henni has not stopped talking about you since."

Joey beamed at this.

Our benefactor continued, "I will tell Henni that I met you. I'm sure she will be thrilled. She is so looking forward to her birthday on Friday and dancing the night away to your music." He turned towards me, and gave me a smile. "She is particularly looking forward to renewing her acquaintance with you, Biffo. I believe she has a little surprise for you."

Joey sniggered, and I promised myself that I would kill him one day.

We finally got back on the road, with Joey happily whistling away at the wheel, smiling at the thought of the money he had just saved. For my own part, I mused on what Henni's father had told me. *She was looking forward to seeing me. Especially me!* That was certainly strange. I thought her daddy will probably end up giving her a new BMW for her birthday surprise. But what was the little surprise she had planned for me? I smiled, at the thought, then decided that no way, it couldn't be that. Could it …?

Strangely enough, we soon found ourselves in a bar in a small town that happened to be on the way to wherever we were going, which could turn out to be anywhere, with Joey's sense of direction. Stu and I nursed our beers while Dave and Joe fought for honour and glory and the odd pfennig, at the billiard table. I noticed Stuart observing me warily, and enquired about his interest in me. "I've just been thinking," he said, "what with Astrid giving me the chop and Trudi hating my guts for messing her about, I suppose it's ripe for you to be sniffing around her now, eh?"

"Sniffing around …? Who? Astrid!"

"Trudi, mate!" he replied. "I know you fancy her, and don't try to deny it, I can see it in your eyes, mate, because they give you away every time."

I was so taken aback by what he said that I admitted it, "Yes, I think she's a beauty, and I do like her. If that's what you want to hear, then yeah, I do fancy her."

Stuart smiled. It was a surprisingly nice smile. "Well, if you promise not to have a hysterical fit, I'll tell you something," he said. "Trudi's got a soft spot for you too. In fact when we first arrived here, she took a shine to you right away." Then he chuckled to himself. "But being you, you didn't even notice, you daft pillock!"

I hadn't noticed a thing, probably because I wasn't expecting any attention from any of the opposite sex, and had been so long away from them that I wouldn't have known the signals if they had been written in block letters.

"Unfortunately for you, Biffo," Stu continued, "I fancied her too, so to enhance my chance of getting into her knickers, I told her you weren't interested because you preferred blokes."

I was mortified and about to berate him but was interrupted as Joe and Dave joined us. Joe was as sour as a lemon having been soundly thrashed by Dave. "Listen Joe," I said, still seething at what I had just been told, "did you know that Stu here has been putting it about that I'm some kind of poofter?"

"Oh, aye," Joey confirmed without a hint of embarrassment, "he told Trudi, and it soon got round to all the other girls."

"You bastards!" I hissed at them. "You frigging bastards! No wonder I never got a leg-over!" I was fuming, and disappointed at being misused like this by my own friends.

Joey chuckled at my reaction, seeming to enjoy it. "I can see that this info would jeopardise your chances with the fairer sex," he admitted, "but there is another major problem which has probably been the real reason for your lack of success."

"And what's that?" I snarled at him.

"Your fucking ugly!" And the unfeeling bastard roared with laughter.

We took the straight road back to Schleswig, partly because I was still seething about what they had done to me, and partly because nobody could get lost on that particular road, since it went straight from where we had been to where we were going, but Joey still managed to take a wrong turn and lose our way. The thought of how he was going to navigate his way through Hamburg on the way to our next gig in Lüneburg was anybody's guess! We finally appeared by the garage at Brodersby, where Erik, Wolfgang, and Lothar all gave us a cheery wave as we rumbled by, and from there even Joey couldn't lose his way.

I found my way to Otto's bar for a drink when we got back. I was the only customer in the premises and Otto greeted me warmly. I mentioned that Henni's father had saved our bacon, but I don't think it was the mention of his name that put a smile to Otto's face, but rather the mention of the beautiful Henni, who he doted on. He planted a foaming beer before me and waved away my attempt to pay. "Henni will be here to celebrate her birthday on Friday," he told me, as if I didn't know, "and she is really looking forward to it."

I finished my beer and walked outside for a breath of air, and the thoughts began to fill my head. I was a loser who hadn't had a girl, sexually or otherwise for a year, and suddenly I now apparently had two beautiful girls showing serious interest in me. I could hardly believe it, but all the signs that I had been unable to read earlier seemed to be telling me it was true. As uplifting as this realisation was, it still made me uncertain and actually nervous. I certainly had no wish to put myself in a position where I could become emotionally hurt. Once had been enough! Then again, I felt something for both these girls that was more than physical attraction, so in a way, I realised that I was already emotionally bonded to them. But I still didn't want to get hurt. Neither did I want to hurt them – I liked them too much. As I stood outside in the cold, I dithered and sighed, then dithered again. I didn't really know what to do about the information that had been injected into me, but it had got into my blood and certainly had me jumping. The trouble was that I didn't know which way to jump.

Back at the room, I found Joey sitting alone on his bed strumming his guitar. For once, he wasn't in a talkative mood, so I just sat down on my own bed to relax with my own thoughts. A sharp knock at the door brought me out of my thoughts. A moment later Joey's head popped around the door, "Oy, dozy," he said, smiling all over his red face, "shape up, you've got a visitor!"

Before I could turn around I heard the door close and felt two arms around my neck and the heavy aroma of a perfume I immediately recognised. "Hi Biffo," Trudi's voice purred, then she planted a kiss on my neck.

I was taken completely by surprise, and could only stammer out, "What are you doing here?"

She slid out of her coat and smiled sweetly. "Did you, or did you not, ask me to come up to see you, and to make you smile?"

"Did I..?" I stuttered. "I really can't remember ..." Then I saw the vision before me, and gasped out, "Trudi, you look stunning!"

"Thank you," she said coyly. She gave me a steady look as she scrutinised my face, giving herself time. "I'm here to make you smile," she whispered, "if you want me to?" She pulled me towards her and kissed me full on the lips. In the heat of the moment, a thought crossed my mind, and I pulled away from her panting, and rushed into the next room.

"Joey," I hissed, "is this one of your bleeding wind-ups or what? I know what you're like, and if it is I'm going to kill you!"

Joe kept strumming, completely unconcerned, and gave me a stupid grin, looking like the idiot he was. "It's got nowt to do with me," he assured me. Then a serious look came into his face. "Look you dozy sod, she's come here to be with you, now get back in there, get the fucking cellophane off it and give her what she wants, and don't even think of coming out again until you do, because I'll be listening!"

I rushed back to my room praying that the apparition that had appeared there had not been an illusion, but Trudi was already lying on the bed with a smile on her face and little else. "Turn off the light," she suggested, so I turned off the light. "Come here by me," she said, and patted the mattress, so I came and lay down beside her. "Is there anything you want?" she asked, cooing in my ear.

"Yes," I breathlessly panted in her ear, "leave your boots on!" and she did, and we did, and we did it all, and I could still do it after all that time, so we did it all again, and again. I had a lot of catching up to do, so I did!

I suddenly became aware of heavy footsteps clumping up the wooden stairs, and then heard Stuart's voice calling out as he burst into the room demanding to know where I was.

"We're on in ten minutes, and I can't find him anywhere!"

"Keep your knickers on," Joey told him, calm as could be, "he's in his room writing some postcards back home."

"What, in the frigging dark? D'ya think I'm stupid? He's got someone in there with him, I can hear the bed springs twanging. So who is it?" he demanded.

Joey remained as calm as the whispering of the Spring breeze. "Maybe he's just restless," he said. "He's just tossing and turning after a long hard day. Leave him alone, he'll be okay. In fact, I know he'll be okay!" and he chuckled loudly. "Anyway, are you ready?"

"Yeah," came the response. Then Stu called to me, "Are you in there Biffo?"

"Definitely, mate!" I called back, and chuckled as I felt Trudi's lithe body thrusting away.

Before they slammed the door behind them, he called out again, "Are you coming or what!"

"Any second now, mate," I gasped back to him, "Any second, now!" then the door slammed shut.

A little later, as we were lying in each others arms, Trudi whispered in my ear, "Did I make you smile?".

"Believe it!" I replied with grateful honesty, and noticed that I actually was smiling.

I was late, and our bedroom antics had to come to a somewhat undignified end as I pulled on my clothes and we rushed down to the dancehall where the lads had already started playing *Sweet Little Sixteen* with Joey thrashing around wildly on my drum kit like a demented octopus, with Stuart taking the vocal. From where I stood, it didn't sound too bad either. Trudi looked on wide-eyed with a bemused look on her face. "I didn't know Joey could play the drums," she said.

I whispered in her ear, "He can't, but don't tell him!" I gave her a quick kiss, "Duty calls, so I'll see you later," and sprang up on stage feeling a new vigour in my body, to took my place behind my kit.

Stu was annoyed by my late arrival. "Where the fuck have you been? What have you been up to?"

I didn't reply, but I could see by the look in Joey's eye and his broad grin that he knew exactly what I had been doing, and knew that I had finally broken my duck – he could see it by the stupid expression on my face which was even more ridiculous than normal.

I exchanged secretive smiles with Trudi as she danced among the other girls in front of the stage, and lascivious images of our time together went racing through my head as I thumped the skins and slashed at the cymbals. My head was still spinning from what I had just experienced, and I wouldn't even have cared if Joey had played *Yesterday* a dozen times that night, because I, the butt of all the banter and abuse I'd had to endure, had just been with the most attractive and stunning girl in the building – the first girl for a year. Poofter, my arse!

The following evening after the gig, I sat at our usual table in the bar with the delectable Trudi, feeling extremely elated by the pleasure of her company. I felt like the cat that had got all the cream, and I couldn't stop grinning. Joey was there with Maria, and he must have been feeling quite happy himself because he bought a round for us all without anyone even having to suggest it.

I was more content than I had been for a year. I was with fun friends doing what we enjoyed, and doing it well as we strutted our stuff on stage and played some really good rock and roll for the appreciative audience that turned up night after night to listen to us. I had new friends around me whose company I enjoyed, and not least, I had the beautiful and enticing Trudi by my side and in my arms, and pleased to be there. I couldn't have been happier!

I should have known it couldn't last! It never does...

Trudi and Maria had to go to work in the morning so they gathered their things together to leave. Trudi leaned towards me and whispered, "I promise I will stay over with you in your room tomorrow," then planted a warm kiss on my face, and walked out. Her final words were a cheery "Auf wiedersehen, see you tomorrow, Biffo!" then she was gone.

Joey was smiling at me from across the table. "Will you stop doing that!" he told me.

"Doing what?"

"Grinning like a Cheshire Cat, that's what!" He gave me a friendly punch on the shoulder. "You two must have been having it off none-stop since you got the green light."

"Too damned right," I told him. "I've got a lot of catching up to do after you buggers spread those rumours about me!"

There was no sign of Dave or Stu so I enquired about their whereabouts. "Stu went to that bar on the Marktplatz to drown his sorrows after you started bedding his girl, and Dave went along to keep an eye on him," Joey informed me.

Johan had joined us. "They won't be there too long, because that place closes at two o'clock, whereas this place only closes when Otto's too tired to fill the glasses," he told us. Just then, the telephone behind the bar started ringing. Otto picked it up, listened, nodded his head and turned around with the phone in his hand, to indicate that Joey or I should come to answer it immediately.

The two of us began our usual juvenile argument about which of us should do the honours, but Otto's increasing agitation at our nonchalance and shouts of *Schnell! Schnell!* finally brought me to the phone. "Hello," I said, wondering who it could be, but not really caring.

A heavy German accent attacked my ear. "Is that The Charters, the English group?"

"Well, not all of them," I chuckled, "but I'm the drummer, if that's good enough for you."

"Good!" The voice was that of a heavy smoker's, and I could hear him exhale as he spoke. "I am calling to tell you that you are to move on to the Star Palast in Lüneburg to play there from tomorrow night. Is that understood?"

I thought that this must be a hoax. Some disgruntled lover wanting us out of the way. "And just who the hell are you, then?" I asked, suspiciously.

"Of course!" The voice was clipped and assured. "My name is Manfred. Manfred Müller. I own the Star Palast Dance-halls."

The clear concise Teutonic manner in which he delivered this statement made it clear that this was no hoax. I quickly pulled myself together to assume my normal simpering servility when in the face of authority. After all, I was speaking to the feared Manfred, the gangster from Kiel. Then the enormity of what he had just told me hit me like a brick and my euphoric state of mind vanished in a blink – we had to leave in the next few hours!

The voice in my ear brought me back. "Hello..! Hello..? Are you still there?" the voice demanded.

"Yes, of course," I replied, gathering my senses.

"You must leave in the morning and be ready to play in Lüneburg at seven o'clock in the evening. Your contact there will be the manager, Herr Helmut Schneider, and he will fill you in on all you need to know."

My heart was in my boots by the time he had finished, and I was hardly listening to what he said. Just to have something to say, I asked, "What's the address of the establishment?" twittering away like a half-soaked cretin.

"Just ask directions when you get there. Everybody knows the Star Palast." Perhaps my silence was what he expected;

receive orders and carry them out without question – the German way of doing things. "Good," he finished, satisfied that I had understood his instructions, "now put me back to Otto, I need to speak to him urgently."

I passed the phone to Otto. "He wants to speak to you," I told him in a dead voice that hardly carried to him, and I saw the worried expression that my words brought to his face.

Feeling despondent, nay even crushed, I rejoined the others and slumped into a chair, down in the mouth and deep in my own thoughts.

"What was that all about?" Joey enquired, suddenly showing concern at the sight of the misery that had replaced the grin that had been glued to my face for the past couple of days.

I took my time before replying, not really wanting to hear the hard facts spoken, even by myself. Eventually I replied in a tired voice, "It's all over for us here, Joe. We have to move on to Lüneburg." My dead eyes stared at the floor between my feet as I spoke.

"What, now?" he barked in dismay.

"No," I mumbled miserably, "tomorrow morning." I heaved a sigh of sadness. "We have to be ready to play by seven o'clock," I told him as I stared disconsolately at my beer. I didn't touch it. I'd lost the taste for it along with my will to live. Joey became silent too, and remained quiet for some time. We both knew that this moment had to come, but why now? Why did it have to come just when I had found a girl I really liked and who even liked me back? Why now, when I was happy and content to be where we were? I sighed, and my face must have shown the depths of my despair, for it was impossible to hide it.

"I am going to miss you guys," Johan said, and by the tone of his voice and the sadness in his eyes, I knew he meant it.

I gave him a brave flicker of a smile to show my appreciation. Then it suddenly hit me like a rock; Trudi would come here tomorrow expecting to see me and I would be gone! And Henni was coming to celebrate her birthday, and was looking forward to seeing me again, and I wouldn't be there! I'd be gone! We would all be gone! I almost tore at my hair in despair. Why now! Why fucking now!

Just then Dave and Stuart happened to come off the street, noisy, laughing and joking, and full of themselves. They stopped up abruptly when they were confronted by our unhappy faces. "What's up?" Stu asked, suddenly looking worried. "Has someone died, or what?"

The smile quickly disappeared from Dave's face as Joey gave them the short version, and he realised that he would not be seeing Doris again. Stu, on the other hand smiled even more broadly, obviously overjoyed by the news, and cheerfully chirped out, "Ah, well, onwards and upwards, and off and away, because tomorrow's always another day!"

Then he looked directly at me with a wicked grin on his face and smirked, "Tough shit, Biffo!" obviously enjoying my pain and his own little revenge.

I packed away my few belongings in my hold-all thinking it would be best to have it done before Joey suddenly decided we were to leave, which would certainly be early because he was bound to panic at the prospect of getting to Lüneburg on time, and for that matter, of finding the place at all. Sleep was out of the question as I alternately paced the floor and sat with my head in my hands on the edge of the bed I had shared with Trudi only hours earlier. Her perfume still lingered there.

I stared at the wall, and smiled as I saw a new addition to the graffiti there. In bold strokes of pink lipstick had appeared the legend *TK & JB*. I felt a lump in my throat. I cast a glance at Eric Burdon's scribbling and said aloud, "Well Eric, I wonder if you felt as lousy as me, when you had to leave this place?" There was no answer, but I doubted that anybody could feel as badly about leaving somewhere, as I did at that moment.

With the van finally loaded up, I nipped back to our rooms for a final look around. It might have been a doss-house, but it had been home for awhile, and fond memories had already formed in the short time we had spent there. Emotion is a strange thing, and I had now come to accept that underneath my veneer of careless, callous banter and nonsense, there hid a vulnerable and sentimental soul.

I emerged into the street to be greeted by Joey's harsh voice demanding that I get myself into the van so we could be off. I hastily shook hands with Otto and begged him to give my love to Henni and wish her the best for her birthday. I'd miss her. Our friend Johan had also come to see us off. He put one arm around my shoulder and shook my hand with the other, then handed me a little note. "This is from the heart, Biffo," he said. "Promise me you will read it later." I folded it carefully and placed it in my pocket. It was quite emotional. Then we were off, with Joey giving extra acceleration as we pulled away, just for show.

We had hardly driven five minutes, before Stuart piped up from the rear, "Hey, Joe, I'm gagging for a coffee, so stop at that transport cafe by the gas station, will y'er!" Joey the Red Nosed Driver duly complied, and we trooped into the cafe. Something made me hold back, and I wandered away from the building and looked across the waters of the Schlei back to the town of Schleswig lying shrouded in the early-morning mist. I sighed, and promised myself that I would come back. Sometime. Somehow.

I was met by Joey's creased and worn face grinning at me as I rejoined the others. "Hey, you dozy bugger, you haven't been crying have you?"

205

"No, of course not," I protested weakly. "I've just got some ash in my eyes, that's all!"

Getting back to basics, Stuart demanded, "Where do we go from here, Joe?" figuring if anyone should know it should be our erstwhile driver.

"Well," Joey began, "according to Otto, we take the third exit on the roundabout then head straight for the Autobahn."

"And then …?" Stu enquired.

"We follow the star to the right, then straight on until morning!" Joey chuckled.

"Sod off, you grinning ginger ape," Stuart responded, laughing quietly, "who do you think you are? Peter fuckin' Pan?"

Then we drove away, leaving Neverland behind us forever.

Zeit Fur
Lüneburg

As we began the fourth lap around the roundabout, I wondered why, and glanced at Joey hunched over the steering wheel concentrating so hard his face contained more lines than ever as his brain grappled with a problem he knew only too well. Sighing and muttering loudly he eventually stopped the rust-mobile and demanded that I find the map in the glove compartment.

"What do you want the map for?" I exclaimed. "We're still in bloody Schleswig!" Which was certainly the case, for since our departure some time ago we had hardly driven more than a mile.

He spread the battered map across the steering wheel once again and studied it carefully. With a look of total confusion still written on his lugubrious red features, and after a couple of minutes pondering the situation, he suddenly stated, "Right! We're here, and we have to get there," he said, pointing his finger and not looking at all confident that this statement was correct.

"So what's the problem?" I wondered, not able to understand why there should be a problem at all.

"Well," he said, taking his time as he spoke, for he was certainly baffled and needed time to think, "what I want to know is, how do we get to this Autobahn thingy from here?"

Clearly rankled by the delay and the fuss that was stopping him from getting some sleep, Stuart snapped out, "You take the third friggin' exit on the roundabout, exactly like Otto told you!" I couldn't decide if he was distraught or merely frustrated, whatever it was he was not happy just then. "What's the matter with you this morning," he chided, "are you already missing Maria or summat?"

I could see by the reaction on his face that Joey wasn't too pleased by Stuart's comments, knowing full well that he would never see her again. I suppose that thought concerned him more than trying to find his directions from the roundabout. I decided to be sympathetic, and gently suggested that he just take the third exit and we would be on our way, but he rounded on me. "Do you think I'm friggin' thick or summat," he howled, "I know it's supposed to be the third exit, but there is sod all there to indicate that's the way to the bloody Autobahn, Lüneburg or anything like that, the only sign there reads Einfahrt!" He was definitely confused. "I've looked at the map and can't find it anywhere," he moaned, "see if you can find it Biffo," he begged.

Despite having a heavy heart from having to leave the tantalising Trudi and Henni behind, I had to smile at Joey's ineptness at reading a map. I tried to explain. "Einfahrt is the slip road that leads to a motorway, Joe," I told him patiently, and is not to be confused with the Autobahn signs that read ausfahrt that you take when you leave the motorway."

Joey's face lit up and the idiot grin came back in place once more. He chuckled good-naturedly. "It seems that I don't know my einfahrt from my ausfahrt," he said, then let drop the kind he did know, probably just to get back at us for knowing more than he did, and roared with laughter at our discomfort.

When we had cleared the air Stu chirped up, "With you mooching around like a dead dog all night, did you remember to get our pay packets so we have something to show for our efforts?"

Still chuckling away, Joey confirmed the fact. "I got them from Otto just before we left," he said, and rummaged through the pockets of his Parka to produce them with a flourish.

As I put my hard-earned cash into my pocket I remembered the note Johan had given me before we left, and opened it to see what he had written. It wasn't much. In fact it was a very simple message, but it was everything it didn't say that made my eyes well up with tears as I scanned it. *The Charters, I will never forget you. I will always remember you with good memories. Johan.* A simple little message written from the heart, as he had told me.

"What's that?" enquired Joe, looking over at me with curiosity stamped on his face. I showed him, and a smile slowly formed on his craggy features. "That's nice of him," he said. "He wasn't a bad old geezer for a shitehousemeister, was he? Very friendly and informative." He seemed to drift away in his own thoughts. Perhaps Johan's little message had even got through Joey's rusty cast-iron veneer. After a few moments of unusual silence, Joey broke it again. "He certainly took a shine to you," he said. "The two of you were forever chin-wagging away nineteen to the dozen like a couple of bloody fish wives."

"Just as well too or I wouldn't have had anyone to talk to after you lot spread the rumour that I was bent!" I pointed out with some feeling, then bit my bottom lip and sighed as the image of Trudi and Henni's smiling faces suddenly appeared in my mind and I knew I would never see them again. Never more Neverland …

It suddenly occurred to Joey that we were still on the roundabout, not an inch closer to our destination than we had been despite the time it had taken to ascertain where we were and where we were hopefully going to end up. "Right," he said, taking command of the situation, "is there anything else before I finally get this show on the road?" The sound of silence gave him the answer he required, so he roared the engine for show, then let out the clutch and we were finally on our way to new adventures taking the old with us as memories that would last a lifetime.

We were soon rattling down the Autobahn, fortunately heading in the right direction for once as was confirmed by the signs that popped up on the way: Kiel, Neumünster, Norderstedt and Hamburg. The only sounds to be heard were the humming of the tyres on the tarmac, the knocks from the engine, the periodic grinding from the gearbox, the occasional strike of a match to light a cigarette, the air gushing through the slightly opened windows and the occasional burst of flatulence from our twitchy driver cum band idiot.

Several miles had passed with no chit chat of merit as I stared through the grimy windscreen at the endless Autobahn that stretched out before us. I kept a good hold on the remnants of what had once been a map for with Joey driving it could turn out to be the lifeline to survival the next time he took an unintended detour. The idiot couldn't even find his way out of Schleswig, and obviously took roundabouts too seriously, apparently thinking that he had to keep going around them until someone told him otherwise. We had only travelled a mile, and that had included a coffee break, before our leader of men had been totally perplexed just trying to ascertain which direction the Autobahn was. Just thinking about it was giving me a headache!

I don't know if Joey had suddenly acquired extra-sensory perception at this point, but just to give me new faith in his abilities, he suddenly croaked out, "Hey, Biffo! Where the fuck are we …?"

I put our minds at ease by confirming that we had just passed Kiel, and were therefore thankfully still going in the right direction. I checked the map and informed those inclined to listen that we would soon come to a long straight stretch of Autobahn before we reached Hamburg.

"A long straight stretch, eh? Well, just to alleviate the boredom, I suggest you all get your heads down and have a kip, 'cos I am!" I glanced at him grinning away like a chimp with a banana, and thought that he might just do it too. Thankfully a thought entered his head to keep him awake a little longer, and he asked, "Did Manfred tell you who was replacing us in Schleswig?"

"They'll probably be there by now," I mused, wishing it was me, and drifting off again with thoughts of what I had left behind.

"Well," Joey demanded impatiently, "are you going to tell me, or what?"

I came back to the present to tell him, "Bodger and the Bulls Hits."

"Bodger!!" I thought he was going to drive us off the road from the shock. "Bodger and that band of bloody maniacs?" He could hardly believe it. "That Manfred can't know what he's letting himself in for," he said with some conviction. "They'll not only bring the house down, they'll bloody wreck it first." He was probably right. Joey was building himself up to a fair degree of righteous wrath at the thought of these stalwarts of British music invading the lodgings he had so painstakingly made liveable. "Those buggers have no scruples," he moaned, "no ethics … and the morals of an alley full of tom cats on the prowl!" He kept shaking his head in disbelief and mumbling, "Bodger …?" at regular intervals as the miles passed by, apparently in shock from the revelation that they had been allowed out of the country at all.

Considering his comments and opinions on Bodger and his cohorts, I realised that Joey must either have some morals hidden underneath his thick skin somewhere after all, or a very short memory, for unless I was mistaken, we hadn't been far off the mark ourselves during the past couple weeks. But then again, apart from Joey's various involvements with the police, emptying stores of their wares and cars of their petrol, and thrashing someone within an inch of his life, we had really only acted like any other healthy young heterosexuals with hormones to spare.

Yes, just like Bodger and his ravaging raiders, I thought, and grimaced at the thought of them running loose back in Schleswig. From the silence of the driver sitting beside me and the worried look on his face, I deducted that his thoughts were occupied with much the same as my own.

We were both brought out of our reverie by sounds emanating from the back seat, and I turned to see Stuart hanging over his backrest with his backside showing his building site cleavage as he tried to reach his guitar in the back of the van. He managed to wake Dave from his dreams of Doris and other delightful damsels. He opened one sleepy eye and grumbled at him, "Just for once, can't you make a noise quietly!" which had me thinking from there to Hamburg trying to decide if he was pretty damned smart or just basically thick. To this day, I still haven't found the answer to that.

Stuart finally found his Rickenbacker and began to strum the strings gently as he tried to formulate the chords he was looking for, but we didn't give much thought to his laboured chord changes and left him to it.

Feeling generous, I lit two cigarettes and passed one on to Joey just to keep him awake. We puffed away contentedly as we heard Stu's chord sequence taking shape. They seemed to have a familiar ring to them, and from somewhere deep in my subconscious I realised that it was something from West Side Story. Just then he piped up, "Got it!" and began to warble, *Maria … I've just met a girl called Maria …*

Joey's face was a picture! His whole body seemed to crumble and his mouth sagged open so the cigarette dropped from it to disappear from view. He desperately fished around with his free hand to try to locate is. "Shit!" he shouted with panic in his voice, "where's the bleeding thing gone? I can't find it anywhere!" He set his eyes on me. "Don't just sit there, give me a hand to find it," he demanded in a shrill voice.

I leaned over him, desperately searching high and low. Just then, Dave decided it was time to come awake. Rubbing the sleep from his eyes, he suddenly sat bolt upright in shock at the sight of the band drummer, in what can only be described as a compromising position, with his head moving in the lap of the ginger singer who was cavorting about on his seat like a spastic on speed.

"What the fuck …!" he exclaimed in dismay, but got no further.

"Shut the fuck up!" came from the front in a stereo scream that left no doubt that we would appreciate his adherence to our request.

Try as I may, I couldn't locate the cigarette, but did become aware of the smell of burning which was quickly followed by a yowl of pain from Joe, who was obviously in acute agony. His hands left the wheel to grasp his nether regions, and the van slewed wildly from side to side completely out of control as the driver concentrated on other matters. The tyres were screeching loudly while Joey, back to business and still screaming with agony desperately attempted to get the slewing vehicle under control.

We nearly side-wiped a passing van in all the panic, but far more frightening was the fact that we were almost under the back wheels of an articulated lorry that had suddenly loomed up very large in front of us. Everything was happening in micro seconds yet seemed to be in super slow motion. Still screaming like a wounded wild animal Joey gripped the steering-wheel with both hands as he fought to bring the van back from two wheels to four before we rolled over.

I suppose our miserable lives must have passed review and I probably begged for divine intervention. Whether it was

Joey or the Divine, doesn't really matter, but all the wheels came back to Terra Firma and Joey desperately jammed on the brakes to slow us down. I dare say he would have thrown out an anchor if he'd had one on board!

To everyone's relief we managed to stop on the hard shoulder, trembling from the shock, but still alive. Joey had other things to think of. Still screaming like a stuck pig, he immediately baled out of the van without so much as a by your leave and began to rub his crotch furiously, cursing and howling in pain as he did so, and, yes, tears rolled down his cheeks. Perhaps he was human after all? They could have been tears of relief at having survived certain death, but I rather thing it had something to do with the glow to his goolies …

From the back I just heard Stuart's voice cracking out, "Christ, I nearly shit myself!" From the smell in the van, he may very well have done just that.

Dave was as white as his bleached hair. "That was bloody lucky," he gasped, sitting stiff as a board in the seat as he held himself in place with rigid arms, as though still expecting the crash to happen.

Lucky must have been the understatement of the year. If the van had rolled over on that Autobahn, the ensuing chaos would have been utter carnage. I shuddered as I thought about it!

With Joey still whining away as he ruefully rubbed his pride and joy, the rest of us joined him where he sat smouldering. To calm our shredded nerves we all lit up for a smoke. Not unnaturally, Joey declined the one I offered him. He had probably smoked enough for a while.

Showing some concern for our ginger-haired invalid, Stuart enquired, "Are you alright, Joe?" and got hammered for his sympathy.

"No I'm not frigging alright, you fat sod!" he hissed through gritted teeth. "And it's all your fault for taking the piss, singing that Maria song!" Whether it was the shock that was coming through or the strain of holding in his anger, he had begun to tremble. "I've burnt me friggin' bell end because of you," he wailed.

It was hard to hear, but somewhere out there I seemed to hear a voice mumble an apology, and I saw Stuart shift his body self-consciously as he stared at the ground.

To our astonishment, Joey suddenly began to unzip his jeans and carefully removed his wounded pride, completely oblivious to the fact that we were there to experience the moment. He spat a load of saliva into the palm of his hand and gingerly massaged his shiny bell-end with it. Transfixed by the enormity of it all we could only stand and stare for there was no point in lending a hand, not that we would have in a month of Sundays – that thing looked likely to bite!

We were about to get back to the van to continue our journey when we were suddenly confronted by an army of police as they leapt out of their patrol cars. The leader, noticing our English registration plates began to converse with us in Ger-Glish, demanding to know who was in charge, so like the true cowards we were, we immediately pointed to the hapless Joe, to indicate that he was the culprit in charge.

Joey glowered at us, and then informed the policeman of the problem in hand. "We just had a little accident inside the van," he told him, "but it was nothing, and everything's alright now."

The policeman didn't seem to agree. There was more than a little arrogance in his voice as he spoke. "That is not what was reported to us on the car radio," he said. "It seems you were driving erratically, without due care and attention and about to cause a serious accident that could have cost lives."

We sighed and shuffled about awkwardly under his withering glare, while the rest of his henchmen gave the van the once-over which included the compulsory practice of tyre-kicking.

He brought out his notebook and flourished a pen ready to put it to paper when one of his companions brought his attention to the fact that there was a severe shortage of hub-caps, and wanted us to explain exactly who *R. Send* happened to be.

The top cop was just about to formally book us, for we must have infringed every Autobahn regulation in the book, including stopping in a no-stopping area, when Joey, with a last throw of the dice, tried to explain what had happened. Just to prove his point, he lobbed his wounded warrior out of his pants to verify the facts, and didn't even blush doing it!

"Look," he said, "there it is …" as though they could have missed it!

"Yes, very impressive," smirked the sergeant sarcastically. Looking closer he could see Joey's point. "Yes, I can see you have had a little accident," he admitted, then wondered, "Is it still sore?"

Joey winced and nodded his head to confirm the fact.

Putting away his notepad, the sergeant smiled at our leader's proud stance, while members of the patrol gathered around to gaze in awe at the wonder of what they saw before them. One even put on his glasses to get a clearer view as he muttered Grosse!

The sergeant seemed satisfied and sympathetically decided to show leniency, probably thinking that Joey had already suffered enough for his crimes, so he let us go with a warning to show more caution on the Autobahn.

Joey smirked as they drove off, then noticed the cold and quickly zipped up again before he got frostbite to go with the burns.

"You're a brazen bugger!" Stuart told him with the awe etched on his face. He couldn't believe what he had just seen any more than I could. "How could you lob it out in front of all those coppers? It's a wonder they didn't arrest you for gross indecent exposure!"

"There's nowt indecent about it," Joe assured him, "in fact it's bloody magnificent, and it held those coppers at bay, didn't it!"

Dave was occupied with other thoughts as usual, and stopped us in our tracks by asking, "I wonder why they do that?"

We all turned to him, wondering what he was on about.

"Do what?" Joey demanded.

"This penchant they have for kicking tyres," he replied.

We looked at each other with the same puzzled expression on our faces, wondering which universe the lad had come from, before Joey consoled him with a reply. "It's probably the first thing they teach them at police school," he informed him. "That's the test they have to pass to become a copper. If they can kick a tyre, they're in!"

We pulled up at the first service area we came to, feeling that we deserved a rest and a coffee break to get our frayed nerves under control, and Joey immediately squeezed the first coins from our hard-earned pay to put some petrol into the tank despite our protests, but as he so delicately put it: "The fucking thing doesn't run on friggin' air!"

I took the opportunity to ease some of the pressure from my bladder, and was commanded to acquire "one of them stadt plan thingies of Hamburg", on my way to the ablutions. I was impressed by the quality of the toilets; they were spotlessly clean, with air fresheners, flowers, and even background music to make your stay both pleasant and relaxing. When I got back to the eatery where the others had just finished their meal, I enthused about this discovery without receiving the interest I thought it deserved.

"Sounds like piss-house heaven," Stuart said laconically, while the other two merely stared into the middle distance through a cloud of cigarette smoke, and paid me no attention at all.

"But there is a downside to it," I informed whoever might be listening.

"Downside?" Stu was interested despite himself. "What do you mean, downside?"

"Well, how should I put it," I said, before deciding to put it to him straight. "You have to pay to pee."

Joey had been awake after all. "Pay to pee!" he exclaimed, apparently offended by such injustice, "I'm fit to burst, but I'm not paying for a friggin' pee!"

"It's only ten pfennigs, Joe," I told him, thinking it was well worth the price.

"I'm still not paying," he grumbled, and crossed his legs to keep his principles in place.

I studied the map and was relieved to register that we could skirt Hamburg to get to our destination. "If we stay on the Autobahn we can pass Hamburg without having to go through it," I informed Joey with a happy smile on my face. I shoved the map into his face to show him. "We just drive over this blue wiggly thing," I looked from the map to Joey's face, "you do remember the blue wiggly thing, Joe?" the scowl that came to his face told me he did, "then it's straight on to Lüneburg!" I finished with a flourish.

He looked from the map to me, then back again, and decided to bow to superior knowledge. He handed me the map without a word, and with that symbolic gesture surrendered his authority as self-acclaimed navigator for the group to someone who could actually read a map. Then, without any further preamble, he stated, "Talking about pantomimes …"

This put us all off track, wondering if he had finally succumbed to acute senility, or if this was a side-effect of his smouldered soldier.

"Pantomimes!" Stuart cried in exasperation, "Who said anything about pantomimes?"

Dave came back from somewhere over the rainbow in the land of Oz, where he usually spent his time when there wasn't a female around to occupy his attention. "Pantomimes?" he exclaimed with an eager look on his face, "What about pantomimes …?" It was obvious that he must have a soft spot for Widow Twankey and her friends.

Joe registered that he had got our undivided attention. "When I was a nipper I used to go to the pantos, and it was from watching them that I got the urge to get on stage to perform for a live audience," he informed us. "Now don't laugh …" he was trying to be serious, which was an unnerving experience to have to witness, but Stu did laugh.

Guffawing loudly, he guessed, "I suppose you wanted to be the arse-end of the donkey!" and howled at his little joke. Even Joey's face creased into a smile.

"Okay, do you lot want to hear this, or not?" he demanded.

Still chuckling away, we nodded our heads to say, *yes please!* because we were all dying to hear what the silly sod was going to come up with next.

"Well, I always fancied being the principal boy because he was the hero who rescued all the damsels in distress and lived happily ever after with the heroine," he had positively wandered back to childhood dreams, and the look on his face told it all.

He was brutally brought out of his whimsical wandering by Stuart, who very rightly pointed out that the principal boy was always played by a woman. "Didn't you know that?" he asked.

"Of course I did!" Joey lied. "It's just that I fancied prancing around in a short tunic and knee-high boots, brandishing a sword and shouting to the audience, asking *How will I kill this dragon?*"

"I suppose you could always sing to it, Joe!" Stu suggested, and cracked up in laughter.

I had to agree that this was a remarkably sensible suggestion. "Sing *Yesterday* and put it out of its misery," I told him. "That should be the death of it!"

With us making mock of his childhood ambitions, Joe had another hissy fit, lit a smoke and sulked alarmingly while we rolled about laughing at the pictures he had conjured up for us, imagining our red-nosed leader strutting about on the stage in his tights with his sword sticking out.

"You're always taking the mickey," Joe moaned, with good reason, "I can't tell you anything without you getting at me all the time." Joey feeling sorry for himself was not a pleasant sight, but I could understand his point of view.

"Look lads," Dave said unexpectedly stern in his voice, "we've got another month or so to go, and we can't go bickering among ourselves, so stop all of this rollicking right here and now, because we're like the three musketeers, all for one and one for all!"

It was a fine speech, and well in place under the circumstances, but surprising that it should have come from Dave. It was probably the longest sentence he had uttered in his life.

" *The three musketeers*," Joey mimicked, suddenly back to basics with his woes forgotten, "how can we be the three musketeers when there are four of us?"

"You're forgetting D'Artagnan, which makes four," Dave put him straight.

Joey brightened considerably. "Bagsie, I'm D'Artagnan!" he called, making heads turn at the other tables.

"You can't be D'Artagnan," Stuart sneered. "Whoever heard of an ugly D'Artagnan with red hair and a nose like a beetroot! It has to be someone handsome and dashing."

"Aye," said Joe, agreeing completely with this opinion, "then I'm D'Artagnan!" That bloke always did have a somewhat twisted perception of reality …

With that matter settled, we ambled out to the van to continue our journey to Lüneburg, nicely refreshed by the coffee and rejuvenated by our intellectual little tête a tête.

The sky was rapidly turning black as we approached Hamburg and getting blacker by the minute. The darkness was lit by occasional flashes of lightning that cracked alarmingly close. It was Dante's Inferno to the goose-step and very frightening.

I cast a nervous glance at Joey to see that the idiot grin had long since gone as he stared straight ahead with a resolute grimace occupying his ruddy features. His hands gripped the steering wheel so tightly that his knuckles had turned white with the strain.

Suddenly we were in the thick of it, with the wind buffeting the van from side to side as Joe valiantly tried to keep it on the road. Then the rain hit us. It was like driving into a wall, and the strength of the deluge had the wipers working overtime and screaming for mercy as they could barely cope. The windscreen became a blurred kaleidoscope of garish colours of which the red of stop lights dominated. Then a tremendous clap of thunder cracked through the bodywork of our rusty van immediately followed by three or four bursts of lightning that lit up the inside of the van in frightening flashes that made us quake.

I turned to see how Stu and Dave were coping with the pandemonium, and another flash of lightning gave me a fleeting glimpse. They were sitting bolt upright gripping on tightly to the back of the front seat with their eyes bulging and ready to pop. I didn't have time to register more than this as my attention was brought back to the driver's seat as Joey's strident voice shouted to be heard, with the cry of, "What the fuck is that!"

Looking ahead, I saw a massive grey curtain rapidly closing in on us, and we hit it with a crash as hail stones the size of marbles attacked us with a vengeance. Whipped by the force of the wind they peppered the van so the noise inside was incredible. The combined force of the howling wind and the millions of hailstones thrashing us was buffeting the van wildly. This was the stuff of nightmares, and the thought that we might not survive did cross my mind as we fought our way through the onslaught.

Then, as suddenly as it had hit us, it was gone, and we were through, thanking our Maker for deliverance and our driver for keeping us on the road. After some initial comments of relief at our salvation, we all settled down with our own thoughts, and quiet ruled inside the van for the next few miles.

I noticed a sign as we passed it, and proudly announced, "Gentlemen, welcome to Lower Saxony!"

This brought Dave back from wherever he had been spending the last few minutes to exclaim, "Hang on, I thought we were in Germany!" which comment caught our attention and once more made us consider him with some degree of uncertainty. "Nobody told me we were going to another country." He seemed somewhat disgruntled by the fact.

"It's not another country," I informed him patiently, "and we're still in Germany."

"Then why did you say we were in Lower Saxony if we're still in Germany?" he asked, all bewildered, wide-eyed innocence and waiting for an explanation.

"Well …" I began, but decided that I really didn't have my heart in it, so I tried to pass the buck to Joey instead, but he declined the invitation with a shake of his head and the revelation that he was now as uncertain as Dave about where we were and where we weren't.

Thankfully our attention was drawn to a perfect rainbow that stood out before us in all its beauty. This had Joey breaking into song to give us a flaky rendition of the old Judy Garland classic as he warbled away, *Somewhere, over the rainbow, way up pie* …

"Way up pie..?" Stu was insulted that he could ruin a perfectly nice song like that. "It's *way up high*, you daft bugger!" he hissed.

"Oh aye?" Joey thought about it, and decided that he was probably right. "Yeah, it does sound better that way," he acknowledged, and went back to humming the tune to his own satisfaction and our irritation.

"There's a crock of gold at the end of the rainbow, you know," Dave suddenly informed us, looking quite pleased at being able to convey this knowledge to us. Knowing him, he probably believed it! But then, Dave probably also believed in the tooth fairies.

We saw the first signs indicating that Lüneburg was somewhere ahead in the distance, and I began to look forward to the end of our journey. However, this thought also brought back the memory of what we had left behind us only hours earlier. I had started the day with a heavy heart knowing that every turn of the wheel would be taking me further away from where I wanted to be and who I wanted to be with. I wondered what Trudi was doing, and what Henni's surprise was to have been. No matter, there was now no way I would ever know, and I felt saddened, already missing them both as the miles between us increased.

Compared to some of the scrapes I had been in with my dysfunctional travelling companions, this journey had been relatively uneventful. Apart from almost causing major motorway mayhem and getting killed in the process, setting fire to Joey's privates, a run-in with the local politzei, and a battle to survive a thunderstorm from hell, the journey had gone quite well.

My daydreams were interrupted by the sound of Joe squawking out, "I can't believe! We're here! Lüneburg..!" with his face so full of relief it was obvious that he had never really believed that we would actually make it.

We found our way into the city centre where we stopped to get directions to the Star Palast. Joey parked by the side of the road, rolled down his window, and called out to someone walking along the pavement, "Oi! You mush! Yeah you!" and beckoned him over. "Where's the dance hall?"

The Lüneburg citizen gave him a withering glare of contempt as if to stiffen him, then sent off a long string of German expletives at our hapless driver before demonstratively spitting at the front wheel and walking off shaking his head and muttering to himself.

Joey was somewhat taken aback by his welcome to our new home. "Was it something I said?" he wondered, clearly amazed at the reaction his polite query had caused.

Clearly embarrassed at being witness to such a spectacle, Dave piped up, "Why don't you show some respect for once, you course foul-mouthed bugger, and ask properly!"

Getting the point, Joe attracts the attention of another passer by, and calls out, "Excuse me please, sir, can you help me?" The bloke stopped to hear what he wanted. Smiling sweetly, Joe then asked as nicely as he could, "Do you know where the dancehall is?"

The candidate looked Joey over for a second, replied, "Ja!" then quickly went on his way, leaving Joe with a face that should have been captured on film for posterity, and Stuart rolling around on the back seat squirming with laughter at his discomfort.

Deciding that someone with a modicum of brain had to take charge, I got out of the van and stopped a youngish guy in a leather jacket. "Wo ist das Star Palast, bitte?" I enquired, in what I hoped was reasonably understandable German.

He gave me a smile. "English group, yes?" I confirmed the fact, noting with relief that he spoke even better English than Joey, which wasn't really saying much, but then … It turned out that his name was Karl, and he was a regular at the venue we were looking for. Karl and I had some moments of pleasant chit chat before he headed on his way with a cheerful wave and an auf wiedersehen, promising to see us later at the dancehall.

All eyes were on me as I returned to the confines of the van. That they appeared to be impressed was an understatement, and I think a more fitting term would be to say that they were positively in awe of my prowess and hidden talent, for they were not to know that Karl and I had been enjoying our conversation in better English than I had heard spoken since we left Blighty some time before.

We soon found the place. It was an imposing white building with huge entrance doors, set in its own grounds, with one hundred yards of road leading from the gate to the car park by the building. We passed a small square building as we approached, and wondered what it was for, but then concentrated on finally putting an end to our long journey. We piled stiffly out of the van, rubbing our legs to get some circulation going, and saw a poster announcing our appearance. "At least they're expecting us," Joe chuckled happily.

They may have been expecting us, but there was nobody there to welcome us, and the place was shut up tight as Fort Knox, so we felt a little deflated, but then we noticed a note taped to the door that informed us that the manager would be back in a couple of hours. After a brief discussion, we concluded that a cold beer and a bite to eat was the answer to our problems, so we climbed back into the van and headed for town to find an establishment that would cater for our needs.

Needless to say, our noisy entrance to our chosen hostelry provoked some degree of interest from the patrons. "Güten tag, Lüneburgers!" Joey called out to the enthralled assembly. "We are the Charters from England!"

"Just sit down and stop making a bloody fool of yourself," Stuart hissed, and dragged him in the direction of an empty table. To stop Joe making a fool of himself was more or less impossible. Although cheerful and good-natured, he was an idiot in anybody's book, and wouldn't have tried to hide the fact even if he had been aware of it himself, which he unfortunately wasn't. Then again, perhaps it was just as well.

A dark haired waitress with a smile on her face and a twinkle in her eye appeared out of nowhere. The sight of our arrival must have brightened her afternoon shift considerably, and was probably what had put the smile on her face. Four beers duly found there way to our table, and we began to unwind after the trials and tribulations of the day.

"What d'ya think," Stuart asked, "are we gonna be happy here?"

We pondered the question and discussed it at some length before we came to the crucial issue. "Where are we going to settle down for a few drinks after we finish playing at nights?"

This was a very pertinent question well deserving of the time we spent discussing it, for when we had finished our five hours on stage, we would be in dire need of fluid relaxation to rejuvenate us, preferably in pleasant company. We finally concluded that our present watering hole would fit the bill, despite the fact that it would mean a short walk from the Star

Palast which had Stuart quaking at the very thought. In the end however, he reluctantly had to agree that since this bar was the nearest one to our place of toil, it would have to do even if it did mean that he would have to take an evening walk.

"I suppose we could always get some booze and drink it in our digs, wherever they may be, just to save us the walk there and back," I suggested, and immediately regretted opening my mouth.

"Drink on our own in the digs?!" they exclaimed in dismay, making it quite clear that my suggestion would not be put on the political agenda in the immediate future. "Having a few drinks is associated with frolicking with the fräuleins," they informed me in a high-pitched chorus, "and we're not going to attract any female attention if we sit forlornly in our digs supping brown ale!"

Herr Sneider, the manager was waiting for us as we found our way back to the dancehall. He was with a young man who introduced himself as Jürgen, then eagerly insisted on helping us carry our equipment inside. As the neon lights flickered into life we had our first glimpse of the Star Palast's dancehall, and were quietly impressed by what we saw. Heavy theatre curtains were pulled back to reveal the sizeable stage with its back-drop showing New York's skyscrapers lit up at night. There were numerous tables at the perimeter of a dance-floor that could accommodate half the population of Luton and the villages nearby to boot. A bar ran the length of the room and had enough pumps to put out a fire, should it happen.

The manager indicated a table and informed us that this would be ours for the duration, then directed Jürgen to show us to our quarters, which turned out to be the square white building we had noticed on our arrival. We went inside to find that our quarters comprised one square room with six framed beds, a couple of wardrobes and a rickety dining set contained within its four green walls. A cast iron stove stood in the middle of the room with its chimney pipe going straight to the roof and through it. The place looked like a barrack room and had no style or substance, but at least it was clean. As it happened, the same thankfully applied to both the kitchenette and the washroom.

"What do you think," Jürgen cheerfully asked, "good, yes?"

"Aye, it'll do," Joey sighed, as resigned as the rest of us to the fact that we would have to share our slumbers in the same room for another week or two.

Jürgen was eager to please, and insisted that he would be only too happy to help us in any way he could. By the look on his face it was obvious that he mean it.

"Tell me Jürgen, what are the girls like in this place?" Dave enquired, apparently now over the loss of Doris and ready to find a new playmate to help him forget. Jürgen could assure him that there were indeed available girls in Lüneburg who frequented the dancehall, and the smile on Dave's face grew broader with each word he heard.

I lowered myself to my creaking bed and stared vacantly at the ceiling with my thoughts winging their way back where I wanted to be, and gradually dipped off with memories of Henni and Trudi to keep me company.

A kick to the mattress and Joey's voice bawling, "Come on, we're on in fifteen minutes!" brought me back to reality with a vengeance, and I quickly donned my group gear to accompany the others on the short walk to our opening night at the Lüneburg Star Palast. A quick beer before we went on was the order of the day, but I felt the need for something stronger to shake me out of the lethargy I could feel beginning to envelope me, and downed a double vodka in one hit to kick-start my engine and get me running.

The place was humming like a hive and the crowd were really getting into the stuff we were dishing out for them to dance to, and obviously enjoying themselves. The fact that it was our first night and they had never heard us before probably made what we played and how we played it more interesting than it really was, but they seemed to be lapping it up.

From my slightly elevated position at the back of the stage I could see how the lads were strutting their stuff, winking and flirting with any available fräulein who caught their eye. As usual Dave was getting most of the attention from the predatory females prowling around the edge of the stage, but Stuart wasn't totally lost either using his trademark twinkle in the eye and winsome smile to attract his fair share of attention.

Sadly for Joey, the girls had still not discovered his potential, and not to be outdone by the others, he strived even harder to rectify the problem, and became hyperactive and put his heart and soul into everything he performed. People began to crowd around the stage just to see him in full flow as he hyperventilated with euphoria. A gaggle of girls were enthralled by his crazy antics, laughing and whooping with delight at his egomaniac performance. They all loved it. But even more importantly, so did Joey, who was revelling in his stage persona and grinning like the maniac he was, for, as he had told us on numerous occasions, he was the star, and actually believed it. I was pleased for him, for if nothing else, the adulation he was receiving had probably taken his mind off his singed sausage.

Not surprisingly, there was little interest in the drummer at the back. The beat behind the band and back-up singer, I didn't get any attention at all no matter how much I shook my head like Ringo. I wondered what was wrong with the fräuleins of the world. After all, I had a genuine warm smile, deep brown puppy-dog eyes and all my own teeth, so what was wrong? So I thumped away at the drums and slashed at the cymbals, oohed and aahed into the microphone and tried to forget that I was ugly and that this might have some bearing on the lack of enthusiasm for the boy at the back of the band.

The closest I came to anyone acknowledging my existence at all, was when my acquaintance from the street earlier in the day, Karl and his girlfriend, gave me a smile and the thumbs-up as they gyrated away in front of the stage. Small comfort, but at least it was something, and a confirmation of the fact that we were going down quite well.

But although people were certainly enthusiastic, we were still not getting the wild uninhibited response we had in Schleswig, and I put this down to the crowd at the Star Palast being accustomed to better acts with bigger names, and egos to match Joey's.

The thought struck me that the best reaction we had ever had was in the wild and woolly hills of North Wales whenever we performed in the concert room of the Red Lion at Llannassa, which is a place that nobody knows exists. The only excitement in the place is watching the sheep munch grass and waiting for the arrival of the bus that turns up once a day. Perhaps that was why, but whatever the reason, we always went down a storm when we played there, and they treated us like gods. Perhaps it was because Lüneburg was neither Llannassa nor Schleswig, and more sophisticated than both, that our reception, although wild enough, still left the roof in place.

The excited chatter of the others as we closed for a break confirmed that they thought it was going well. Joey's charismatic performance had achieved the desired effect for he was surrounded by smiling girls chattering excitedly at him. One young fräulein seemed particularly enamoured, despite actually seeing him up close, and was fluttering her eyes at him wickedly. Stu was enjoying the attention of a few fräuleins and was wreathed in smiles at all the attention he was receiving from them, but it was naturally Dave who was getting the most slavish attention.

Among the many who crowded around him, were two identical twin sisters. They were stunning girls with blonde hair, a double dose of delight that would have the blood rushing to the head and elsewhere in the anatomy of any heterosexual of the species, and there they were, both of them cooing over our bleach-blonde bass player, much to the consternation of Joe, who was almost salivating at the sight of them.

When we finally finished for the night and settled down to relax in a haze of cigarette smoke, a few of the girls who had been hovering around us all night drifted over to our table. Female company was always welcome, especially pretty girls with a ready smile and a friendly disposition, and all of these fitted the description, but none more-so than the vivacious and tantalising twins.

The next couple of hours passed too quickly and our convivial night was brought to an end by flashing lights that told us it was over. Our newly acquired set of groupies made their collective departure with cheery goodbyes and blown kisses. and promises of another tomorrow, when they assured us they would be back for more.

So we headed back to our spartan but clean quarters with more than a modicum of contentment, happy that we had got a good reception both musically and otherwise, and looking forward to further developments in both departments. Joey began to wax lyrical about the particular fräulein who had taken his fancy, and made it known that he had high hopes of getting to know her better on the morrow.

"You'd better wait for a bit," Stuart advised him, "or it might spark a new flame that'll burn it off!" and chuckled away at the memory of Joe's smouldering member hanging out to dry with the traffic whizzing by.

We noticed Dave looking more introverted than usual, apparently working his brain at some mathematical problem of gigantic proportions. We managed to bring him back from wherever he was, to learn that he was having considerable difficulty in deciding which of the twins he should endow with the benefit of his charms. "The other one is bound to be disappointed," he sighed, taking it for granted that they were both his for the asking, "and I don't like to hurt anyone."

"Then take them both, you soft bugger!" Joey couldn't see what the problem was, and was positively irritated by such dithering. "That way they'll both be happy," he pointed out, feeling as wise as Solomon and quite pleased with his conclusion.

I had had enough for one day and heard enough for one night, so I rolled over and promptly fell asleep, leaving them to their deliberations.

Trying to
Make an Impression

Once again I awoke to pistons merrily pumping away in my head and a pain that even overrode the ghastly taste in my mouth that felt like an overflowing ashtray. Why I couldn't learn from previous miseries was a mystery to me. I might well have had an enjoyable evening but I was now paying for the pleasure with some genuine pain.

I managed to manoeuvre myself into a sitting position and concentrated my befuddled mind on what was happening around me in that spartan room. I could hear Stuart before my eyes managed to focus and actually see him. His bloated belly rose and fell with each deep breath he took. This was accompanied by a noisy rattling snore that ended with a high-pitched whistle at the end of each cycle and jarred my nerves to the very edge of human endurance.

"Dave," I wailed, "give that snoring sod a dig in the ribs to wake him up or he'll be the death of me."

Sadly his sharp dig did nothing to solve the problem. Stu merely rolled over on his side and kept snoring and whistling, but now even louder. Somewhere far, far way, my mind registered the tinkle of coffee cups being stirred, and Joey chuckling away to himself, before he suddenly appeared with a smile on his face and four cups of steaming coffee on a tray. "It's a lovely day outside, campers!" he enthused, and handed me a cup.

The sight of Joey wondering around dispensing coffee to the wounded like Florence Nightingale was something to behold. With his tousled red hair, throbbing nose, an old t-shirt that had clearly seen better days, and his Dennis the Menace underpants all askew, he limped through the mess on the floor wearing just one sock. The fantasy of rock and roll? The women swooning for the singer and the band? They should have seen us then!

"What about Stu?" he wondered. I brought his attention to the fact that the aforementioned was still asleep and creating a commotion in the process. "Well, give him a poke in the eye and wake him up," he suggested, then decided to enjoy the procedure himself, and gave him a poke that could have killed him and shouted, "'Ere, d'ya want this?" as he thrust the steaming coffee at him. Stuart reacted immediately and rose up ready to poke back, but decided he had more pressing matters to take care of, and wobbled off to the bathroom grasping his slack underpants from falling off on the way to his destination.

Dave had been silent during this little interlude, lost in his own thoughts, he gazed forlornly at the floor and sighed deeply as though the cares of the world were his to solve and he knew not where to begin. You didn't need to be Einstein to know that he was thinking about girls, for that was all he ever thought about, but even at that early hour our brains had sufficient oxygen to understand that he must have the tantalising twins on his mind.

"I can't decide which one I fancy most, if it's Mai or Eva," he moaned, and sighed yet again. "Whichever one I choose, the other's going to be disappointed." Dave took such things for granted – he actually expected women to fall under his spell.

"Well, have them both, then," Stuart suggested, then everybody's happy."

Dave wasn't keen on the idea, because he was basically a monogamous bloke who was completely faithful to whoever happened to be in his bed at any given moment, and was too set in his conservative ways to share his attributes between the sisters.

"Then let me have one of them," Stuart demanded, thinking it only reasonable since there would be one twin to spare.

"Which one?" Dave wondered, hoping that the answer would decide the issue for him.

"Either one, mate," Stuart smirked, "after all they're just the same, so who would notice the difference."

Since this answer hardly lifted the burden of decision from his shoulders, ave felt no obligation to pay Stu for services not rendered, so decided to keep both the twins in his personal custody until he was able to make his choice.

At this, Stuart announced that he would then give his attention to one of the other new acquaintances, a blonde called Heidi who had taken his fancy. Not to be outdone, Joey informed us of his choice. "I'm going to take off with that Clara who was giving me the eye all last night," he told us.

"The one with the bad eyesight?" Stuart smirked. "You'd better tell her to leave her glasses at home or she'll get a shock when she can actually see you!"

Joey ignored him and turned to me instead. "What about you Biffo," he asked. "Has anyone caught your eye yet?"

The honest answer would have been, everything on two legs with tits, but instead I replied, "Not really, but if pushed I would have to admit that I quite fancy Mai from Dave's double trouble, but since the selfish sod has decided to keep both for himself, I suppose I'll just have to bring me knitting with me tonight to alleviate the loneliness of the long-distance drummer."

It wasn't far off the mark, for I had fallen back to accepting my fate as the group's wall-flower and had no illusions that the girls would suddenly drool over my looks or my charm. I thought of Trudi and felt sad. Henni's smiling face pushed itself into my mind, and I felt miserable. I missed them both. They were both where I wanted to be but couldn't be. I sighed at the fate that had taken from me what had been given, and left me to mourn the loss on my own with nobody to comfort me and share my pain.

To get my mind off my problems I suggested that we went into town to get something to eat. This enlivened my fellow musicians sufficiently to put their clothes on, which was a blessing considering the spectacle they presented without them. Dave demanded that we should drive in the van because he had been having some considerable pain from his corns and could hardly walk. This was hardly surprising, since he insisted on wearing his high-heeled Chelsea boots that were one size too small whenever he was out of bed, and probably sometimes when he was in it too. What a rocker! Sex, drugs, rock and roll, and corn plasters with it … Had they only known, all those squealing young things wetting themselves at the sight of him on stage!

As it turned out we drove straight into the Saturday Market in the town square. The place was packed with various stalls that were selling a variety of goods and hordes of people milling about and generally enjoying themselves. We finally found a space to park, and began to move into the crowd and feel the atmosphere of the place. The market was really buzzing with throngs of people scurrying to and fro between the stalls, and there were jugglers and entertainers of various sorts. Smoke billowed from various stalls that sold all varieties of sausages, and there was a stand that sold booze and beer that had a sizable crowd congregated around it. Many were drinking a dark red liquid that was obviously hot since there was steam coming off it. It turned out to be something called glühwein and was very popular, as we could witness from the happy faces and raucous laughter of those sipping it.

We found a snug café called the Lüneburghof and made our usual noisy entrance, turning a few heads in the process. Although it was quite full, we managed to find a table to accommodate us all, and were immediately confronted by an attractive young waitress with a pleasant welcoming smile on her lips. Hoppell Poppell was on the menu, so Hoppell Poppell it was for all four, this having now been established as being a healthy portion of scrambled eggs, sausages and mushrooms, which was just what the doctor ordered.

Looking after the waitress as she left us I had to acknowledge that Joey had been right for once. "You did promise that there would be beautiful, blonde and blue-eyed fräulines, Joe," I told him, "and that was sure as hell one of them!"

"What's up with you," Stu piped in, sneering at me as he spoke, "are we going to have to go through this every time we go to a café? You go slack every time you see a bloody waitress. Do we really have to go through this ritual every time we have a coffee?" I had to admit that he did have a point, for Henni was still heavy on my mind after falling in love with her over my first cup of coffee in Schleswig.

As it turned out, the waitress had seen us performing the previous evening, and delighted Joe by actually complimenting us on our performance, even admitting to Joey's questioning, that he did have a certain stage presence, which for my money was as sweet and diplomatic a put-down as anything.

"You should have come over and joined us at our table," Joe told her. "We would have given you a good time," he assured her, but to no avail.

"I'm sure you would," she answered with a smile, "but from where I was sitting, you seemed to have plenty of female company." Joey nodded his head to acknowledge the fact. "Anyway," our new-found friend informed him, "I don't think my boyfriend Klaus would be overjoyed if I had left him to sit with you."

Joey's ardour dampened immediately when he heard the dreaded word *boyfriend*, and he pulled back in his seat to review the situation and think out new strategies.

"Lucky boyfriend," I sighed on hearing the news, and noticed her eyes flash in my direction.

She informed us that Klaus the boyfriend was also in a band called The Axemeisters. Unlike us, they apparently had ambitions that went beyond drinking themselves stupid and chasing women with their tongues hanging out, and old Klaus had a tendency to hang out at the Star Palast to get new inspiration from the groups that played there.

Well, I couldn't see him getting much inspiration from us for basically we were only there for the beer, as they say, and because our agent wanted us at arm's length for a while. Joey however, suddenly finding a way to worm his way into her affections, offered to help. "If Klaus wants a few tips on techniques and that," he told her, "tell him to have a word with me tonight, and I'll show him a few chord changes and rocking riffs, because I'm very good at them," he gushed at her.

"The only thing you're good at is bullshitting!" Stuart sneered at him to destroy his moment, and Dave and I nodded our heads in mute agreement, for there was no disputing the fact that Joe could sprout inane drivel in his sleep, and often did.

We finally filed out of the café and into the square outside to mingle with the crowd in the colourful marketplace. The smoke from the grilled bratwurst stalls billowed into the air, and the smell from the sausages was tempting, but we had our priorities and decided to keep our cash for other temptations. It didn't take too long before alternative suggestions came to the fore.

"'Ere Biffo," Joe nudged me and pointed, "you were keen to try that red, hot stuff at the beer stand, Gluewingy, or summat," he said, "so now's you're chance."

I corrected him, "Glühwein," then decided that it might be interesting to see what it was like. So we headed for the bar area where they had placed tables and chairs, and commandeered a glass for each of us. Whatever magic ingredient was in this steaming brew it certainly seemed to bring out the Christmas spirits of those drinking it, because everyone around us was in pearly paradise and happy as punch. Out of normal curiosity I asked one happy imbiber what Glühwein actually consisted of, to which he replied in a slurred voice that informed me that it was hot and spicy mulled wine, which didn't make me much wiser.

We looked uncertainly at our steaming drinks and mentally dared the others to take the first tentative sip. Tired of waiting, Stuart finally raised the glass to his lips and took a long swig as we stared intently at him to see his reaction. We didn't have to wait long. Before he had replaced the glass on the table, his face had flushed red, his eyes sparkled and he was positively glowing.

"That's potent stuff, and no mistake!" he exclaimed. "I can feel it burning all the way down," he seemed to concentrate to get the full benefit of the experience. "You can get seriously hammered supping this stuff, lads," he said, then immediately grabbed the glass and emptied the rest of its contents.

On registering the fact that he had survived the ordeal with honours, we all quickly downed our own drinks and soon became as red in the face and as sparkly-eyed as Stu. This first glass was so enjoyable that we quickly had three more which soon had us at a slant, finding everything uproariously funny and giggling hysterically without really knowing why.

A juggler was manipulating his balls with such dexterity that he caught our attention, and Stuart roared out, "Hey, Dave! Could that Doris bird manipulate your balls that high?" and doubled up laughing. Dave swayed unsteadily on his feet and couldn't find a suitable retort because he was concentrating so hard on staying upright. Joe was in hysterics, holding his stomach in place with both hands and had to steady himself against the table to stop himself from falling down, whereas Dave then did just that to Joey's roar of "Timber!!" I decided that discretion was the better part of valour, and quickly sat down before I joined him on the floor. "Bloody hell, that was funny!" I gasped, trying to get myself under control.

I wasn't the only one who thought so, for a few yards away we were being observed by the politzei who stood with smiles on their faces as the sergeant mouthed *What do you expect? They're English!*

The glühwein had certainly made an impact on us, and the other drinkers observing the effect of their local brew on the mindless foreigners, and apparently finding this to be enjoyable entertainment, joined in our laughter, which did nothing to aid the concentration of the hard-working juggler. In a sequence of rapid hand-movements he missed with the inevitable result that all the balls came crashing down. One hit him on the head, and the rest bounced at crazy angles off the cobbled ground to jump and roll under various stalls and between people's feet. Unfortunately one middle-aged woman trod on one and promptly fell, spilling the contents of her shopping bag to add to the general carnage with potatoes, onions, apples and oranges rolling about all over the place.

The juggler was far from happy and sent his assistant to retrieve the balls while he glowered at us and ruefully rubbed his head, then shouted expletives at us that we didn't understand, but nonetheless knew to be less than complimentary.

Stuart was giggling so uncontrollably that he had to hold on to a table with one hand, while he used the other to thump it repeatedly, with tears of laughter streaming down his cheeks. Joey was completely out of control in pleats of laughter, shaking his head from side to side, while Dave still lay prone on the cobbles where he had unceremoniously fallen, missing out on the fun.

We finally managed to get some degree of control. Stu lit a cigarette with trembling fingers, then glanced down at Dave. "Is he dead?" he wondered, then took another deep drag to steady his nerves.

I shouted down at Dave's inert body to ascertain how he was. "Dave!" I called, and prodded him with my foot. "Dave, are you dead?"

He eventually gave a response. "What …?" he moaned.

"Stuart wants to know if you're dead," I informed him.

"Am I?" he groaned, and didn't seem too convinced either way.

Joey took command, as was his wont. "Shift yourself," he ordered, "you can't lie there all day." At that moment, I think Dave saw it differently, but in his condition he had no vote. "It's becoming embarrassing," Joey told him, "we've got a bigger audience than the juggler had!" I looked over at aforementioned and could clearly see that he was still distraught despite the fact that he had managed to retrieve his balls, for he was still cursing loudly and far from happy.

The spectacle we had made of ourselves prompted the politzei to come over to move us on and allow the market to return to normal. Two of them helped Dave to his feet but his knees immediately buckled under him and his body slumped like a new-born giraffe. The officers were in a benevolent mood, and suggested that Joey and I should take our comrade somewhere else to sober him up, and that a bottle of wonder-medicine from the pharmacy would put him right in double quick time.

We were given a round of applause from our assembled audience as we helped our hapless bass player away, and Stuart took the opportunity to thank them with a gracious bow and a flutter of his hand, like a bent actor acknowledging the adulation of his fawning fans.

Somehow it only seemed natural that we should head straight for the nearest bar to bring our hero back to the land of the living. As it happened, Das Bären was the closest, and we dragged him inside and dumped him at the first empty table parking him on the bench seat. Without our support to keep him upright, he immediately slumped forward to hit his head with a hefty thump on the table, and groaned loudly at the impact. At least, he wasn't dead …

Taking pity on him, I wandered over to the pharmacy and explained the situation for them there. Apparently, Dave's case was not the first they had dealt with, and they carefully explained that the elixir was to be administered in small regular doses. I returned to the bar to find a glass of beer ready for me on the table and Dave still comatose on the bench. Producing the bottle, I explained what I had been told by the pharmacist, but Stu wasn't having it. He unscrewed the bottle, pulled Dave's head back by the hair and poured half the contents down his throat, shook him vigorously to make sure he had swallowed it, then allowed him to drop back on the bench with a mighty crash.

This amused a group of young men who had been observing us from a nearby table. Stuart bristled at their levity, and Joey threatened to go over and do them physical harm unless they stopped their cat-calls and laughter. We may as often as not be quite brutal with each other and never mind, but it was quite another matter for complete strangers to throw ridicule at us, for we were the three musketeers and although D'Artagnan was indisposed, we were not inclined to be the butt of ridicule from other than ourselves.

So, leaving D'Artagnan to his slumber, we rose as one and made our way towards our tormentors with menace in our eyes, one for all and all for one. Their sneering laughter ceased as we stood before them, but the smirks on their faces were still hanging on until Joey stood over them punching the flat of his palm with his clenched fist and staring daggers. The smirks then drained from their faces in seconds. He leaned towards them and placed his huge bricklayer hands on the table and glared threateningly at each of our tormentors in turn and demanded to know what they found to be so amusing.

They shuffled awkwardly as they nervously glanced at each other for guidance, but no explanation was forthcoming. To get a response, Stuart snarled at them, "Are you deaf, dumb or thick?" he growled, "You've been asked a question so answer it, or you will find, ve haf vays of making you talk!" The twinkle in his eyes told me he was enjoying himself.

But Joey wasn't. He was just mad. He grabbed the nearest available culprit by the neck and roughly dragged him to the floor, hissing, "Well! I'm waiting!" It was obvious that he had no intention of waiting too long, so he finally got a response.

Gasping for breath, he gushed out, "The blonde one!" and pointed at Dave's lifeless body. "We watched him getting drunk on the glühwein outside!" Joe considered this for a moment, then pushed his victim back into his seat. The expression on their faces showed that they now knew that Joey meant business. They outnumbered us two to one but still cowered before us, with good reason, knowing as I did, what Joey was capable of when his temper flared.

One of the others addressed us curtly telling us, "We watched you getting intoxicated on the glühwein and making fools of yourselves …"

"Oh, really …!" Stuart commented in a clipped and icy voice dripping with sarcasm. "That's what we English guys do," he told them. "It's called having fun!"

Looking at them, I thought they looked vaguely familiar but I couldn't place them, so I put it from my mind as Joey demanded to know why they had aimed their scorn at our bass player. Yet another of the gang opened his mouth to inform us that the two in the middle, one Wülf and one Holger, harboured a grudge because of the slavish attention the terrific twins had lavished on Dave the previous evening, and had taken great delight at his present plight, thinking that if Mai and Eva had seen him like this it might have them looking in a better light.

"Better light?" snapped Joe. "No light is better for this gruesome twosome. They're so ugly I bet the midwife smacked their father when they were born!" Both Stuart and I chuckled at his joking banter, for Joe was now back in relaxed mode as we all realised that this particular stand-off was now over. There were even one or two wry smiles from the Germans, except for Wülf and Holger who only scowled and muttered, for what Joey had said in jest had not been taken lightly and had obviously hit a chord.

The threat of devastation now over, we returned to our seats when I noticed a poster on the wall that informed the people of Lüneburg that The Axemeisters would be playing live in this establishment at 20.00 hours on Sonntag. "It's a pity we're playing," said Joey, "or we could have come to watch somebody else play while we just relaxed with a beer or three."

"You can come to watch!" It was the handsome one with the leather jacket. "The Star Palast will be closed tomorrow because it is Sunday, so you can come here and listen to a good German group." He swung his arm in an arch that enveloped his assorted cronies, and with some bravado he announced, "We are The Axemeisters!" For a moment I thought he was expecting applause at this announcement for he did seem quite pleased with himself.

"So you're the famous Axemeisters, eh?" Joey seemed impressed, which for us who knew him, meant that trouble was brewing. "We've heard a lot about you …"

Taking interest at this piece of news, their faces brightened. Even Wülf and Holger began to show signs of thawing out. "What have you heard about us?" the handsome one just had to know.

"That you're crap, and the manager at the Star Palast wouldn't let you on the stage if you paid him," Joey replied with an innocent smile on his craggy features, then guffawed at the expression that slapped onto their faces and left them gawking at him.

"Only joking, lads," Joe assured them. "Actually it was a blonde waitress called Heinke who told us about you." On hearing this, the handsome fellah smiled proudly, and informed us that she was his girlfriend.

"Then you must be Klaus," Stuart piped in with the twinkle back in his eye. "We've heard a lot about you. Heinke says you're a bit of a guitarist."

By now Klaus's face was wreathed in smiles as he realised that the star attraction at the Star Palast actually knew of him and his group, and his girlfriend. "Yes," he admitted smugly, "I am the lead guitarist and singer in the group. I think that is why she fell for me in the first place, and she adores me."

Now that was really to set himself up for our red-nosed leader. "Are you really sure about that Klaus?" Joe wondered, looking somewhat uncertain. "If you don't mind me saying so, I thought she looked as though her affections could quite easily be swayed." The smile dropped off Klaus's face and he looked dumbstruck, but Joe plodded on regardless to avenge their taunting of our blonde bass, who was still lying dead to the world somewhere behind us. "She was giving me the eye, and making it clear that she fancied Stuart, and even our ugly drummer here's in with a chance judging by the attention she was giving him earlier."

A worried look had crept into his handsome features as Joey spoke, and he shook his head from side to side saying, "No, you are wrong. Heinke is my girl and she adores me …"

Joey was ready for the coup de grace and leaned down towards him looking him straight in the eye, "Are you sure?" he asked. "Are you really sure, Klaus?" Leaving him wide-eyed and gawking as we made our way back to our table with Joey cackling away merrily, saying "That'll give the smug git something to think about."

To our surprise we now noticed that the hapless Dave had got company in our absence, and now lay snuggled up close against one of the twins, who was whispering in his ear and planting kisses on his face. Whether it was due to the elixir Stuart had poured down him or the presence of the delectable twin is uncertain, but whatever it was he had certainly made a remarkable recovery.

We knew it was Eva and not Mai because she had on a necklace with an E on it, otherwise we would have been stumped. With Eva wrapped around him, Dave looked a lot happier than when we had left him, and who wouldn't have, for she was a stunning girl, as was her sister, but then if one was, then the other couldn't be less attractive with them being the same, as Stu had put it.

They both managed to take time off from their canoodling to give us a smile. Dave even had the presence of mind to ask what Stuart had put in him earlier to bring him back to life, and promised eternal gratitude to me for getting the stuff from the pharmacy. For my own part, he could keep his gratitude, for I was seriously worried that he wouldn't make the performance that night, which would have given me some serious problems without his bass line to follow, so I was as happy to see him alive and kicking as was Eva.

Deciding that this little digression had gone on long enough, Dave and Eva resumed their previous sport of eating each other alive. Her face was a picture of passion, which could hardly be said of Wülf who was watching this little performance from his nearby viewpoint with seething envy green on his face. He was not a happy bunny.

For my own part, I was becoming quite content now that the unpleasantness with the German group seemed to have become history and I had a couple of beers inside me. I was beginning to relax and enjoy myself in the company of the others, and found that I was considering our present hostelry, Das Bären with some satisfaction, almost feeling at home there. I looked across at Dave and Eva at ease in each others company. They smiled contentedly at each other as she stared lovingly into his simple face. I decided that he must now finally have made his choice, and Eva was it.

He caught me looking and confirmed the fact. "Eva's for me," he told, "so you can have Mai," which I thought was very generous of him, but what Mai thought of the suggestion would be another matter entirely.

"Dave," I told him patiently, "it doesn't really work like that, you know. You can't give her away, you're not the bride's father."

I should have kept my mouth shut, because he then began to dither again, worrying about how she was going to take the disappointment of being off-loaded for her sister. The thought of how terrible it would be for her to be told that she would not have the Greenfield Gigolo to play with was hard for him to come to terms with, knowing as he assuredly did, that it could break a woman's heart to be held at bay from his charms.

In the end, Eva informed us all that she would tell her twin herself, and get the whole triangle sorted out to everyone's satisfaction, particularly her own and David's. In recognition of services rendered in saving him from himself, he offered to buy a round and got up to go to the bar. Eva immediately followed, obviously not wishing to be left on her own to be gawked at by three slightly intoxicated grinning idiots with semi-erections to keep them awake. As she wiggled along linking arms with her hero, Joe gazed lustily after her and I could see her clothes falling off inside his head as he dreamed and drooled for the unattainable. Gazing across at The Axemeisters, it would seem that the gruesome twosome were also dreaming but theirs were nightmares, and they were staring daggers as Dave stood at the bar with one of the two women of their dreams wrapped around him.

Just then a red-haired girl entered the establishment and went to the Axemeister table. Stuart noticed and exclaimed, "Uncanny!" then turned to enquire of Joe if his father had been in Germany after the war. Having confirmed this, Joe was naturally interested in what had prompted the question. Stu then pointed at the girl and gave it as his considered opinion that she was the spitting image of Joe. "And just as ugly too!"

The resemblance was remarkable, and for a few moments Joe could only study her in amazement, hardly believing what he saw, for it was himself he was looking at, but in skirts and a beehive hairdo. He seemed to be mightily impressed by the sight before him.

Totally unaware that she was the centre of attention, she gave the long Axemeister a kiss, so she was presumable his girlfriend. Joey however, was already on the way. Striding across to her table he called out in a voice that could be heard throughout the establishment, "I just saw you come in, and I want to ask you a question." She stared at the ginger apparition before her and mutely nodded her head. "Tell me," Joey continued, "how would you like your first child to look like me?"

I couldn't understand her reply, but the gist of it was that she would rather wander in eternal damnation. Joey decided that the answer was probably a negative, and returned to our table chuckling to himself, while Klaus wisely held the long one back from addressing the situation, no doubt thinking that all hell would break loose, which it would have knowing Joey.

Although it was all only meant in fun, Joey was definitely working hard to reduce our popularity stakes in our temporary home-town, and we now had more scowls aimed at us than was comfortable for a peace-loving drummer from Chester who was only there for the beer. Joey was fun to be with and a tremendous friend who would do anything for you, but he could also be completely obnoxious without even knowing it. A pain in the arse would sometimes be preferable to being witness to some of his antics, and he made enemies as quickly as he made friends, and had enough of both, but just then I had an uneasy feeling that we were getting more of the one and less of the other in the otherwise so peaceful town of Lüneburg.

Dave and Eva decided to continue their conversation elsewhere and removed themselves with the promise that he would be on time for the show, so then we were three. Looking after them as they departed Stuart was heard to mutter, "The jammy bugger will be getting his leg over now," and apparently not too happy about the fact.

"Stop moaning," Joe chided him, "it's Saturday and you never know, we might get lucky ourselves tonight." Always the optimist was Joe.

"Might get lucky, Joe?" I asked. "Coming from a bloke who would screw anything that had a pulse, I find that kind of pessimism somewhat daunting."

We had a show to do, so decided we would have to do it, and headed for the door to find our way back home. As we were leaving, Heinke the waitress entered looking for her Axemeister boyfriend. Joe pointed them out, "Oh yes, Karl and his merry band are definitely here," he said.

She gave me a sweet smile as she passed me, and said "See you later," then the doors closed between us and we were gone.

We immediately crashed out on our creaky beds when we got back to the barrack room, knowing too well that we only had a couple of hours before we were due on stage and would need some rest to bring us to scratch before we went on. I stared at the ceiling and thought back to events of the day and couldn't help but smile, for it was days like these that lifted your spirits. It had been a nugget of a day among the rubble that otherwise filled our time, and an intoxicating break from the tedium of it all. Life on the road for a collection of incompetents like us was definitely not sex, drugs and rock and roll, but rather the tedium of sleeping, snoring, farting and drinking, just to pass the time, and time passed very slowly when you had nothing in particular to do but the aforementioned.

Joey was concerned about the morrow. We had already decided that we would be spending the next evening listening to The Axemeisters perform in what had now become our local bar, but as usual, it was the long hours of daylight that had to be filled in one way or another. "We have to find something to do or I'll go bleedin' barmy," Joe whined, and had us nodding our heads sympathetically, for we all felt the same way.

There were no suggestions, so I changed the subject by wondering what we should start the show with, for I felt that we really needed something that would get the evening to a jumping start since it was Saturday and the big night of the week. Again, there were no suggestions, and I began to think that they had gone to sleep. "Right," I told them, having taken the matter in my own hands, "we'll start with the old Contours hit *Do You Love Me*. That's a cracking song to get the punters on their feet."

My suggestion was immediately forgotten as the door opened and Dave entered with Eva hanging on his arm. He had a smug grin on his face while she positively glowed, and their expressions told the whole story, we simply need not ask. Eva sat on his bed and crossed her legs provocatively and tugged at the hem of her skirt to preserve a modicum of modesty with three slack-jawed morons staring at her with our tongues hanging out. She was a vision of beauty and illuminated our spartan barracks with the radiance of her smile. I had never seen her looking so gorgeous before.

Dave couldn't help but notice the effect their entrance had upon us, and smirked, "Put your eyes back in your head, Biffo," he told me, chuckling at the sight of me drooling, "you look like a mangy mongrel with a hard on." He wasn't far wrong there …

Joey cupped his chin in his hands and stared adoringly at the beauty before him. "D'ya know what, Eva?" he asked her disarmingly. "When I look at you I think of spanners."

"Spanners," she wondered, giggling, "why spanners?"

"When I see you I can feel my nuts tighten up," he told her, and gave her an ingratiating smile that made him look even more moronic than usual. Dave gave him a look of displeasure, but Eva only laughed and was obviously enjoying the attention she was receiving from the lovelorn losers lusting for her unattainable charm.

We found our way to the location and sat at our designated table for a quick drink before the doors opened, and called

Jürgen the gopher over so Joe could explain our requirements for the stage lighting of our first number. He was as eager as ever and made a note of his instructions assuring us that he would take care of it. "By the way," he said, "you will also have the day off on Wednesday," which news bucked us up no end.

"Why's that," Stuart wondered, "is it the anniversary of Adolf's birthday?" He had a deep grudge against all things German after they had bombed his local chippie.

Dave was already back in clinch with twin one, and Joe was beginning to show signs of jealousy when he was suddenly confronted by a young lass who had been giving him the eye the previous evening. She babbled happily away at him, but he had probably forgotten who she was and where she had come from, for recall was not one of Joey's greatest assets. "Live for the moment, Biffo," he would often tell me, "fuck 'em and leave 'em, because like buses there'll always be another on the way shortly!"

Stuart's potential bed-warmer Heidi dropped by to say hello to her Scouse hero, and breathlessly informed him that she would be joining him later. A satisfied smile spread across his cherubic face, for Heidi was a classy gal with a demure smile, and he was no doubt already contemplating how he was going to keep that smile on her pretty face through the coming night.

I looked around and saw quite a few faces I recognised, including most of our adversaries, The Axemeisters. The tall one was there with his Joey-clone in attendance, as were Klaus and Holger, while Wülf glared menacingly at Dave as Eva caressed our blonde bass to his obvious delight. I didn't see Heinke, so she had probably not come, which I thought a pity for she was both fun and very attractive. I cursed Joey for taunting Klaus and his storm troopers about her earlier in Das Bären, and hoped it hadn't given her any problems. Mai, the other twin, was also missing, and I assumed she was staying away to hide the disappointment of coming in second best to her sister.

We were on. I hoped Jürgen managed to follow our instructions for our intro, because we had actually given it some thought and hoped it would work. He announced our presence on stage, saying, "Mein Damen und Herren, directly from England, the Star Palast presents The Charters!" The curtains drew back to reveal a stage in total darkness with only the super trouper stage light picking me out on my raised platform at the back, All this brought out a gasp from the audience, for they had never experienced anything like it before. I began the song, *You broke my heart – 'cause I couldn't dance – you never wanted me around – but now I'm back to let you know – I can really shake it down,* then the stage lights exploded into action to reveal Joe, Stu and Dave posing in his dark glasses as we launched into a rousing version of *Do You Love me.* The dance floor immediately filled up with writhing bodies and happy faces. This was undoubtedly the musical zenith of our trip so far and gave me a huge adrenaline rush. We received a rousing ovation when we finished, which also gave me a huge buzz.

We kept it bouncy throughout the first session, which suited me fine. It was hard work, but very rewarding for the impression it made on the audience. I became even happier when Joey sidled up to me to say that he wouldn't be doing any slow stuff until the end of the second session, which meant another couple of hours before I would have to suffer through his painful rendition of *Yesterday.*

The first session of an hour and a half flashed by very quickly; it's surprising how quickly time passes when you're enjoying yourself. Even so, the break was welcome when it came. Dave was immediately surrounded by adoring girls as we made our way to our table, and Eva hurriedly made a bee-line towards him to make it plain who's fellah he was.

As the battle lines had already been drawn the previous evening, it wasn't as crowded around our table as it had been the night before. Eva had her manicured claws into Dave and he was clearly delighted at having her undivided attention. Stu had Heidi smiling and cooing at him, and they looked perfectly happy to be in one another's company. They had seemed to click straight away when they had met. That could not be said of Joey who was clearly restless with the wide-eyed attention that Clara was lavishing on him. I had the distinct impression that he was more interested in her friend who was lingering close by. To put Clara's nose out of joint he invited her friend to join us. She was a pretty, dark-haired girl with mascara that accentuated her laughing eyes. Judging by the look on his face Rudolf the Red Nose was quite taken by the vision before him. Whether or not Clara was aware of Joey's obvious interest was hard to tell as she desperately tried to hang on to her conquest, but she did introduce her opponent. "This is my friend, Maria," she told him. I thought that was her big mistake. Giving him that little nugget of information would have blown her chances. Maria? Now that was a coincidence ...

The look on Joey's face on hearing this, said it all. He made up his mind on the spot and decided that Maria was for him, and the grin that spread across his face confirmed the fact. It didn't take many minutes before the new couple were showing their affection for each other, and poor Clara left us with tears in her eyes. I pointed this out to Joe and suggested that he might have been a less callous in his switch of allegiance, but he wasn't having it. "I've told you before, that they're like buses and there's always a new one on the way." He gazed lustily at his latest conquest and continued, "And I'm really looking forward to clambering aboard this one." She laughed at his crude innuendo, put an arm around his neck and gave him a peck on the cheek as encouragement.

Following our next hard-driving and hectic session I was looking forward to a beer to wind down for a while, for I was getting extremely tired with all the effort of keeping the pace going. With it being Saturday night, we were desperate to look and sound good and give the punters a really good show, so we were putting everything into each new song we played. It didn't harm if we could also blow The Axemeisters away, and so far it seemed that we had succeeded for they were watching and listening avidly as we played, and they were no longer smirking and sneering at us.

The concentration on my beer was interrupted by a voice asking for a word. I looked up to see a young man with a mass of curly hair standing before me. It turned out that he was a junior reporter in the local newspaper, and was so impressed by our performance that he wanted to do an interview.

"You are very charismatic," he told me, and I had to laugh at that for although we had been called many things, charismatic was not one of them. We were just ordinary blokes doing our best and boozing and hopefully dallying with the girls was about the height of our ambition. I explained this to him, but he wasn't having it.

"You underestimate yourselves," he insisted. "You are a very good group, as you can see by the response you are getting from the audience," he pointed out, then repeated his request, "so can I take a set of photographs and do an interview with you?" I suggested that he came back when we had finished for the night so he could ask when we were all gathered, and he toddled off promising to return later.

Joey was excited when I told him. "Photos and an article," he enthused, "that's bloody brilliant!" and went on, "Our fame is obviously spreading if they want to do an interview!"

Although I thought it sounded like fun, my enthusiasm was tempered by the fact that this was only a local newspaper, and more importantly, because I had already gone through a similar experience some time earlier when my previous group had appeared on the pages of our home-town paper.

I was then in a group called John E. Byrnes and the Dateliners which apart from myself and the aforementioned John E. included Peter Williams on lead and Vic Button on rhythm, with Bill the Bass completing the line-up. The happy snapper who was to take our photograph had us in all sorts of ridiculous poses in the high street, but had finally settled on one where we were all holding the singer in our arms, while getting soaked in the rain that had been pouring down throughout the shoot. We were all dressed in our new group suits and quite frankly looked like a collection of tailors' dummies.

When the picture appeared in the local newspaper we became the laughing stock of the local beat-scene, and it took us months to live it down. Our "street creed" went straight out of the window, not that we were endowed with that much of it in the first place, but then ... So I couldn't quite manage to share Joey's unbridled enthusiasm at the prospect of finding ourselves in print.

"It's only a local rag, Joe," I told him, trying to bring him back to earth.

"Stop being so bloody negative," he retorted, "it's going to be great!"

A breathless Stuart returned at the last minute from his sojourn at our lodgings with Heidi, flushed and excited, just in time for our first number. He pulled the guitar strap over his shoulder and waited for Joey's announcement of the first song. Speaking into the microphone, he said, "Peter, zip yourself up because your brain is showing," to the delight of the audience and the embarrassment of the owner of the equipment on view.

We found the reporter waiting when we were finally finished for the evening, and quickly agreed to do the photographs on Monday and the initial interview the next day. This certainly seemed to make him happy, and he beamed with delight at the prospect of being the first to introduce The Charters to the German mass public.

As the night wore on I became comfortably numb with beer inside me and, once again alone with my thoughts, when I came awake at the sound of a female voice saying, "Hello Biffo!"

I turned to see that it was Heinke, and immediately shook myself out my lethargy.

"Hi," I said, returning her smile, and before I knew it I was complimenting her, "you're a sight for sore eyes," I told her, "and may I say how very attractive you're looking tonight." It must have been the booze, for I was normally very reticent with the opposite sex. Then again, I was desperate for some female company, present company definitely included.

She thanked me with a smile, then told me that we had been brilliant that night. Those were her own words; brilliant, not good! "You certainly put a lot of effort into the performance, and Klaus and the boys were very impressed," she trilled. I was hardly listening for I was enamoured by the beauty of this pretty blue-eyed waitress with the blonde hair who served a mean hoppell popell to the hungry.

Before I had properly had the chance to register that she was there, she was already on her way again. "I have to go now, or Klaus will be jealous," she told me, "but promise me you'll come to Das Bären to hear The Axemeisters play tomorrow. I'm sure they'll take it as a compliment if you do." I wasn't so sure of that myself, but if she was going to be there, then I'd certainly go to cheer them on. She gave me a peck on the cheek, and left me to my own devises.

"Any luck, Biffo?" Stu called from across the table.

"With her friggin' boyfriend watching us like a hawk? You must be joking!"

He wasn't letting up. "She can easily be swayed away from him," he informed me like the connoisseur he thought he was. "I can see it in her eyes and the way she looks at you, so go for it, you dozy bugger, and stop trying to be Mr. Nice Guy!"

I promised to keep his advice in mind, then promptly forgot it as I saw that the other twin, Mai, had finally arrived on the premises. She was a stunner and no mistake, and obviously knew it by the way she flaunted her ample charms before the male population gawking at her. It must have been the beer, for I decided that I would do as Stu had suggested, and go for it.

I got my chance as I stood by her at the bar. "Hi, I'm Biffo, the drummer," I told her, already thinking what a ridiculous come-on that was. Surprisingly she informed me that she knew the fact, which immediately put me out of my rhythm. But I fought on. "Would you like to join me at Das Bären tomorrow to watch The Axemeisters play?" I asked.

She seemed interested by the suggestion, but declined. "My sister will be there with Dave, so I don't want to be there to see them together," she pouted.

"I'm only asking you to join me for a drink," I told her, "for I would really like the pleasure of your company, for you are a really classy lass." It was all lame stuff, but all I could come up with in my desperation.

On overhearing my pleading attempts at flirtation two girls at the bar turned on me to sneer, "Yes, you would undoubtedly like to enjoy the pleasure of her company, you lecherous

English bastard! What makes you thing we'll all come running when you people click your fingers? Some of us actually have some taste, so go away and leave her alone, English bastard!"

They may as well have punched me on the nose. I was shocked by the venom they poured at me, and completely distraught and humiliated, and left with their mocking laughter ringing in my ears.

I felt a touch on my sleeve as I began to walk away clutching my beer for comfort, and turned to see Mai smiling warmly at me. "I'm sorry about that outburst," she said. "Forget what they said." She waited for some response but all she got was a senseless mumble. "Look, I'm not promising anything, but I'll try to call in at Das Bären tomorrow night, okay?" No doubt she was trying to cheer me up after my brutal assault.

I decided that I had experienced enough discouraging humiliation for one night and wandered forlornly back to our digs feeling miserable. Wallowing in self-pity in our drab barrack room I lashed out at a chair in frustration, and missed. It just wasn't my night!

To top it all, the door suddenly burst open to reveal Joey in full steam with Maria hanging on for dear life, making their noisy entrance and giggling away like two naughty kids caught in the act. "You don't mind, do you, Biffo?"

"Mind? Why the fuck should I mind? The night couldn't get any worse anyway."

But I was wrong. Again … Although I could thankfully not see them in the darkness, I was kept awake half of what remained of the night listening to the bedsprings working away and the intermittent sounds of Joey's crazy cackle and Maria's moans of "Grosse!" as I tried to remember the receipt for tripe or anything else that might possibly take my mind off the copulating couple by my side.

259

Sonntag was
an Interesting Day

God knows what time it was when the strident maniacal laughter woke me, but whatever it was, it was too damned early for my liking. The sight that greeted me wasn't anymore agreeable either, for Joey held Maria in a close embrace before opening the door for her to leave. Then they kissed tenderly, and that sight alone made me want to rush for the toilet, for Joey's features were never the best at any time, but to see him doing tender was quite nauseating. To make me feel even worse, Maria trilled, "Thank you for an interesting night, Joe. You've worn me out and it will take me all day to recover, but I'll be back tonight, big boy." That's when I felt the bile coming. Then the door slammed shut and she was thankfully finally gone.

Joey was grinning broadly, and well he might from what I had had to endure listening to through the night. "I take it she was impressed by your prowess?" I said, although not particularly interested in a reply, but it came anyway.

Oh, yes," he sniggered. "Let's just say that I gave her something to chew on." He sighed. "I think I'm in love."

"Come on ..." I moaned barely able to listen to his drivel, "What about your little theory about another bus always on the way?"

He chuckled. "Right now I'm on a bus that's taking me where I want to go, so move along, there's plenty of room on top, and she can definitely ding my bell any time she feels like a ride." He was obviously in a poetic frame of mind.

I had the temerity to ask, "Since you're obviously so besotted by Maria, the second Maria in two weeks I might add, have you given any thought to the little lady back home?"

"What? Who? Oh, Mandy!" He shook his head. "No, that's over," he said, "I'm in love with Maria, and I'm seriously thinking of taking her back home with me." Looking at him, I could see that he actually was, for his face was screwed up in a grotesque mask of concentration as he thought about it.

"You don't half talk a load of shit!" I told him, shaking my head at his latest stupidity.

He considered my remark at length, and finally agreed. "Yes, I do, don't I," he acknowledged. "I haven't really thought this scheme through properly have I?"

"The pfennig has finally dropped!" I exclaimed, relieved that he had seen the futility of his puerile plan and come to his senses, but then he had always kept his brain in his nether regions and they were probably still thinking for him after his night of passion.

"I'll just have to bonk her silly for the next week or so to get her out of my mind," Joey surmised, and was apparently content with this conclusion. "After all, there will be other buses on the way." So much for love.

"She'll probably need an M.O.T. by the time you've finished with her," I told him.

"What d'ya mean, M.O.T.?"

"After the rattling you've been giving her, she'll need a service to pick up the pieces and put her back together again."

I recalled the humiliation I had suffered at the hands of Mai's callous lady friends at the bar only a few hours earlier, and winced at the memory. There was little sympathy from Joe when I told him of my experience. "That Mai wouldn't have owt to do with you," he chided, "she's got too much class." As if I didn't know, without him telling me. "Anyway, I don't know why you're sniffing around her when you attracted the attention of that waitress last night."

"I didn't," I protested. "She only came over to ask if we were going to watch her boyfriend play in the bar tonight."

Joey wouldn't have it. "I'm telling you, Biffo, she's interested and you could have her if you could only get your arse in gear." I didn't believe him, but didn't have the stamina at that time of the morning to get into a discussion with him, for that would never end until I gave in, for Joey always had the last word regardless.

It seemed I would have a hard time before me, for Stuart was nicely shacked up in Heidi's flat, and Dave was doing the honours with Eva at her parents house after they had found slumber, so it looked like I would be spending my sleepless nights in complete frustration with only Joey's heavy breathing and Maria's gasps to keep me company. It was not a happy thought.

The reporter turned up at our quarters with Stu in tow and was immediately besieged by Joe who was beside himself at the thought of appearing in a German newspaper with glowing reports of his many talents, and with a picture to boot! "Would you like a coffee, Thomas?" he asked as courteously as an old spinster with her favourite nephew on a visit. Thomas would, so Joe barked out, "Stuart, get the coffee!" then returned his attentive attention to our visitor from the media.

Thomas the reporter began to set up his tape recorder and find his notes. He noticed Dave's absence and wondered where he was. When we told him he was with the delectable Eva, he lit up with a smile, "Ah, Eva!" he said, and sighed. "She and her sister are stunning girls," he told us, as though that was necessary, for we had seen them ourselves.

Thomas decided to get started despite Dave's truancy for which he now had full understanding. He explained that he already written a glowing report from our performance the previous evening, which news had us all smiling at each other like kids in kindergarten being told they'd been clever little things. He then went on to tell us that he had made a questionnaire to give a profile of each member of the group for the benefit of the readers who would then get to know more about the idiots who were attempting to entertain them.

"Let me start with you, Joey," he suggested, and I watched Joe grow at being picked out to be first in line, which was where he always took it for granted that he belonged. Joey considered each question at some length before giving a very serious reply. I had never seen him so concentrated. Stu and I glanced at each other and signalled our opinion with the eyeballs heading for the skull, and we finally began to chuckle for this was not Joey, but just Joe trying to be something he wasn't, which was intelligent. He was answering like Malcolm Muggeridge with a hernia, but still just Joe trying too hard.

Somewhat offended by our mirth, the interviewee enquired, "Are you taking the piss?" which had us sniggering even more than before. Forgetting all previous pretensions of intellectual reasoning, he allowed his fiery temper to get the upper hand and the rest of the interview developed into a complete farce, and he gave flippant answers that were simply stupid, which was more like him. The one that hit the bell and made us burst was Joey's answer to what our most prestigious venue had been, when he replied without a hint of embarrassment; The Whisky a-Go-Go Club in Pontybodkin.

Just then Dave arrived panting from the walk and limping from his corns, and just in time to save the day. "Sorry I'm late," he apologised, "but I had to wait until Eva's parents had left for church." This new information took our interest, and we begged for more, wondering if they were a religious family. "Well, her old fellah certainly put the fear of God in me," Dave told us. "I sneaked down the stairs in the early hours of the morning for a pee, then I heard their bedroom door open, and almost wet myself where I stood. He went down the stairs to the same destination I had been heading for, while I was stuck stock still on the landing with my bladder ready to burst and my heart pumping away at full throttle."

Even Thomas was listening as wide-eyed as the rest of us, hanging on to every word. "So what did you do?" Stu asked, clearly intrigued by his predicament.

"With me fairly bursting at the seams there was no choice but to use the window, and it cascaded onto the corrugated tin roof of the outhouse below like a waterfall. It was a hell of a relief, but the noise brought her old man out in the yard to find out what it was, so I almost shit myself as well, but by the time he was out in the open I was finished and he couldn't figure out what it was." We thought this an impressive story and made the right noises to confirm the fact.

"You didn't splash the dog?" Stu asked.

Dave started. "Dog! What dog?!" Suddenly he looked worried. No doubt the memory of his intermezzo with Adolf still caused some degree of paranoia.

"But how did you get out of there?" Joe wondered, completely engrossed in this new escapade, and simply gasping to know.

"I had to shin down the friggin' drainpipe, and leg it," he said in a shocked voice. "So that's why I'm late." He looked around for sympathy, but despite us having enjoyed his tale, he found none, which was basically the norm in our merry little group.

As we were all hungry we decided to continue the interview in a café that happened to be open on a Sunday. On entering the establishment Stuart looked around and stated, "Thank God there are no blonde blue-eyed waitresses for Biffo to gape at and simper over!" Personally I was disappointed, and thought that every café should have one.

When we were finished, Thomas the Pen decided that it was time to take some photos, and demanded that we traipse around the town for some scenic backgrounds. We grumbled but complied, and he soon had us standing on walls, hanging from lamp-posts and sitting on steps, always smiling like the buffoons we were, and generally looking like simpletons on a day outing.

Walking about wasn't our forte so we were soon tired and bored and ready for some relaxation and found it in a local bar called the Hofbrauhaus where Thomas kindly bought the drinks and something to eat. He also took the opportunity to take a few more candid pictures, one of which showed us raising our steins of beer to him in salute. "That's the one!" he exclaimed. "That's the one we'll use in the newspaper!" Personally I couldn't see what was so exciting about the pose, but frankly I no longer cared.

He sat down next to me and opened his pad. "Right, Biffo," he told me as he crossed his legs to rest the pad on his knee, "now it's your turn." I sailed through the séance without so much as a titter from the others who were hanging on my every word. Then he came to the final question. "What has impressed you most since you came to Germany, and particularly Lüneburg?"

I was in the process of opening my mouth to enthuse about the picturesque ambience of the town, when I was interrupted by Joey's voice rasping, "Blonde blue-eyed waitresses, and in particular the waitress at the Lüneburgerhof Café. He's crackers about Heinke!"

Thomas was all interest. "So you are acquainted with that café and with Heinke?"

I shuffled awkwardly on my seat as I glared daggers at Joey's grinning face, wanting to kill him where he sat. I shrugged my shoulders and mumbled, "Yeah ... I suppose so ..."

With that Thomas was content and packed his things to go. "I'll come in and do the stage shots when you're playing tomorrow," he said.

"Make sure you take me from my best side," Joey told him.

"You haven't got a best side to take," Stuart taunted him. "You're ugly all around!"

Having been with us for a number of hours Thomas had got to know the innocence of the banter and no longer took it seriously. He promised to bring copies of the photos with him to Das Bären that evening so we could see them, then he gave us a smile and a wave and left us to ourselves.

The unaccustomed activity of walking and breathing fresh air had taken their toll on us so we decided to go back to our barracks to rest from the exertion and build up strength for the evening that lay before us. It turned out to be a sensible decision for a couple of hours later we were back on the square refreshed from our rest, shaved, showered and ready for whatever the night had to offer.

Our appearance caused a buzz of raised voices as we entered a bar on the square, not least among the younger clientele, and a gaggle of young girls got particularly excited at the sight of Dave posing in his sunglasses, which he insisted on wearing despite the fact that it was pitch-black outside and not much lighter in the bar. He was loving the attention, and not one to miss any opportunity, he took his drink and went to join his fans to bring some magic into their lives.

With him out of the way and Stuart feeding coins to a slot-machine, I took the opportunity to berate Joe for the remark he had made to the reporter about Heinke, but he only told me to relax and assured me that Thomas would have known he was only joking and would not include it in the article. "Stop worrying," he told me, "you're getting all worked up for nowt."

We gathered the troops and crossed the square for our destination. Parked directly behind our van was The Axemeister vehicle. We were surprised to see that it was a brand new Mercedes with superbly crafted sign-writing emblazoned on the sides. In comparison our rusty hulk looked like a candidate for the scrap yard, which was what it was. But as we neared the entrance to Das Bären I noticed that some young frauleins had written messages of love with lipstick on the sides of the old Commer. Joey was intrigued, and circumnavigated the van to find if any messages had been inscribed in his honour, but came out from his inspection disappointed. "The only way you'll get any declaration of love on there is if you write it yourself," Stu said. "But then we'd know it was you, because you can't friggin' spell."

There was still an hour to go before the music began but the place was already filling up, so it took some time before we found a table. It was obvious that the local heroes had there fans and many were coming to hear them that evening. What impressed me was the quality of their equipment. My eyes almost popped out of my head as I espied the drum-kit, a super-smart glittering Ludwig set with umpteen cymbals of various diameters. There were top of the range Vox amplifiers, huge P/A speakers either side of the stage and an impressive row of shiny guitars including Gretsch, Fender and even a Les Paul Gibson all standing neatly at attention on guitar stands. They even had a mixing desk and monitor speakers! The thing was that it all looked brand new. The Axemeisters must have been making mega-money, or have a rich backer to sponsor them. Whatever, they were in a different league from us as far as equipment was concerned.

I could see that Joe had also registered the equipment and sat gazing at it with envy written all over his face. "It's alright having all that flashy equipment, but what's the point if they can't play it?" but I could hear from the tone of his voice that he no longer felt quite so confident.

A hand touched my shoulder and there was Heinke smiling down at me. "I'm glad you came to see Klaus and the group and I hope you will enjoy their music." Frankly, at that moment I couldn't have cared less about Klaus and his music, I was only happy to see her, but she disappeared as quickly as she had come, and returned to the table where The Axemeisters were gathered. By now Maria had joined Joe, and Eva and Heidi were already embroiled with the other musketeers, so I was on my own once again. I gazed longingly towards Heinke and got a sweet smile in return. Perhaps I wasn't alone after all?

The band eventually began to play, with Klaus strutting his stuff with an air of confidence as he milked the slavish attention he was getting for all it was worth. Heinke sat by the stage smiling at him. Despite Joey's initial reservations, the band was competent and very together, but Klaus was the focal point and seemed to share the self-same delusions of grandeur that afflicted Joey. However, Klaus won hands down in the looks department, for he was handsome and dashing whereas Joey was definitely neither.

Heinke popped up again and we got chatting. She really had a way to make me lighten up, and I found that we were getting along like a house on fire, but our convivial conversation was interrupted by Klaus announcing that they were now going to do some Beatles songs to make the English group feel at home, which I thought to be a fine gesture. He pointed us out and Joey, being Joe, got to his feet to bow and acknowledge the applause, grinning like a lunatic on pot. Heinke gave me a peck on the cheek and got up. "I'll have to go now or Klaus will be jealous," she said then slalomed her way through the crowd back to her table.

The next couple of hours were spent on conversation and booze, and not necessarily in that order, and I was in pleasant mood, relaxed and in a world of my own when my senses were sharply brought back in focus by the voice of Eva trying to attract my attention from across the table. "Biffo," she called, "if you're still interested, my sister Mai has just come in!"

"Where?" I enquired suddenly awake and intrigued, and turned to see her looking as gorgeous as her sister, but then she would, wouldn't she? My pulse throbbed faster as I concentrated on her exquisite features, but my joy was deflated by the sight of her cronies by her side. They had given me enough misery the previous evening and I didn't want any more. Just then she caught sight of me and waved, then began to move towards me but her cronies held her back and tried to persuade her to stay, but whatever they said was not making much impression on her for she only shrugged and continued on her way in my direction.

Every male eye in the place followed her progress as she crossed the room, eager to see who the magnificent Mai had chosen to spend her time with and sighed with disappointment as she sidled up to me with a smile on her face. My hormones were suddenly in overdrive and wildly out of control as her skirt hitched up higher than my expectations. Seeing my reaction she whispered in my ear, "You like, Biffo?"

Like? I was in orbit and grinning like a Cheshire Cat. "Mai, I most definitely like," I assured her. "You're looking incredibly stunning tonight." She was exceedingly attentive and I felt the thrill as she caressed me. She was bouncing me like a ball. I was giddy with lust and certainly rising to the occasion, which she acknowledged with a smile of triumph. She gave me a kiss that I wouldn't let go, then smiled wickedly at the power she had over my emotions knowing that I had become putty in her hands and that she could knead me to any shape she wanted. I was desperate for her and she knew it only too well and kept cranking up my ardour knowing that I was powerless to do anything about it where we sat in the middle of the crowded bar. I was as taut as a violin string and she was plucking me at will to make her own music.

Her breath sent shivers down my spine as she leaned against me and whispered in my ear, "Where is your group van, Biffo?" As it was parked in the middle of the square it was hardly the right location for what she so obviously had in mind, so she pouted showing disappointment, "That's a pity, for I was rather hoping to …" She didn't need to finish, for I knew only too well what she was hoping for, but if she was hoping, then I was most certainly begging on my knees.

She considered her options then took me by the hand and got up. "Kommen sie mit mir," she said with a wanton smile spreading, and like the slack-jawed cretin I was, I let her drag me away to the sound of cat-calls and general derision from my friends and their women. I felt very embarrassed, not so much at the thought of what might be in store for me with the ravishing creature who was leading me to my fate, but because I had such an erection that I had to wobble through the bar in a stoop to try to camouflage the bulge in my pants. I felt like Quasimodo with the hunch misplaced.

She dragged me down a dark alley and leaned wantonly against the wall as she pulled me towards her and kissed me breathlessly. My hands wandered feverishly over the slender body and she arched her body with excitement and pleasure and gasped. Then she deftly unzipped me to release the tiger from its cage. She had certainly been around the block a few times, for she knew exactly what was what, where it was and why. Before I knew it, she had danced us around so I was now with my back against the wall groaning with pleasure, then she went down and I thought I had come to heaven without a harp and moaned a thanksgiving and three hallelujahs as she worked her magic.

It was first when it was over that I realised how cold it was. Despite the temperature I was hot and sweating, but I could now feel how the frost was beginning to take hold of the perspiration and turning it to ice.

"Good, yes?" she purred with a contented smile on her lips.

"Yes, very good!" I gasped, and sighed happily.

With the deed done and the cold beginning to creep into our bones, the surroundings were hardly ideal for prolonged after-play, so we found our way back to the bar and our table there. My trembling legs could hardly carry me but we held unto each other like drunken sailors and with a little support I finally made it.

Mai toddled off to the little girls' room to put her face back on, while I good-naturedly took the winks, nudges and smirking innuendos aimed at me.

As we all tumbled out of Das Bären with the other patrons, we decided to leave the van where it was and walk back to base, for there was a sizeable politzei presence in the square and Joe was hardly in a state to drive. In fact, without Maria's support to keep him upright, he would hardly have been able to walk. Stuart took Heidi off for another night of passion in her comfortable bed, while the rest of us stumbled up the square with our girls hanging on for dear life. Apparently thinking that there would be little satisfaction from Joey in his present state, Maria headed home on her own with kisses and promises of a better tomorrow. Then the twins made their departure giggling as they walked away with arms linked and promising to see us the next night.

As we unsteadily made our way back to our quarters Joey's back legs had definitely gone and he was lurching all over the place, but still merrily chuckling away to himself. Although Joe was happy enough, Dave apparently was not, and had become silent and sullen. On enquiring what ailed him, he snapped at me, "You, that's who!"

"Me …?" I was somewhat taken aback by his response and the way he had despatched it. "What have I done?" I wondered, for I couldn't see that I had done anything at all to rattle his marbles.

"You've put the kybosh on me sneaking in with Eva tonight, that's what. After you went with her sister she decided that she wants to spend the night with sister-talk to get all the dirty details." He gave me a nasty look. "If you hadn't gone off with that Mai I would be spending another night in a warm and cosy bed with a smooth and ready body for company instead of having to sleep with you lot!" He was evidently too unhappy to appreciate that I was also entitled to a moment of happiness when it happened along.

Joe finally lost his grip and his wobbling balancing act ended up in a giggling heap in the gutter, where some might say he belonged. We picked him up and pointed him in the right direction and he staggered on manfully. I noticed that he was slouching along with one foot on the pavement and the other in the gutter, making his passage jerky and lopsided, and wondered why.

"So that's it," he gleefully exclaimed in a drunken slur, "for a moment I thought I'd gone lame!" Having to think and speak at the same time as balancing was too much for him, and he promptly fell once again into the gutter, where he remained muttering and chuckling to himself until we managed to pick him up and drag him back to the barracks where we unceremoniously dropped him on his bed to live or die as he chose, for we no longer cared either way.

I sat on my bed to get my breath and gather my thoughts. I called across to Dave, "It's been an interesting day, hasn't it?" but he was already under his blankets sulking for having to be there at all, and I got no reply. Another day over, a new one soon to come ...

Pushing
My Luck

The mother of all hangovers greeted me in the morning and I swore once again that I would never touch another drop. For some reason the devil entered my head in the form of Joey as I remembered how he had once told us, "We are the kiddies and this is what we do. We're up-front and in their faces, full of shit and bravado, and nothing fazes us. We pull the birds, but above all we sup booze and get pissed if we feel like it because that's who we are and that's what the Krauts expect from us!" But somehow I still felt like a repentant sinner and was ready to go into cloisters to keep me from another morning like this.

Joey lay exactly as we had dumped him a few hours earlier. His bulbous nose was merrily throbbing away like a warning beacon, and his rattling snores jarred my brain. It was like listening to someone trying to start up a chainsaw.

My gaze wandered the room and I noticed that there was something missing, but I couldn't quite decide what it was. Then it slowly dawned on me that the central stove and its smoke-extractor were no longer where they were supposed to be. It was as though they had been spirited away in the night by the stove fairies. I blinked to see if it could be my imagination, but no, still nothing. I scratched my head to help me think. It had definitely been there when we came in because I remembered that Dave had tripped over it when we were aligning the red-head ready for the drop to his bed. So where was it now? It couldn't just disappear on its own.

I lit a cigarette to help me concentrate as I wrestled with the mystery of the missing stove, then noticed a trail of soot that lead to the door with several footprints from whoever had spirited the stove and smoke-stack away. I couldn't fathom who would want to steal a rusty old stove. I knew that Joey would be up for it under the right circumstances, but he was still deep in his beauty sleep and as innocent as Joey possibly could be. It must have been a hell of a night if we had been so smashed that we didn't even notice someone removing the stove.

Dave stirred and finally managed to get to his feet looking less like the sex symbol he otherwise presented himself as and more like a normal mortal after a night on too much of what doesn't always do you good after all. As we now had a shared affinity in the form of the delicious twins, I offered to make the coffee. "Give Joe a poke, and see if you can get some life into him," I suggested.

Dave complied with a vicious smile, probably happy to get some of last night's frustration out of his system, and poked our leader of men in the eye with a vengeance. The result would have frightened the wits out of anybody not used to such a sight. Joey awoke with a snort and a snarl that turned into a loud and prolonged groan. He was a hideous sight to behold as he sat there blinking and trying to find his brain with no apparent success. Then again, on a good day you would need a microscope to find anything inside Joey's head, and where he kept his brain was anybody's guess. "Where's Maria?" he rasped through the sanded Sahara of his tonsils. "Don't tell me she's gone."

"What the hell are you talking about? She wasn't here, you daft bugger!"

"Are you sure?" he managed to ask. Taking our silence for confirmation, he sighed and sagged back. "In that case, I must just have been dreaming about her," he said and fell back on his mattress grateful that he had nothing to prove and knowing he couldn't if he had wanted to in the state he was in.

"Anyone fancy a game of I Spy With My Little Eye?" I asked cheerfully. The abuse came as expected. "Let me put it another way," I said, "have a look around the room and see if you can see anything that isn't there." They gazed vacantly around with puzzled expressions on their faces, but saw nothing that wasn't there. I smirked across at them and informed them, "The friggin' stove's gone!"

"Fuck me, you're right!" The nose had found his brain. "Where's it gone?" he wondered.

"The stove fairies came last night to take it away," I told him.

"What stove fairies?" Dave piped in, suddenly more than interested with an expectant expression creasing his innocent features.

Before I could reply there was an anguished cry from the window where Joe had managed to crawl, "Shit!" he howled, "somebody's nicked the bleedin' van!" We chuckled then laughed aloud as we saw the alarm on his face. "What's so funny," he screamed at us, "this is serious, I'm telling you, somebody's nicked the bloody van!"

"You left it in the square, stupid!" we informed him. "Don't you remember?"

He looked as blank as only Joey could and eventually answered, "No …" Then a thought struck him, and he asked, "How did we get back here, then?"

"Well, Joe," I explained, "we walked, but you crawled and could hardly stay upright even when you were on your knees."

"Was I drunk then?" We exchanged a glance, then answered in chorus, "Naw …"

The Lüneburgerhof Café was warm and welcoming as we entered to find Stuart waiting by a table. Heinke came up to get our order and gave me a special smile to get my day off to a good start. As it was quiet she sidled up beside me and

asked what we had thought about The Axemeister's performance. For once Stuart gave a serious answer, giving it as his
opinion that they were much better than he had thought they
would be. She glowed at this, and pressed on to know what
we thought about her boyfriend Klaus. Stu gave her what she
was hoping for, and told her that he had been excellent and
was obviously the star of the combo. This made her very happy. "Yes he is, and I am very proud of him," she informed us.
Then she opened up to tell us that he would never have her
along when they went away to gigs, and that this made her
feel insecure with all the girls vying for his attention, but she
trusted him and was lucky to be his girl.

"It's Klaus who should feel lucky," I told her, "having
a beautiful girl like you." Where it came from, God alone
knows. Perhaps I was still floating from my success the previous night. I got a blush and a smile for my trouble, and was
ready to follow it up when Joey broke the trance demanding to know where they had got the cash for all their expensive equipment. It turned out that the drummer's daddy was
stinking rich and had paid for the lot, which didn't seem to
make Joe happy. I could understand why, because we were
no-hopers who had to battle for our cash and fight to pay
for the dented tools of our trade that enabled us to make the
music we loved to play, whereas The Axemeisters had got all
that they needed and more just by keeping Daddy happy. Joe
was jealous, and if pushed, I would have to admit that I wasn't
far behind him on that score.

Heinke returned her attention to me. "How are you, Biffo?
She asked and gave me a warm smile.

"I'm fine," I assured her, "and even better for seeing you
again." I really meant it.

She seemed surprised. "Me?" she retorted. "Even after you
had the gorgeous Mai giving you so much attention at Das

Bären last night?" I didn't know what to say to that so didn't say anything, and she let it slip. She leaned closer and whispered, "Thank you for your kind compliment, Biffo. It was very sweet of you, but I won't tell Klaus or he'll just be jealous. Let it just be our little secret." She gave me a wink that had me wondering, then left us to get back to her chores.

Not surprisingly, the van was still standing when we went outside to check, for who in their right mind would think of stealing such a rust-heap. Joe walked slowly around it to see if any words of endearment had appeared with his name on it during the night, but was disappointed once again. In comparison, there were several messages of love and kisses for Stu and Dave, which didn't exactly help to bolster his failing ego. I noticed a little statement on the back door and had to smile as I read the magical words written in a lipstick I knew and had tasted *I loveBiffo!*

I was still enthralled by what I had discovered when Stuart's voice brought me back as he called to Joe. "'Ere Joe, how many hub-caps have you got left?"

"One, I think. Why?"

"Wrong again, mate," Stu chuckled. "Try none."

"The robbin' bastards!" Joe wailed in dismay, and kicked at a tyre in frustration as though taking the exam for admittance to the Politzei corps.

"Right," I announced, "I'm off to mooch around the town and take a couple of photos for the album, so I'll see you later," then wandered off leaving them to their troubles. I had a wonderful feeling of freedom as I walked through the town enjoying the peace around me and feeling liberated at being alone without my three constant companions to pander to. However, as much as I enjoyed being rid of them for a while, I had an ulterior motive for escaping from their clutches, for I had a cunning and devious plan.

It was closing on one o'clock as I entered a news agency and bought a couple of postcards. I paid my money then hurried off to Das Bären knowing full well that Heinke had a date with Klaus there, and wanted to get there before them. When she entered the premises she found me at a table with a beer and a pen in my hand as I wrote on a card. She was surprised but pleased to see me. I invited her to join me. She cast a nervous glance at the door then sat down. "I'm meeting Klaus for lunch in a few minutes," she informed me, but I suggested she could keep me company while she waited for his arrival. Another quick glance at the door, then she relaxed. "Of course," she said, and gave me one her smiles that were worth dying for.

She noticed the postcards and asked who I was writing to, if it was a girlfriend or a wife. "No and no again," I told her. "I haven't got either." She seemed to make a note of the fact "Actually I'm writing to my parents," I said. She wondered what I was writing, and I suggested that she gave me some suggestions. She mentioned historical buildings and the view from the river, and I wrote it all down as she spoke. I looked up to ask if there was anything else I should mention.

She giggled. "You could tell them about the beautiful waitress you've met at the café – your words by the way – and that her name is Heinke." I wrote each word as she said it. She looked at me wide-eyed and gasped "Surely you are not writing that down!" I showed her the card to prove that I was. "You are a crazy guy!" she said, and the smile was even warmer than before. She placed her hand on mine and I could feel the warmth course through my body at the thrill of her touch.

Our moment passed only too quickly as the door opened and Klaus appeared with the long one by his side. As Heinke had her back to the door I informed her of their arrival. She turned and got up with a happy smile on her face to embrace him, but Klaus hardly reacted to her but only bored his eyes threateningly into mine with suspicion plastered all over his face.

"Klaus," Heinke trilled eagerly, obviously unaware of the friction in the air, "Biffo and the group have paid some glowing compliments to The Axemeisters for your performance last night, let me tell you what they said."

But her handsome hero was clearly not listening as he continued to stare me out. He barked, "Heinke, come with me now!"

I know I'm not the sharpest tool in the box, but even I know when I'm not wanted, so I said, "Look, you don't have to leave on my account for I'm about to join my pals at the bar across the square." With that I got up, gave them a nod and headed for the door. Before I closed it behind me, I looked back to see Klaus in an agitated state speaking to her in clipped tones and far from happy.

The bass and rhythm were hammering balls on the pool table when I entered and found Joe alone and irritated by my late arrival. He had soon drained the events of the past couple of hours from me, and having got the details, enquired about how I liked hospital food, for in his opinion, the way Dave and I were going on, we would soon have to learn to like it.

"I'm not worried," I replied laconically, "as long as I've got you to stand up for me."

I could see that he liked me saying it, but he retorted in the only way he could, "Get stuffed, Biffo! What do you think I am, your bloody minder or summat?"

"Yes please! Please be my minder, Joe. Say you will, Joe. Please!" This was the kind of thing his ego fed on, and with an ego as big as his, it needed a lot of feeding.

"Bollocks, you daft sod!" he said, and shook his head wondering what kind of idiot he had before him, but not altogether displeased by my grovelling. "Now eff off and get me a beer, and I.. er... might think about it." I could see him thinking already.

Our conversation was taken up again later as we sat at our table at the dancehall waiting for the doors to open. I was deep in my own thoughts when Joe wondered what I was moping about. "You're not still thinking about that waitress?" He knew me better than I thought. "Get real, Biffo," he said, "she's got a fellah, you dozy bugger, so she's off limits and unavailable, full stop!" He didn't end there. "That sex-on-legs twin will be in here shortly draping herself all over you and working you into a lather, so forget the waitress, will you!"

The doors opened and the happy crowd entered for their night's entertainment. The girls were soon clinging to their respective conquests around our table but there was no sign of Mai. Her twin must have noticed my crestfallen expression and leaned over to assure me that she would soon be coming, and was actually looking forward to seeing me again, which was reassuring enough to buck me up.

The first session seemed to flash past and Mai had still not arrived, but to alleviate my gloom Heinke had. Strangely she was without Klaus. Oddly enough the rest of his gang were also absent. The mystery was explained when she came over to sit with me and informed me that The Axemeisters were playing somewhere outside town. I wondered why she hadn't gone with them.

"Klaus insists that no girlfriends travel with the group because he thinks they are a distraction, and he wants them to concentrate on their music so they will be successful." She was very earnest. I wondered if she was happy with such an arrangement. As it happened, she wasn't, not least because she happened to be in love with the handsome Klaus whose looks also happened to attract many other interested females. "I do feel insecure about it," she admitted, "but I trust him." Poor girl, I thought, I only hope you won't be disappointed.

She changed the subject by pointing out that I was alone once again. "I would have thought that Mai would be here with you," she said.

"She's supposed to be," I told her, crossing my fingers that she would, "but she's working late."

I thought I noticed a blink of disappointment in her eye, but then she gave me that smile that made me tremble, a quick peck on the cheek, and left, wishing me "good luck!"

Halfway through the second set I noticed that Mai had finally arrived. She was dancing with her sister, so I knew that one of them had to be her. She looked stunning and highly desirable as she gyrated in front of the stage in a white micro skirt, a pale blue sweater and a pair of knee-length boots. She simply oozed sexuality, and knew it. I could hardly wait to be with her, which was at our next break when she breathlessly put me on the boil by whispering, "Are you ready for some fun?"

I was grinning like the village idiot and probably drooling as much as she led me away. "Where do we go?" she purred in my ear.

The only suggestions I had were the van or our spartan lodgings. "I'm sure you've had sex in less flattering surroundings than either of these options," I dared to say.

She wasn't bashful. "Oh yes," she admitted readily enough, and smiled wickedly. "You'd be surprised at the places I've had my fun." She was a man-eater and not afraid to admit it, but I didn't care, for now I was to be her meal.

She kissed me passionately. She was good. Very good! Sex with her was a mind-blowing experience. It was pure animal lust. No feelings. No talking. Just raw sex.

She caught me admiring her body when we had finished and flashed me a smile as she held up her panties. "Souvenier?" she asked, and I took it.

There and then the events of the coming week were set in stone: get up late and tired, toddle off to the café for breakfast to bring me back to life, drink too many beers in the town square, flog my guts out for the punters of Lüneburg, more beer, and then the ultimate pleasure of the majestic Mai to round off the day. What more could I ask of life? Unless … But then, she had a fellah and was unfortunately off limits.

The only deviation from the routine came on our free day while drinking in Das Bären. We were all in high spirits that were only spoilt by the constant badgering Dave and I were getting from Wülf and Holger: The Brothers Grimm personified. They drunkenly taunted us from their unsteady position at the bar, jealous and seething at the fact that we were jollying the delectable twins.

Tiring of their racket, the ever diplomatic Joe marched up to them to advise them to cool down. He did it in his own inimitable way by telling them, "Shut the fuck up!!" Neither of them chose to heed these words of wisdom and paid the ultimate price for their stupidity when Joe butted them in quick succession.

Their noses exploded in blood and their wailing cries brought reinforcements and not surprisingly there followed an unseemly melee between us and the rest of the bar who apparently decided to side with the local team, and the politzei had to come to restore order. Not surprisingly we were banned forthwith from this particular hostelry, which was a shame for they had good beer.

"You're gonna have to learn to control that temper of yours, Joe," chuckled Stuart as he licked his grazed knuckles.

"No way!" Joe disagreed. "This is what makes life worth living!" and his crazy cackle echoed between the buildings as we wandered through the night back to barracks for another night in our creaking beds.

Another morning arrived as unwelcome as they all were. A couple of uneventful days had passed since the fracas in Das Bären and life had returned to the daily routine of trying to keep our sanity alive under the very trying circumstances of having to live close twenty four hours a day week after week without actually attacking each other. We were all basically nice blokes and had enjoyed each others company when we were just a local group doing a few performances during the week and breaking up to live our own lives between each gig. But this was different, for we no longer had our own separate lives, but were joined at the hip to the rest of the group for the duration, and the fact that we had not yet become sullen enemies could only be put down to our common love of rock and roll and that we all shared the same zany sense of humour that saved many a situation from developing too far for retreat.

"Here you go, Biffo. Get your laughing tackle around that," said Joe, and passed me a steaming cup of coffee. For some reason, Joey had taken upon himself the role of mother-hen from the very beginning, getting up early to make coffee and generally fussing about to make our lives a little more comfortable. It was a bizarre contrast to the brazen and aggressive bloke who was completely devoid of any inhibition and was a one-man army just waiting for a war to happen. But Joey couldn't do enough for us, and played mother when we were in our quarters.

"Ta!" I acknowledged, and took the first tentative sip. Joe made good coffee and the best was the first of the day. He lounged nonchalantly on the rickety chair and stared at me with a broad grin on his face. Eventually tiring of being under his constant gaze I demanded to know what he was looking at.

"Well, from where I'm sitting, that cut over your eye is clearing up nicely after the punch-up in the bar on Wednesday night." He seemed pleased for me.

I winced as I gingerly touched it with my finger, and muttered, "Is it? It certainly doesn't feel any better." Neither did my ribs. I still felt as though I had been run over by a bus, and I had been in agony when we were playing the previous night. "I got a right kicking in there because of you and your bloody temper," I told him miserably. "What the hell made you kick off like that anyway?"

Joey was hurt by my insinuation that it was all his fault. "Well, there's gratitude for you, you ungrateful swine!" he moaned. "I only did it to stop those two bastards from hurling abuse at you and Dave. They got me dander up, that's all!"

"But that was all it was, Joe. Just abuse! It was sticks and stones may break my bones etc., and as touchy as I am, I could easily put up with that for I'm well versed in taking abuse, not least from you I might add!"

Dave decided to get his penny's worth. "Yes, you started a bleeding riot in there and we could all have ended up in hospital because of you. Quite frankly, you should be bloody well hung!"

Joey countered immediately. "I am!"

"You're what?"

"Bloody well hung," Joe smirked. "Just ask Maria!" The criticism rolled off him without even ruffling his feathers.

I allowed him to bathe in the luxury of this retort and lit a cigarette before I returned to the attack. "The worst part of this bloody ruckus apart from the pain, is the fact that we've been banned from the place, and given the amount of broken glasses, tables and chairs, it's a wonder we weren't arrested for criminal damage!"

Joey stopped laughing and quietly pondered on my words, hopefully deciding that he would try to control his temper in the future. He stared into space with his chin resting on his hands and his elbows on the table, and finally sighed and admitted, "Yeah, you're right. I suppose I was a bit hot-headed and foolhardy." We said nothing, preferring to let him think it through himself. "The worst part was that Maria was so hacked off by it all that she left me in a flood of tears." I could see what little conscience he had, begin to be pricked.

"I'm not surprised that she left in tears," Dave primly told him, "especially after that dumpy red-head of the drummer's smashed her over the head with a chair!"

Joey sighed deeply at this reminder of what he had tried to push from his mind, for since the incident he hadn't seen hide or hair of Maria and was obviously missing her sparkling company. "It's just me and my big gob!" he moaned. "From now on I'll keep it zipped shut!"

"Can we have that in writing?" We asked.

Our conversation was interrupted by a knocking on the door, and we were confronted by Herr Sneider the manager, withholding his disgust as he looked around our humble abode. He handed us our wage packets and smirked as we grabbed them, for by now we were once again totally bankrupt. It was obvious that he had something on his mind as he paced around the room with three pairs of eyes following him closely and wondering what it was. We could almost hear his brain ticking over as he wrestled with the problem of how to broach whatever it was that was bothering him. He finally decided to get straight to the point.

"It has been brought to my attention that you were involved in an ugly altercation in Das Bären a couple of days ago, involving brutal violence that resulted in people having to have hospital treatment." We were like three truant schoolboys being scolded by the headmaster and not liking it too well. "There were considerable damages to the premises and the politzei had to be called to stop the whole unseemly incident." He looked at us as we looked down at the floor, waiting for more and wondering where this was taking us. "Now, would you please explain to me what happened and how this started?" He stared at Joe. "You first."

Joe looked back at him with his face drained of its normal ruddy complexion, but no words were forthcoming. He just shuffled is feet awkwardly under the German's withering glare, probably thinking, *What's up with him? It was only a bar punch-up after all …*

Sitting on the edge of my bed and taking more than a passing interest in this interrogation, I decided to rescue Joey. "We were just having an enjoyable conversation with some frauleins when two of The Axemeisters began to taunt me and Dave because they were drunk and jealous."

He wondered who our lady friends had been, and when I told him, he lit up. "Ah, yes, of course! The twins!" he said it as though that explained everything. "They are two stunning girls who enjoy being the centre of attraction, and often excite jealousy." That settled, he then wanted to know who had been taunting us, so we told him that too. At this news, he broke into good-natured laughter, and exclaimed, "Wülf and Holger! Those two dumbkoffs are brain-dead!" He chuckled to himself, "They could start a riot in an empty room."

Pointing to Joe who was still strangely silent and looking uneasy, he continued, "I suppose it was him who retaliated," he said with a knowing smile, "I can tell by just looking at him." Joey was about to open his mouth, but wisely decided that it was better to keep it closed. "So bitte, how did he approach them, was it in a friendly manner or aggressively?"

"Oh, definitely in a very friendly manner," I lied. "Joe politely asked them if they would please desist in their taunting and to please moderate their language as there were ladies present."

"I take it they refused to comply?" the manager asked, and Joey nodded sheepishly. "And then what happened?" he asked, trying to suppress a smile, for he knew we were lying through our teeth.

From then on, we could stick to the truth, so I told him, "Joey decked them both, sweet as a nut, and they went down like two sacks of potatoes howling to wake the dead. Then it turned into a riot with everyone barging in on the fun until the police came to break it up, but by then the damage was done."

He considered our lies against the facts he already knew, and decided that the best course of action was to take our lies at face value and brazen it out. After all, we were bringing in the punters and he wanted to keep us. "I shall ban Wülf and Holger from the Palast for a month to avoid further trouble," he informed us.

Dave's face paled at this suggestion, and begged him to change his mind. "It'll only cause further aggravation and we'll have to keep checking behind us for reprisals when we're out in the streets." With his own nocturnal escapades and his early morning escapes down the drainpipe to wander home on his own, he would be a prime temptation for retribution, so he was naturally worried.

"Please remember to be on your best behaviour when you are at the Star Palast," he requested, "for we do not want any trouble there, and I would have to report it to Manfred Müller if there was." He gave us an ominous look that told more than a thousand words that this was not a desirable option.

Joey collapsed in a fit of laughter when the door had closed and our visitor had left. This rankled Dave who, like me, had been quite concerned for the possible outcome of our confrontation with Herr Sneider. He snapped at him, "Shut up the fuck up will you!" There was no response from Joe who only laughed louder. "You really are a sneaky, despicable and callous bastard!" Dave sneered at him.

At this, Joey stopped laughing, but the grin remained planted on his face. "Yes, I know," he said. "Isn't it great!"

We found Stuart wandering down by the square waiting for us, and went to the café for some breakfast. He informed Joe that he had met Maria and she would be coming to see Joe that evening. This news brightened him considerably and for a moment I thought he was about to offer to pay for our food, but unfortunately he changed his mind. He was happy, but not that happy!

I noticed that Heinke acted quite reserved as we entered. Although she returned my smile it held none of the warmth and radiance I was used to seeing in it. She loitered by the counter apparently reticent about coming over to take our orders. When she did, she was stiff and formal, and I wondered what had caused this as she was normally very open and friendly with us. She handed us a newspaper. "Here you are," she said with no enthusiasm, "you've made the front page."

We crowded around excitedly to see ourselves grinning away on the front page. The main article was on the entertainment page, and we had it all to ourselves, with photos of each of us in live action plus a long shot of the whole group on stage. We thought it was brilliant. The problem was that we couldn't understand the many columns of print that accompanied the pictures, so Heinke agreed to translate it for us, and we listened intently, hanging on to every word.

Our reporter friend certainly had a way with words and his glowing report on our performance had us all brimming over with pride. I was particularly pleased with his praise of our presentation of the opening number *Do You Love Me* which seemed to have made an exceptional impression on him.

Heinke then translated the individual profiles, and we chuckled and nudged each other at the inane information we had offered the good burghers of Lüneburg for posterity. Then she turned her eyes on me, "And now the drummer's profile," she said, and I thought I noted a hint of irritation in her voice as she said it. I nodded my approval at each answer as they were exactly as I remembered them when Thomas had written them down. I smiled a contented smile and lit a cigarette as he she continued. Then she set her eyes on me as she read out the question *What has impressed you most since your arrival in Germany?* and then read what Joey had jocularly answered for me about being crackers in love with the waitress in the café.

My smile fell from my face as I heard what had been written. My feeling of dismay was hardly helped by the sight of Joey grinning wickedly at my acute embarrassment. "I didn't say that," I protested, looking at her for mercy, "honest!"

A smile crept to her face. "So you're not crazy about me after all?"

"Well, yeah … I mean, no … Er, yeah …" I muttered. I felt like an idiot and really didn't know what to say.

Coming to my aid in my hour of need, Joey admitted that he was responsible, and that it had only been meant as a joke, but Thomas had obviously taken it at face value and included it in his article.

"I see," she said slowly. "So all I am to you is a joke?"

"Of course not!" Stuart told her, as he tried to bring some sense to the situation. "It was just Joey trying to be funny at Biffo's expense. No harm was intended, certainly not towards you, for we all like you."

She seemed to forgive us, but then frowned as she informed us, "Klaus will be very angry with me when he reads this." We couldn't understand why this should be the case, but she had us thinking when she explained, "He knows I talk with you and enjoy your company, and he caught me with Biffo at Das Bären the other day. Despite my explanation that it had all been a coincidence that we had met there and just a chance meeting, he was very angry with me." I could see the worry in her eyes, and I felt guilty for putting it there. "Now he will see this in the newspaper and be very unhappy!"

The ramifications of Joey's joke backfiring finally registered, and we all sagged and shuffled and felt responsible, which we had good reason to do. Because of Joey's thoughtless remarks the shit was about to hit the fan, not only with Klaus, but more importantly, with Mai, for when she read about the feelings I had for the waitress, she would not be a happy bunny and that no doubt would be the end of our happy relationship.

I think he must have realised the problems he had caused, because Joe stayed with me when the others left on another errand, and even offered me a cigarette as a token of appeasement.

Heinke turned to me to ask, "Are you really crackers about me, or was that also just a joke?"

I couldn't deny it any longer. With a sheepish grin I admitted, "Yes, I suppose I am."

She was about to leave the table when the café door burst open and Klaus strode in. His face was contorted with rage as he spotted us together. "So it's true!" he snarled. "How long has this been going on behind my back?" He grasped Heinke by the shoulder and shook her and berated her in strong Teutonic terms that even Joe understood to be less than flattering. He released her and she ran out of sight behind the counter where we could hear her sobbing.

Angered by what we had witnessed we rose to our feet to confront him about his attitude, with Joey shouting at him, "Do yourself a favour and fuck off out of here before I do something you will regret!" There was no doubt that corporal punishment was likely to be the menu of the day, so Klaus decided to comply with Joey's suggestion and skulked off lashing out at a chair as he left.

The day that had started with such optimism was rapidly going down-hill tits up and pear shaped, and I was becoming thoroughly depressed. My fears were confirmed that evening at the dancehall when neither Mai nor Heinke put in an appearance. Others however were present to rub salt in the wound, and I got a good rubbing from my two lady acquaintances of the previous night who took delight at my plight and the fact that Mai had apparently finally decided to dump me. Holger was also there to enjoy my downfall. He looked resplendent with his plastered nose, but despite his broken hooter he made it clear that he enjoyed my gloom.

The people at our table also seemed happy enough. Dave and Eva showed little sympathy for my predicament, for with her twin no longer on the scene he could once again begin to sneak into Eva's boudoir, and he was positively salivating at the prospect of a new liaison in the warm comfort of her bed. I knew Stuart would be spending the night with Heidi, but the news that Joey had been invited to spend the night with Maria really sent me into deep despair, for that meant that I would be spending the night in the barrack room on my own. I shuddered at the thought, but that solved nothing.

After a miserable night on my own I was dragged out of my blankets by Joey who had decided to come and take me for breakfast. He was irritatingly cheerful and in stark contrast to my own mood, but he finally got me into the open and into the van. I took a walk around it, and wiped Mai's lipstick message off the carcass as though by doing this I was permanently terminating what once had been. My eyes caught a new message. *I love Joey!* it stated in sparkling pink lipstick. I thought that he had probably written it himself just to have his name in lights, so I asked him. "No, it wasn't me!" he insisted. "Honest injun! Maria did it."

As we drove towards the square we turned a sharp corner and something caught my eye as it rolled from under the seat. It was a lipstick in baby pink. I looked across at Joey and smiled, but said nothing.

He noticed me looking, and asked, "What?!" but I left him to wonder.

It was Saturday market again, busy and bustling, but we found space to park then headed for our breakfast café, where Stu and Dave were waiting. We were attended by a plump waitress who smiled as she recognised us from the pictures in the newspaper. We wondered where Heinke was, and she informed us that she had called in sick and wouldn't be coming in that day. We ventured to ask what was wrong with her, and the smile was replaced by a scowl as she told us.

"She had an argument here yesterday with her boyfriend who accused her of all manner of things, then slapped her and said it was over between them," she informed us. "She collapsed in a flood of tears and was very distraught. I think that is why she is not working today."

I sat open-mouthed as I listened to what she had to say. The others were as shocked as myself, especially Joey, who knew that it was his stupidity that had caused her problems. His voice was calm but cold, "I warned that bastard yesterday," he said. "The next time I see him I'm going to deck him."

"You'll have to join the queue, Joe," I told him, "because I'm first in line."

With these thoughts at the back of our minds, we ambled around the various market stalls trying to put the picture that had just been painted for us on hold. The market seemed busier than it had been the previous week. There was much animated chatter among friends and neighbours as they exchanged gossip and the air hung heavy with smoke from the sausage stalls. By now my anger had begun to subside from stark to gently simmering. We came to the bar area and decided to have a brew or two. "Right," said Joe, gleefully rubbing his hands together, "four glühweins is it?" The look of horror that appeared on Dave's face at the mention of glühwein soon had us in a better mood.

We found a table and relaxed with a couple of beers, feeling completely at ease as we laughed and joked and enjoyed the general ambience of the market. Our old friend, the juggler, turned up to entertain the crowd, but caught sight of us sitting there, and hurriedly moved to another spot further away.

His place was soon taken by another entertainer who was sprayed from head to foot in silver paint. We waited for him to do something, but he did nothing at all. He just stood stock still without an inclination of movement, so we lost interest. A sudden movement caught my eye as he moved into another position, and then held it. "He's playing at being a statue!" I announced as though I was Archimedes in the bathtub exclaiming Eureka!

"He reminds me off Dave at work," Stuart chuckled, "only livelier."

Just then I saw Klaus with a girl on his arm coming through the crowd. Incredibly, he had the gall to sit down at the table next to ours, and kiss the girl. He smirked at us in triumph and the arrogance on his face was intended for our benefit.

"Considering what's happened, you have to admire his brazen nerve," Dave acknowledged.

"Look at the smug fucker!" Stuart snarled.

But I wasn't listening. Joey tried to call me back as I rose from my seat. "Leave it, Biffo!" he warned, but I ignored him.

I stood over Klaus the waitress-slapper, nose to nose and eyeball to eyeball, and grabbed him by the throat. I hissed a warning at him, "Treat Heinke that way again and you'll find I'm going to be your worst nightmare, do you hear?" I released my grip and began to walk away when I saw him grinning at me. That did it. I lost my cool and smacked him right between the eyes with such force that he fell backwards off the chair and lay in a heap on the ground. I glared darkly at him, then noticed that our performance had attracted a bigger crowd than the juggler so we decided to find other happy hunting grounds before the politzei took interest.

Once in the secure confines of a bar I ruefully rubbed my knuckles and gave Joey a smile. "D'ya know what? In a perverse way I actually enjoyed that!"

"As a matter of fact, so did I," he chuckled. "I honestly didn't think you had it in you."

"You know why I hit him, don't you?" I asked, then gave the answer myself. "It was that smirk, that arrogant supercilious smirk that really blew my mind! Actually Joe, he's a lot like you," I pointed out, "bloody irritating!"

"I don't do supercilious," Joe protested. "In fact I don't even know what it means."

Stuart came from the bar with four frothing beers and put them down before us. "Just what is it with you pair?" he asked. "Are you trying to provoke them enough to give us a good kicking, or what?"

Dave nodded in agreement. "After that little show of violence and Joey decking those two in the bar the other night, they're going to have all The Axemeister fans and an assortment of local thugs to back them up when they come looking for us. You've turned us into public enemy number one and every bloody nutcase will be after our blood now."

Joey was full of bravado as usual. "Are you listening to yourself? Don't forget that we are the kiddies and nobody messes with us, I'm telling you now!"

Just then a couple of girls came up to our table to actually thank me for having put Klaus to shame. Apparently they were friends of Heinke, and knew that he had been two-timing her every time her back had been turned. One of them noticed the grazing on my swollen knuckles and assured me that she would be telling Heinke of my exploits. As they were in the process of leaving they gave us an ominous warning. "Watch your backs, for Klaus will never allow this insult to go unavenged, and he has many friends."

We considered the warning over another beer and decided that we should heed the advice given, and keep an eye on each other, for we were the three musketeers, one for all and all for one. However D'Artagnan was somewhat hesitant about this arrangement as he felt it would put him off his stride to have us about when he was giving of his best.

The atmosphere at the dancehall that night was definitely sparky with enough electricity to power the lights in Blackpool. Klaus and his merry band of dysfunctionals kept taunting us as we played, enjoying each loud jibe they sent at us. How Joey kept his volatile temper under control was anybody's guess, but the fact that Manfred Müller would seriously disapprove if we caused any bother in his Star Palast was probably helping to hold him back. But he was definitely bristling, and it was touch and go how long he would hold.

It was a huge relief when the first break came so we could get away from the continual hectoring from Klaus and his cretins. We found our reporter friend waiting at our table, and told him the whole sorry mess his article had caused. At first he was apologetic and distressed, but then he gradually pulled a smile from his pocket and gave a chuckle. We looked at him in surprise and waited for an explanation. "I was just thinking, "he said. "You see, I have a photo-shoot of The Ax-emeisters tomorrow for the newspaper, and I imagine Klaus will not be looking too handsome in the picture."

"He won't be the only one," Joe pointed out.

"The Brothers Grimm are both sporting patched-up broken noses after Joey rearranged their faces last Wednesday," I informed him, then suggested that he might balance the picture of Klaus's happy band by placing one of the nose fractures at each end and have Klaus with his panda eyes in the middle. "That should make an interesting picture for the paper."

Seeing me alone in the crowd, Eva suggested that she could have a word with her sister to get her back in my lonely arms. I shrugged my shoulders but didn't reply, thinking of Herr Sneider's lecture when he had remarked on the affect the stunning twins had on those enamoured by their charms, and how they loved to have attention and the jealousy they caused among their suitors.

Despite the constant barracking from Klaus and his hordes we managed to get through the night without incident. Joey showed remarkable restraint, no doubt influenced by Maria's threat to leave him on his own if he got into trouble.

As I sat getting comfortably numb on copious amounts of beer, a girl appeared to inform me that she had a message from Heinke, and would I meet her at the bar on the square at eight the next evening. "Can I tell her you will be there?"

I brightened considerably at this but tried to remain cool, calm and collected. "I'll think about it," I replied, and left it at that.

With the rest of the English out for the second night running getting their collective jollies, I was once again alone with my drink-fuddled brain, and the nagging thought kept popping up that my invitation for the morrow might be a cunning plan to lure me there for Klaus and his cretins pleasure and my own pain. It was a sobering thought.

Waking up on your own in a strange barren room can be quite depressing and the complete silence was deafening in comparison to the dawn chorus I was used to with the others around. To my surprise I found that I particularly missed the sound of Joey's high-pitched whinnying laughter which would normally send a shiver down my spine and rusty nails into my head. After having lived in each others pockets night and day for a month or so, it was hardly surprising that we sometimes reacted with irritation at the various quirks and eccentricities that we had merely laughed off earlier. Joey could be the most irritating person dead or alive when he was in the mood, which he was most of the time, but he was basically a warm and kind-hearted lad who couldn't do enough for us, but it was nonetheless a shock to the system to realise that I was actually missing him!

Although it meant a day off from our labours, Sunday was not my favourite day of the week, for time passed so slowly and it never seemed to end. Somehow this particular Sunday had made a very slow start, dragging its feet and taking its time simply because there was no one there to help me speed it on its way.

The church bells eventually brought me into the open and I wandered through the streets looking for an eatery that was open so I could get some breakfast, but everything was closed.

It was quiet and there was nobody to be seen in the street. It was as though the whole population had been spirited away in the course of the night, for I was alone wherever I went.

I finally found another survivor slouched on a bench in the distance, and was delighted to see it had ginger hair and a green parka to keep it warm. I never thought I would say it, but it was really good to see Joey again and I suddenly felt that life was worth living once more. As though my luck had changed with Joey's appearance, we saw that a bar was finally in the process of opening for business and went in for the first food I had tasted for twenty four hours.

Dave joined us after his night with Eva. Knowing that he wouldn't be seeing her again until the evening and that Sunday was a long day to fill, he suggested that we might take a drive, but Joey refused, pointing out that the knocks, bangs and grinding noises that came from the van were of such a nature that we should spare the vehicle in the hope that it might make it back to Blighty with us inside.

"Those noises have been there for four weeks now," Dave scolded him, "so why haven't you got them fixed?"

Joe didn't even smile when he replied. "I was rather hoping they would go away by themselves." Joey had always been an optimist, but this time his optimism was disappointed.

With a Sunday drive out of the question, I suggested that we could take a walk in the park to feed the ducks. "Are you friggin' quackers?" Joey responded. "Feed the ducks, my arse!" So with no further suggestions forthcoming we decided to pass that day like any other, drinking beer and waiting for it to end.

During the conversation Dave let slip that he had been invited to dinner that evening to meet Eva's parents. Joey's eyes almost popped out of his head at hearing this, and he spluttered incredulously, "You've been what?!" then harangued him good style. "Remember your wedding day, Dave?" he wondered. "That was when you and your missus got married, remember? Her folks provided you with a lovely white wedding with all the trimmings." He looked at me. "D'ya know Biffo, her old fellah was even considerate enough to paint the shotgun white." He looked back at Dave, shook his head derisively and snorted, "Meet her parents indeed!"

This little moral sermon and reminder of vows already made and obligations waiting at home had little effect on Dave. On the contrary, he seemed to find it all quite amusing, especially that Joe of all people should be taking the moral stand, for let's face it, that didn't exactly fit the image he portrayed for the world at large. In fact our happy-go-lucky ladies man was actually looking forward to meeting Mum and Dad, but then his mind was rarely tuned in to the realities of life, so he knew no better.

As coincidence would have it, we had all agreed to meet our respective lady friends in the same establishment that night, which meant that we would have the pleasure of each others company for a change. A thought crossed my mind, and I suggested that Joe might be advised to leave the van at base since our friends The Axemeisters would be playing in the bar across the square from where we would be gathered. "Bearing in mind the warnings we've had, we don't have to tempt providence, so if you don't mind, I'd like to keep a low profile."

"Oh, have a day off, Biffo," Joe sneered at my caution, "those cretins aren't going to have a pop at us. We're the kiddies, remember!"

"Even so," Dave pointed out, looking quite serious, "we have to watch our backs, because you know what these Kraut's are like." He was probably remembering that they had something to do with the war, and were not to be trusted.

Walking back to our barracks, Joe turned to me to say, "I've got some good news for you, Biffo. I'll be back in my own bed tonight so you'll have some company." It turned out that Maria's parents had been away for the weekend and were now on the way back. "I know you've been missing me, haven't you, mate?" he asked, giving me a toady smile.

"Missing you?" I replied disdainfully. "You must be joking!"

Later that evening we diplomatically crossed to the other side of the square on our way to our rendezvous to avoid further confrontations as The Axemeisters and their road managers unloaded the equipment from their van.

We found a table by a window that gave us a broad view of the square between us and The Axemeister's bar. Following our recent altercation with The Axemeisters, it seemed an odd choice of table. Personally I would have chosen a secluded corner where we could keep a low profile with our backs to the wall and a clear view to the door, but Joey had insisted that we should sit where we were in the full glare of those passing by outside. It was as if he was tempting fate, and daring someone, anyone, to provoke him. He was coiled and ready to pounce, probably in retribution for the vocal hammering we had received while on stage the previous night. Maria's influence had held him back then, but I could now see that he was bristling with his shiny red nose pulsing away more than usual, which was always a bad sign.

Considering that it was a Sunday evening there were quite a few people about, most of them gathering to hear Klaus and Company play across the square. Their fans were easy to spot as most of them had the double axe logo on the back of their leather jackets. To keep order in case of trouble, there were a couple of politzei patrol cars parked nearby, which given the warning we had received was quite comforting.

A sudden sharp gust of wind rattled the glass in the windows and the door shuddered. Within seconds a heavy downpour battered the window panes and emptied the square as people ran for cover. There was a loud clap of thunder immediately followed by a blinding flash of lightning that had Joey beaming away with a huge grin on his face.

"What's up with you?" I wondered.

"Nothing," he replied, "I just thought someone was taking me photo."

As quickly as it had begun, the downpour stopped, and people moved back into the square. I noticed the police officers had left their car for a crafty smoke. I stared into the lights of the square and drifted off with Joey merrily chatting away in the background. I didn't listen to what he had to say, for it was usually not worth the trouble. I wondered if Heinke would turn up, and why she had invited me to meet her at all. I looked at my watch to see if she was late, and Joey recognised my nervousness and comforted me, "Don't worry, mate," he told me, "I'll be here." That statement certainly did little to help my nerves.

Just then the tall one from The Axemeiters entered the establishment and stared fixedly in our direction before joining a bunch of fans for a drink at the bar. He pointed us out to the others, indicating where we sat and more importantly, who we were. Joey had his back to the door and was blissfully unaware of the scowling troopers muttering among themselves.

"Don't look now, Joe," I said as calmly as I could, "but one those Axemeisters just came in and I think we're in for trouble."

Joey immediately turned towards them and gave them the two-fingered salute. "Stop worrying. What are they going to do about it? They start playing at eight o'clock." He showed no concern whatever, and pointedly turned his back to the assembled troops.

I decided that he was probably right, and settled down to what I hoped would be a convivial night off, which began at that moment as the door opened and Heinke came in and headed for our table with a huge smile on her face. Her natural exuberance and beauty came shining through. She took my hand and rubbed her finger over my grazed knuckles. "Why did you hit him?" she asked and put those baby-blue eyes on me.

"Because of what he did to you," I told her honestly. "You should never allow anyone to treat you like that. He deserved what he got."

"So you did it for me?" I nodded silently in reply. "So you are crackers about me, then?"

"That's what it said in the newspaper, so it must be true."

She smiled, squeezed my hand and gave me a peck on the cheek. Joey had been a model of restraint and a perfect gentleman throughout, and now only smiled as he watched this simple act of affection. This ended promptly when a couple of girls from the dancehall joined us. Joe immediately cornered them to impress them with his talents, gushing out the usual nonsense about how brilliant he was in every conceivable way. He finally noticed how their eyes had clouded over, so he tried another approach, telling them that he was really a shy and modest bloke. "I'm really a self-defecating kind of bloke," he told them, and I almost choked on my beer when I heard what he said.

"We already know that, Joey!" I spluttered.

"Know what?" he asked in all innocence.

"That you're full of shit!"

Joey realised that he had got himself into a corner and tried to fight himself out by regaling the girls with a few little nuggets of information that he thought might interest them. "When I was a youngster I used to stick a straw into a frog and blow it up until its eyes popped out of its head," he gleefully told them. When this information failed to set them

303

alight, he ventured on regardless. "We had a mongrel that only had one back leg and when it cocked its leg to take a pee it fell in a pile of piss!" he laughed himself silly at this fond memory without noticing the icy expression that had appeared on the girls' faces. They decided that Joey was not for them, and hurriedly left.

Heinke took the opportunity to ask me about various aspects of my life. Some of it was quite personal but I didn't mind, at least she was showing some genuine interest in me, and the more interest she showed, the more intimate I felt we were becoming.

Just then the door swung open and in strode Klaus and the gruesome twosome, Wülf and Holger. They really did look a sight with their patched-up noses and Klaus with his eyes blackened like a panda bear. They had obviously been informed of our presence by the long one and had come across from the bar to sate their curiosity during their break.

On spotting them, Joey took a threatening step forward, while the Brothers Grimm took three back, but Klaus resolutely stood his ground as he fixed Heinke and I with a steely glare. Heinke leaned her head against my shoulder and smiled sweetly back at him, and he promptly turned on his heel and stormed away with Wülf and Holger quickly bringing up the rearguard, following him like lapdogs.

I remarked on her little cameo performance and that it had probably hurt him more than the punch I had given him, and that seemed to put her in a fine frame of mind. "Good," she exclaimed, "for he really hurt me and deserves it!" Then she grabbed my neck and gave me another peck on the cheek.

"Oh pu-leeease!" Joey wailed, ready to puke. "Get me the sick-bag!"

"Shut up, Joe, and I'll tell you who played the Star Palast here before we came on." That got him interested. "I'll give you a hint," I told him, "it wasn't Bodger and Bulls Hits." He looked blank, so I gave further information. "In fact, it was somebody very famous, so see if you can guess."

"Famous eh? Eric Burdon and the Animals? Billy J. Kramer? The Searchers? The Undertakers?" I kept shaking my head with each new suggestion. "So who is it then?"

"I'll give you a clue. It's not a British group. They're a very famous American outfit. World famous in fact!"

The guessing began again. "Johnny and the Hurricanes? The Ventures? Gene Vincent and the Blue Caps? Buddy Holly and the Crickets?"

"Buddy Holly and the Crickets? He died years ago, you chuff!"

He fought on. "The Four Tops? No? The Beach Boys? No?" He was getting frustrated. "So who is it?"

"Think of a legend, Joe," I suggested.

"Then it has to be Elvis!" he exclaimed with glee, sure that he had finally busted it.

"No it wasn't bloody Elvis, you stupid bugger. He's stuck in Hollywood making crap films, and wouldn't be seen dead in a place like this."

"Then who the fuck was it?" He had come to the end of his tether, so I told him.

"It was Bill Haley and the Comets, mate!"

"You're kidding!" he gasped. He thought about. "I bet they didn't have to sleep in that shitty barrack room! With the kiss curl king and all his entourage there would have been a bleeding long queue waiting for the lav in the mornings."

Heinke butted in to give her opinion. "They were all old men in check jackets, and the singer with that silly curl on his forehead really loved himself," she told us, "but they were quite good in their own way." Then she gave us an ingratiating smile and added, "But they weren't exciting like you are."

"Aye, we are, aren't we!" Joey brightened at the compliment.

She put her hand on his and giggled, "You're sweet, Joey."

Joey may have blushed at this but it was difficult to be certain because of his ruddy complexion. I was a little surprised by what she had said, because although Joey could be described in many ways, most of them less than flattering, I would never have chosen to call him sweet. Thankfully Maria arrived to claim his interest.

Dave appeared soon afterwards. He was alone, which was the probable explanation for why his vaguely handsome features were the picture of dejection. He was clearly not a happy chappie. The ever sympathetic Joe greeted him with an evil smile, "Where's your bird, then? Had a bit of a barney have you?"

"No, I haven't," he answered miserably, "but I did have a difference of opinion with her father."

"How could you have a difference of opinion with her father, when you've never had an opinion in your life?" Joe sniggered.

"He probably forgot the order in which the cutlery is used," I suggested. "But then he only knows how to use a frigging spoon anyway."

Exasperated by the adolescent jibes, Dave decided to explain, if only to make us stop tormenting him with our inane remarks. It turned out that they had enjoyed a good bottle of wine after the meal and were having a pleasant conversation about football. "He's a Liverpool fan, and thinks they're going to do well under the new manager, a bloke called Bill Shankley, whoever he is."

Joey yawned and his eyes glazed over in terminal boredom as he enquired, "Is this going to take long, because I've got a bus to catch."

Dave ignored him, which was usually the best course of action with Joey, and continued with his tale. "By the time we were on the second bottle of wine I was becoming a bit lopsided, and feeling that we were getting along like a house on fire, so I broached the question of the war and how terrible Hitler and the Nazis had been, thinking he would have to agree on that particular issue." He sighed and frowned and otherwise looked as despondent as only Dave could when without the company of a woman. "That was a bit of a mistake," he admitted, "because it turned out that he had been in the SS, and didn't take too kindly to my point of view."

"Well, what happened, then?" we demanded, waiting in tense anticipation for all the gory details.

"Nothing much," he said, to our disappointment. "He just booted me out of the house, and sent Eva packing to her bedroom."

"You should have asked him if you could go with her," Joe taunted him. "That would save you from having to sneak in later."

Despite Dave's misery the evening passed pleasantly enough, and we all had an enjoyable time together. Heinke took my hand as I walked her home with the others crowding behind us, and I felt the thrill of her touch vibrating right into my brain. It was all very innocent and a far cry from the worldly-wise Mai, and I liked it. We agreed to meet again the next day, then she reached up and gave me another peck on the cheek and disappeared into the house leaving me floating and feeling quite pleased with myself.

"Was that all you got?" Joey sneered disdainfully. "Just a peck on the bloody cheek?" He might not have thought it much reward for such a long and enjoyable evening, but I was blissfully content and whistled most of the way back to our base.

It was morning again and we hadn't seen a hair of Stuart's head since Saturday night, which was unusual enough for Joe to comment on the fact, but Dave assured him that he was only enjoying himself at Heidi's flat. "Aye, I know that, but it's still a little worrying isn't it?" Joe mumbled. Joey was not known to worry unduly, but it was obvious that he was concerned. "He said he would see us tonight at the bar but he never turned up, now did he? That's not like him at all," and he knit his brow in concentration as he tried to think what might have happened to Stu.

As we ate our breakfast, the waitress confirmed that he had not put in an appearance there either. It was becoming like Alice in Wonderland, getting curiouser and curiouser by the hour, but we put it to the back of our minds and bantered away with the usual banalities that had very little intellectual stimulus or academic merit but got us through the days.

Heinke popped over in her break to inform us that there was to be a football match on the television and we could all go to watch it in the Black Eagle. "That sounds just like a pub," Joey said, the bright lad.

"That's because it is a pub you gormless git," Dave pointed out. "What did you think it was with a name like that, a frigging haberdashery store? In fact it's the bar we were in all last night." Joey was never one for details so he wouldn't have noticed.

A car pulled up as we crossed the square on our way to the bar, and the driver called to us. "I would like a word with you," and began to scold us for having ruined a perfectly good photo-shoot for The Axemeisters by leaving the souvenirs of our violence on their faces.

"Oh diddums," Joey chuckled cheekily, "we're really sorry about that, aren't we lads?" Then his attitude changed and he became threatening. "Those buggers deserved all they got, mate, so if that's all you've got to say, then fuck off!"

As we wandered on, Dave asked, "Who the hell was that?"

"Dunno," says I, "but it's good to see that Joey hasn't lost any of his legendary tact and diplomacy."

"Bollocks!" Joe sniggered. "I just know how to make friends and influence people that's all."

"Is that why we haven't got any then?" I retorted.

"Got any what?"

Talking with Joe was never easy. "Friends!" I told him. "We've got no frigging friends!" This was true enough, for apart from the girls we had met at the dancehall, we had found neither friends nor acquaintances in Lüneburg, unlike Schleswig where he had both. Joey couldn't see the point in trying, as we would soon be off on our travels again, and this was possibly a valid point.

Much to the disgust of the others I had spent good drinking money on an old English newspaper I had seen in a shop by the square. I scanned through the various pages and an article caught my eye. "Blimey," I gasped, "Arthur Haines the comedian's died!"

I was saddened by the news for old Arthur had given me a laugh or two through the years, but Dave seemed quite upset by the news of his demise. He began to reminisce by regaling us with some of the funny anecdotes he used to crack the audience up with. "Some of his stuff was very risqué," he lectured us, "and he was always getting into trouble, but the audiences loved him and called him the Cheeky Chappie."

Joe and I stopped drinking in mid-sup and stared at each in disbelief. "That's Max Miller you're talking about, you daft sod, and he died years ago!"

"I didn't know that!" Dave looked amazed. "Nobody ever told me," he sighed and looked quite crestfallen. He recovered enough to demand, "Then who's this Arthur Haines, then, because I've never heard of him?"

"I dare say he never heard of you either, mate," Joe retorted, and chuckled at the confusion on his face.

Just after one o'clock Heinke popped in to have her lunch with us. Now that her relationship with Klaus and The Axemeisters had come to an end it seemed that she had chosen our company to cheer her up and make her smile again. For me it was quite flattering because as it had said in the newspaper, I was crackers about her. She smiled at me, she smiled at Dave and she smiled at Joey and made us all happy to be with her. She was bright and bubbly and fun to be with. After having described the intermezzo in the square earlier for her, she could inform us that the gentleman in the car must have been the editor of the local newspaper, and as such we might find ourselves in print once again for having done violence to the local heroes.

When she had left to go back to work, I found Joey eyeing me. "Aren't you going to do something about that girl, Biffo?" he asked. "Don't the words, *mouth and gift horse* mean anything to you, at all, mate?"

I was enamoured by the girl but the truth was that I didn't want to become emotionally involved since we would be leaving in a few days, and I had still not forgotten how wretched I had felt when I had left Schleswig when I had finally got something going with Trudi, and I was even now still haunted by the memory of Henni's beautiful face. She had promised me a nice surprise on her birthday, and I knew I would spend the rest of my life wondering what it was.

The football match was nothing to get excited about, but it did help to pass the time. The highlight of the game came when a fight broke out between the rival fans at a dubious penalty decision, but they could have spared themselves the trouble for the ball went six feet over the cross bar. It was a boring game and we watched it with indifference. Dave commented on the fact that the bald-headed bloke in black didn't seem to be doing anything but running about on his own. He seemed quite perturbed by the fact. "He hasn't kicked that frigging ball once!" he snorted in disgust.

Stuart was slumped on his bed blowing smoke rings when we arrived back at the barrack. He was content and completely at ease. "Oh, there you are," he chuckled, "I was wondering where you shower had been!"

Joey had been worried by his absence, but on seeing him alive and well there was no sign of relief, only irritation. "And just where the fuckin' hell have you been, you fat bugger? We haven't seen hide nor hair of you for two bloody days!"

Stu had been playing the family man, enjoying Heidi's company, watching television, taking short walks around the town and generally behaving himself. "It was great to be away from you shower for a bit, I can tell you," he told us truthfully, and I could understand him. After the weeks we had spent cramped together, I'm sure we could all understand him.

The dancehall could hardly be described as being full when we kicked off our first spot of the night. Sparse was probably a more correct description. Hopefully it would fill up during the course of the evening, but there was no guarantee for this since it was Monday and the punters had already spent their hard-earned cash during the week-end. To depress me even further, Heinke and her friends had still not turned up. There is nothing more dispiriting for a musician, and by now we could loosely claim to be called by that name, than having to perform for an empty hall, but we had a contract to fulfil so we had to go on and play as gut-wrenching as it was.

Judging by their expressions, the others were as despondent as myself. There was no spark, no on-stage banter, simply nothing at all. It was as though we were on automatic pilot. I counted in each new song thinking that the sooner we got through it, the sooner we were closing in on our break so we could escape from the stage to the sanctuary of our table for a beer to anaesthetize ourselves with. I began to feel like a goldfish in a bowl going round and round endlessly but getting nowhere. The only thing to lift my spirits was the arrival of Heinke and her friends who managed to get in a couple of dances before our break. This brief lift was however tempered by the fact that Klaus and his clan had arrived en block and were looking particularly aggressive, which was quite worrying as they outnumbered us considerably.

Before we went back on stage I added a double vodka to my previous intake in the hope that it might brighten me up a bit, but sadly it didn't. Joey called out to me, "Cheer up, Biffo, it could be worse!" So heeding his advice I did try to cheer up, but unfortunately it got worse anyway."

I glanced across to the table where Heinke and her friends sat, and saw that Klaus and two of his cronies were standing over them. Judging by the look on the girls' faces they were clearly not happy at all with his presence there. He was shouting and gesticulating at Heinke. Thankfully Stuart had the presence of mind to restrain me as I was in the process of leaving the stage to go to her assistance, for just then Klaus walked away muttering to himself as he rejoined his cretins at the bar. Bearing in mind the lecture we had received from the manager about causing trouble on the premises and the invariable repercussions from Manfred Müller, it was as well that Peter stopped me.

The second spot was much better with more people in the building and more importantly, on the floor dancing to our music, and this raised our spirits considerably. Even so, it was a relief when the next break came along and I could rejoin Heinke, who had by then calmed down again after Klaus's tongue-lashing.

It's funny how time drags when you're doing something you don't particularly enjoy, but sitting there with such a sweet and charming young girl, time simply flashed by, and I saw that we were soon due to go back on stage again. She nestled up closer to me and asked, "This tour that you're doing must be very exciting, but is it really as exciting as it seems?"

Now that was a question worth thinking about! There had certainly been some highs, but by and large I would have to admit that there had been more lows, and the long hours on stage were back-breaking work for anybody's money. I told her so, then added, "But it's all been worth it to meet you." I meant it, but I said it just to make her happy, and got a smile in return.

She lit up when I told her where we had been playing before. "Schleswig!" she exclaimed with pleasure in her voice. "That's where I was born, and I lived there until a couple of years ago." She knew of the dancehall where we had played, and claimed that Otto the barman was a nice bloke. By was enjoying reliving my days there, but I wasn't expecting what came next. "Did you meet my cousin, Henni?" she trilled. "She is Otto's niece, did you know that?" I almost choked on my beer, then agreed that yes, I did vaguely remember a Henni. Then perhaps you also knew my best friend, Trudi. She is a year older than me but we have been friends since we were at school together. She also goes to the dancehall and is very popular. Did you meet her?"

I was dumbstruck as I listened to her, hardly able to believe what I heard, and wondering what to reply, but I had to say something, so I was honest with her, "Eh, no! I don't seem to recall her at all. Sorry." Just then the lights flashed to indicate that our services were once again required on stage so I had an excuse to extricate myself from what was proving to be a difficult situation. "I'll see you later before I go," she said and planted a kiss on my cheek.

"Go where?" I asked, suddenly feeling despair and disappointment filling my head.

"Home of course," she informed me. "I have to get up early for work, remember?"

Of course she did. Unlike us, she lived a normal life where day was day and night was night, whereas we had turned them a quarter clockwise and no longer knew the difference. My introduction to Heinke's family tree and school-chums had got my mind churning sufficiently to make me lose my concentration and make a number of annoying clangers that had my fellow musicians scowling their irritation at me. Joey finally gave me a bark that brought me back so we sailed through the rest of the set happily enough much to the chagrin of The Axemeister drummer who had been taking a perverse delight at my incompetence.

We spent a few minutes together before we split up for the night. Stu left early with Heidi, and Dave sneaked off with Eva for another night of passion and drainpipe-climbing. To Joey's dismay, Maria decided to take a taxi with Heinke, and that left just me and Joey to disconsolately finish off our drinks at the table.

"That was a really shite night, wasn't it," he commented. "And what the hell was up with you dropping all those clangers? You were a bloody shambles!" He was right there, but he graciously accepted my apologies, and left it at that.

We found our way back to our depressing room when Joey suddenly decided to discuss that evening's less than perfect performance. Apparently he found the post mortem as discouraging as the surroundings, and stopped himself in mid-sentence.

"What are we doing sitting here like two bleeding bookends?" he exclaimed. "The bar on the square's still open, so shift yourself and let's go!"

Frankly I was quite reticent, for I had already had my belly-full and was really ready for bed, but I knew I would never get any peace with Joey moody and restless in the room, so I reluctantly agreed on the condition that we went in the van.

Considering that it was twelve forty-five on a Monday night, there were still quite a few revellers left in the Black Eagle, including a bunch of blokes hunched up around a table drinking and laughing loudly. One of them wore a black leather jacket with the double axe logo on the back. They all stopped what they were doing and stared menacingly at us as we entered. I felt knots of tension tighten in my stomach for we were in a very vulnerable position, and I wished myself back in my creaky old bed at the barracks with the light off and asleep. I mentioned my fears to Joey but he dismissed them by assuring me that they wouldn't start anything inside the premises.

"Right," he said, getting down to business, "are you going to tell me what was up with you tonight, or what?" Knowing full well that he would drag it out of me sometime, anyway, I eventually told him. "Bleeding hell, that was some coincidence and no mistake!"

Having acquired this nugget of information, he bore on. "Now then," he said, "what, if anything, are you going to do about that Heinke?"

"Like what?" I demanded, becoming irritated at him prying into my privates.

"Are you for real! The question is, are you or are you not planning to give her one? For if you fancy her as much as you claim to do, then I would remind you that you're seriously running out of time!"

"The problem is that you and Stu and Dave all have got places you can take the girls, but I haven't."

Grinning broadly Joe chided me, "Are you listening to yourself, stupid? What's up with your bed back at the barracks, or the van? Correct me if I'm wrong, but they were deemed to in order when you were giving that Mai girl her come-uppance"

"I know," I protested, "but that was different."

"Different?" he chuckled to himself. "What d'ya mean, different?"

"It just was!" I snapped at him. "That's all I'm saying about it, okay!" I went to the bar for a refill and was relieved to see that gang who had been giving us the evil eye had left, and we enjoyed our last drink of the evening in peaceful small-talk.

They were waiting when we left the bar at closing time and attacked us without any warning, laying into us good-style without a by your leave. We desperately tried to defend ourselves but we were outnumbered and didn't stand a chance. They soon had us on the ground and used us for kicking practice and the only thing that stopped us from being killed was the arrival of a patrol car that had them fleeing to safety. We could hear them calling to us from a distance, taunting us as we lay on the ground spitting blood.

I felt as though I had been run over by a bus, and must have been black and blue from the kicks I had received. My face was throbbing like hell and I could feel blood all over it, but mainly from my mouth. My lips were as swollen as a cows udder and when I gingerly poked at my gums I realized that I had lost a tooth that would never see Blighty again. I must have looked terrible. Joey certainly did. He sat on the pavement with his head resting on his knees. His face was covered in cuts from the punches he had taken and his bulbous nose was pouring blood. I noticed that he was crying.

Trying to cheer him up, I sidled over to him and we sat there side by side. "What's all this then?" I asked through my bloody, swollen mouth, "Joey the hard-knock crying because of a punch-up. Wonders never cease," I muttered.

He didn't look up. "I'm not crying over the barney you bugger. I'm crying because of the frigging pain, because I've just bitten half my tongue off, and it's killing me," he moaned. Feeling the way I was, I could understand him, because I was ready for a tear or two, myself. But even through my pain I managed a smile at the thought that Joey was only human after all.

We finally managed to pick ourselves up and stagger back to the van and painfully clamber inside. Each movement was a nightmare, and the grimace of pain on Joe's face as he carefully started the engine and eased the clutch out confirmed his suffering. In spite of it all he began to chuckle then quickly broke it off again as a new stab of pain hit him, but the semblance of a smile still lingered on his bleeding lips. "Well, that was fun, wasn't it?"

He steered with his body, stiffly leaning into the wheel with his hands close to his chest and pressing his arms to his sides as though to alleviate some of the throbbing pain in his carcase. "At least it wasn't premeditated," he surmised, "because nobody knew we would be going there." He spoke slowly, like an old man, which was unlike Joe who's mouth usually rattled away like a well-used machinegun. "I didn't see any of those Axemeisters, but they'll be fuckin' chuffed when they hear about this." For a moment the fire sparked in his eye again, so I knew that the old Joey was still in there somewhere. "Biffo, this means friggin' war!" he declared with some determination, then gasped as his sudden excitement ripped some cut in his mouth wider.

After the brutal beating we had just received I had had quite enough of war for this lifetime and the next. "In that case, will you please wait until tomorrow before you start it because right now I'm in pain and all I want is my bed."

"That's the trouble with you, mate. You've got no bleeding sense of adventure!"

The night was long and slow and very painful, but it finally came to an end and we managed to manoeuvre our battered bodies into an upright position. The meeting with the mirror was almost as painful as the night itself, for the sight that met me there confirmed that my face was as cut and swollen and ugly as the one I saw on Joey.

Not surprisingly our appearance raised a few eyebrows when we finally managed to find our way to the café for some sustenance. Heinke was shocked and demanded to know what had happened to us, as she gently caressed me, while Dave merely gasped at the sight of us and stammered incomprehensible sounds as he gaped and stuttered.

"It was just a little accident," Joe informed them. "I fell out of bed face first on the floor and Biffo fumbled about in the dark trying to figure out what the racket was and walked straight into the door."

Dave wasn't convinced. "Do you think I'm stupid or summat!"

"Do I really have to answer that?" Joe wondered, and I could just make out the smirk that tried to put in an appearance on his bruised lips.

They heard our tale in wide-eyed silence, then we had to repeat it for Stuart who had just arrived. There was little sympathy but probably a lot of common sense from our Liverpudlian loverboy. "You're a pair of dozy pillocks going out on your own at that time of night after the warnings we got," he scolded, and reminded me of an old school teacher I had once offended. "Forget it happened and drop it," he demanded, "for there's been enough animosity between us and them already!" He really meant it.

Joe and I nodded our heads in grudging acceptance of the fact, but judging from the glint in his eye, Joey wasn't happy with such a capitulation and was already planning his revenge.

The next few days flashed by without any further unseemly incidents, and we were once again back in the daily routine; get up, go to the café, a couple of hours in the Black Eagle with a beer or two, lunch with Heinke, mooching about the town doing nothing, playing our nightly spot at the Star Palast with Heinke's agreeable company during the breaks. They weren't exciting days, but still preferable to the kind of excitement we had witnessed of late.

Heinke was a lovely girl in every way and I found myself being drawn closer to her with each passing day. Despite the fact that I had promised myself not to become emotionally involved, I realised that I was falling in love, and there was nothing I could do about it, so I relaxed in her company and decided to enjoy it as long as I could.

It was now Thursday and Joe decided that we should walk into town and leave the van in the hope that a rest would do it good and possibly rid it of its aches and pains. We were all cheerful as we partook of our morning meal. All that is, but Stuart who had fallen deep in thought and obviously had something that troubled him. Quite suddenly he got to his feet and left with the parting promise that he would hopefully see us all in the evening.

We wondered at this, and Dave worried in case he didn't show up for the show. *I'll hopefully see you,* Stu had said, and Dave found this declaration somewhat ominous. We discussed what might have been the cause of his obvious despondency, and worried in case he had rowed with Heidi. With the outcome of his previous romantic debacle still fresh in our memories, we prayed that his love-affair with Heidi was still alive and kicking, but with him, you never could tell.

We gradually lost interest in Stuart and his problems and spent the rest of the day just passing time and making small-talk. The drudgery of the rock and roll band on the road waiting to play and with nothing to do while waiting was a withering waste of time and energy, but still part of the devil's contract we had signed to make our music.

Our premonition proved to be well founded. When we arrived back at our lodgings around five o'clock, we found Stuart stretched out on his bed drunk as a lord and dead to the world, with a tell-tale vodka bottle lying empty on the floor.

We stared at him aghast. We were due on stage in two hours and by the look of him, it would take two days to get him out of his comatose state. Joey exploded and screamed abuse at the lifeless form before him. Getting angrier by the minute he popped Stu in the eye, slapped him around the face and even threw a mug of water over his head, but to no avail.

"The frigging, stupid, inconsiderate bastard!" he howled in frustration as he paced the room desperately trying to find a solution to the problem but obviously finding no inspiration. Dave and I followed his every movement in silence as we took in the enormity of it all. Joey finally tired of pacing and slumped heavily down on his bed to light a cigarette and glare daggers at Stuart's dead body.

"What are we going to do now?" Dave asked, clearly perturbed.

Joey considered this very relevant question for a few moments before replying. "If we can't get the bastard to come around, we're going to have to go on without him and hope for the best."

"What do we tell the manager if he asks?" I asked.

"We'll tell him that the bugger's sick," Joe decided.

As it transpired, this was perfectly true, for prior to us leaving for the venue, the group drunk had come around sufficiently to make his way to the toilet, and was calling for Hughie down the big white telephone, when we left. Yes, he was absolutely sick!

It was strange taking the stage with just the three of us, for Stuart was the lead singer and as such had his place in the middle of the line-up, positioned directly in front of me. More importantly, his rhythm chords were missing to back up and fill in the rest of the instruments. It's funny how you never miss something until it isn't there anymore, and just then we were really missing his input. This meant that Joey, bless him, had to work twice as hard to keep everything going. He was a good hardworking guitarist, but now even he was struggling to cope, for when he played one of his sparky solo breaks, the whole number went thin and flat without the constant backing of fill-in chords to keep it moving.

The dancers must have picked up on the fact that one of us was missing and that the sound wasn't what it should be, but they kept dancing. However others found perverse delight in our plight, and in the forefront were Klaus and his cretins with an assortment of their moronic fans. I recognised two of them from the kicking Joe and I had been given a few days earlier. They were all overjoyed at being witness to our struggle on stage and laughed and taunted us with jibes and ribaldry throughout the first set. I glanced at Joe and saw that he was seething with fury, and it was a relief in every way when we could finally escape from the stage to take our first break of the evening.

I was greeted by Heinke's warm smile and a cooling beer as I found our table, and was well pleased to see both. Stuart's girl Heidi, had also found her place among us, so I reasoned that she could not have been the instigator of our problems after all.

Our cosy chat was interrupted by the crowing jibes of Klaus and his merry men as they gathered around our table. Joe decided that he had contained himself long enough and jumped to his feet to confront their leader. Eye-ball to eye-ball he snarled, "Right! You and me outside, now!" This had a calming influence on the gathering, but Joe wanted satisfaction and went on, "C'mon you friggin' weasel, right now!" He was trembling with contained fury. The threat of violence and the rage on Joey's face had them sensibly edging away, although the jibes kept coming as they retreated.

Half-way through our second set, the evening rapidly deteriorated from frustratingly difficult to completely farcical as Stuart staggered on stage and promptly fell in a heap, laughing drunkenly. The undignified mass of wobbling mirth slowly got to his feet and just as slowly crumbled back to the floor again. His appearance had drawn gasps from the audience who had never seen anything like it on the stage before, but it only added to the merriment of the Klaus and his morons who all rushed to the edge of the stage to gloat and jeer at this unannounced spectacle.

Joey's volatile temper finally snapped and he lashed out at the nearest taunter and smashed his foot into his ugly face. The jibes immediately turned to anger as they tried to clamber onto the stage to get at us. Stepping back from their grasping clutches, Joey slipped off his guitar in one swift motion and began to swing it like an axe at them. With the guitar set at a very high volume the sound, each time it connected with a skull, screamed out through the amplifier like The Who on speed. All hell broke loose during the mayhem and the bouncers rushed in belatedly to try to restore some order, but they were too late for Dave and Joey were already off the stage weighing into the nearest protagonists.

Maria was screaming for Joe to stop as she tried to drag him away from the melee and for her trouble received a stray punch that was aimed at Joey. Seeing this, Joe went out of his mind, and roared like a Viking with no ale, and butted the nearest attacker, who happened to be the unfortunate Klaus who went down to writhe on the floor holding his splattered nose, and probably wishing he had stayed at home to do his knitting.

The combined forces of the bouncers and the newly-arrived politzei finally managed to break things up. I noticed the policemen looking in our direction with an expression on their faces that seemed to say *not them again*, as the survivors staggered back to their seats now that the cabaret was over.

Klaus was stretched out on the floor where Joey had put him, lying in a pool of blood. He was not having a particularly good week. Some of his henchmen were in various stages of distress after their meeting with Joey's trusted Telecaster, which had apparently suffered no damage.

I had remained on the stage throughout the affair, a spectator with the best seat in the house. "Thanks a lot, Biffo," Joe said sarcastically, "it was kind of you to give us a hand there!"

"I thought you were doing alright on your own, mate," I answered sheepishly. "I've already lost one tooth thanks to you, and I'm happy with what I've still got left," I excused myself with.

Joey bucked up. He was back to the old Joey again, brimming over with confidence and full of himself. It was good to have him back. "Aye, you're right," he agreed, "I was doing alright on me own, and I particularly enjoyed decking that smug bugger, Klaus. That really made my day!" He was glowing.

Stuart was not. The town drunk was still lying in a heap on the stage where he had collapsed and had slept through the whole fiasco and missed all the fun.

Of course this was not the end of the matter, and the police began to take statements from all of those involved. I figured that this was going to take some time so I found my place at the table where Heinke was waiting, still wide-eyed at what she had seen. "I was rather hoping I could take happier memories than this with me from Lüneburg," I sighed.

"You have," Heinke quite rightly pointed out. "You have me." She giggled breathlessly, and took me by the hand to lead me out of the dancehall to our quarters to spend a little time together. At last …

We returned a little later just in time to see some of the walking wounded making their way out. As we entered the hall I caught sight of Klaus being helped out, supported by a couple of his cronies, all of them looking decidedly second-hand. I had hoped that the fiasco would have been boxed in and smoothed over by then, but waiting for me to arrive back at the table were my musical associates, a police officer and Herr Sneider who was looking none too pleased.

"I have told the officer here that you were put under tremendous pressure tonight by these hooligans, and they will therefore not be pressing charges against you," he told us stiffly. We all breathed a sigh of relief at this news. "However," he continued, "I should send you all packing right now because of your behaviour and report you to Manfred Müller." The worry returned to show on our features. "Unfortunately I don't have a replacement group until Saturday so you will perform here as usual tomorrow before moving on to Kiel to take up your residency there." This lightened us somewhat. "And I have chosen not to report this matter to Herr Müller because you have otherwise performed admirably during your stay here." That really brought us back on top.

With his confidence restored, Joey had the temerity to ask if it would be Bodger and the Bulls Hits who would be replacing us. "Certainly not!" The words were clipped and very German. "They caused mayhem at the dancehall in Schleswig, vandalised their quarters and set fire to the stage." Old Bodger and his band had been sent home in disgrace after three days, just as we had predicted, but the thought struck me, if we were still here after all the problems we had caused, what else had Bodger been up to?

Our hopes of an early evening were quashed when the manager gleefully insisted that we get back on stage and play until midnight so we grudgingly returned to work relieved that we still had a job at all. With Stuart finally back in the land of the living we managed to complete the rest of the evening without any further hitches.

"Wake up and smell the coffee, Biffo," chuckled Joey as he passed me a steaming cup of what I needed to start the day. I could never understand how he managed to be so cheerful in the morning, or for that matter, actually be up so early at all, but he was always the first on his feet and playing mother before anyone else had even stirred.

I rubbed my eyes vigorously to remove the sleep from them and to enable me to focus on my surroundings. I looked around to see that for the first time since God knows when, we had actually all spent the night under the same roof, which was now something of a rarity. It must have been a hell of a night, for the life of me I couldn't remember Stu and Dave coming in.

With the coffee warming my innards and giving resuscitation to my brain the events of the previous evening came flooding back to me with vivid clarity. The extraordinary scenes at the dancehall, the punch-ups and general free for all, and Joey weighing in like a berserk Viking as he wielded his Telecaster like a battle axe, Stuart drunk as a toad and twice as ugly, finally finding my way with Heinke, and the news that we were to move on to Kiel on Saturday.

There wasn't the usual sparky atmosphere within the confines of the barrack room this particular morning, for we were all engaged with our own thoughts and the fact that this would be our last full day in Lüneburg. The memories of the past two weeks kept running through my mind, the good, the bad and the downright ugly. I had previously made up my mind that I would not get emotional when it was time to leave, unlike in Schleswig where a night-time telephone call had us packing and out of the place before we even knew it. The suddenness of our departure had made it impossible to say our goodbyes to people who had become important to us. For me that was a wretched feeling and I was determined that I would not allow it to happen again. But I knew that the hardest part would be to leave Heinke, for she had grown on me and I knew I would miss her. However, this time, I would at least be able to bid her farewell.

That night we gave it our all and played like there was no tomorrow, which in a way, there wasn't. It was the least we could do for all the punters who had supported us through our stay, and we really wanted to leave a lasting impression that people would remember us by, so we played our hearts out for them, and then some.

Then it was over, and the moment we had dreaded eventually arrived. We said our final goodbyes with heavy hearts and many tears, Stuart to Heidi, Dave to Eva, Joey to Maria, and me to the lovely Heinke.

I turned to Joey as he started up the van the next morning, "Can you do me a favour Joe, because it's important to me?" I asked. "Can we call in at the café just one more time, please?" I actually said please to Joe!

"Why not," he replied, "a bit of breakfast will set us up for the journey, eh!" he replied with a chuckle and a knowing wink.

"Ta, Joe," I said feeling grateful, "I owe you one."

"You don't owe me owt," he said and gave me a friendly smile, "just let's not be too long, okay?"

Heinke's face was a picture when she saw me come through the door and we were overjoyed to be reunited again if only for a short while, but it was a bitter-sweet reunion and much too short, and we soon found ourselves saying our goodbyes once again, knowing that this time they would be final and we would never see each other again. She followed me to the van and held my hand through the open window as Joey impatiently drummed his fingers on the steering wheel eager to take off on our travels. She reached up to give me a last kiss, whispered, "Don't forget me, Biffo, ever!" and wiped the tears from her eyes as she watched us drive away. I never did …

Silence ruled inside the confines of the van as we drove away and stayed with us for many miles. I studied the route map to try to take my mind off my misery, and I noticed how intensely Joey studied the road ahead, no doubt concentrating to forget. As irritating as his chatter could be, I needed him to talk if only to break the silence that had built up on the journey so far. The longer it lasted the harder I found it to say anything at all.

Joey was an in-yer-face, noisy, grinning hooligan who became very aggressive if anyone rattled his cage and could start a riot in an empty room, or as he had just proved, in a very full one. But he also had a softer side and a more caring nature that was totally at odds with the image he projected, and I could see that he was already missing Maria as much as I was missing Heinke. I know he thought a lot of her, despite his protests that another bus would soon be on the way, ding, dong, there's always room on top, and the like, he was definitely very fond of her, and was as miserable at having to leave her as his passengers were for having to leave their own girls behind.

We were now heading for Kiel, which was a much bigger place than those we had played at so far on the trip, and I imagined that it would therefore be more difficult to make an impact on the punters there. We would also be playing at Germany's biggest Star Palast, and longer hours than before, all under the watchful eyes of the infamous Manfred Müller and the ominous Black Bob, and none of these prospects had reason to raise my spirits.

I could hear Snitch and Snatch awakening from their slumbers in the back seat as they stretched and yawned. Looking anxious, Dave asked if we could soon stop because he felt a pressing need to do so, but all thoughts of easing his bladder were forgotten when a green light suddenly appeared and began to flash on the dashboard. Joey noticed it, but decided to ignore it. After a minute or two with no reaction, I felt compelled to anxiously enquire about what it might mean, but was not exactly reassured by the answer I got.

"Dunno," Joey replied, as he stared fixedly at the road before him, "got no idea." He banged the dashboard with his fist without looking at it. "Has it stopped now?" he asked with hope in his voice.

"Sad to report, Joe, but no, it's still flashing," I told him.

"Oh, bollocks!" he moaned, which did nothing to hearten me.

"It's probably the oil warning lamp," Stuart suggested. As if he knew anything! "When was the last time you put oil in?"

"I haven't," Joe replied. "I only bought the bloody thing to bring us over here, and the only thing I've put in is petrol."

"Well that'll go a long way in explaining all the rattling noises from the engine, won't it you dozy bugger!" Stu chided him. "It's just metal grinding on metal. You need lubrication, you sod! You should know what that is by now."

With this intelligence registered, we stopped at the first garage we came to and Joe scuttled off to purchase a gallon of oil which he immediately poured into the hole marked oil. It was as well that it was marked or he might have put it into any opening that presented itself, as was his wont. "How much do I need to put in?" Joey asked, clearly confused, and got an answer from Stuart that had little bearing on the problem at hand.

"Stop pouring, Joe!" I shouted at him. "The oil's running out of the bottom of the engine!" He stopped immediately with dismay written on his face, but the oil kept coming and made an ever increasing puddle that spread out on the fore-court. The garage owner would be less than happy with this development, so we scrambled back inside and quickly made our escape. Four pairs of eyes could register that the green light had stopped flashing, but the constant knocking and grinding had not, and now we were beginning to get really worried.

With only twenty miles to go, we decided that if we drove quickly we might just make it to our destination before the van died on us, so Joey resolutely drove on with the accelera-tor pressed down as hard as he dared. The gods of dysfunc-tional layabouts and abysmal drivers must have looked down and taken pity on us, for we eventually arrived in Kiel to a collective sigh of relief from all involved. Now all we had to do was to find the Star Palast.

In his infinite wisdom, and fearing that he might lose the paper on which it had been written, Joey had copied it onto his cigarette packet, feeling that he wouldn't lose that as he could actually feel it in his pocket. Very reassuring, he had informed us, and we all agreed with his reasoning, even go-ing as far as to praise him for his ingenuity. Unfortunately, unbeknown to the rest of us, on finishing his last cigarette he had thrown the pack out of the van window since it was empty anyway.

This suddenly dawned on him as we parked by a curb in the middle of Kiel, and he sat hunched over the steering wheel looking forlorn as we berated him for his stupidity. To add to our woes, we were parked facing the wrong way on a one-way street, which explained why every car that passed us gave a severe blast on their horns.

But soon we had something else to worry about as flashing blue lights announced the arrival of a politzei patrol car that pulled up behind us. I watched the officers climb out and begin to circle the van then engage in the time-honoured pastime of kicking the tyres. They checked Joey's papers and seemed to find them in order. When they finally understood that we were an English group looking for the Star Palast, they lightened up, apparently used to people like us being helpless imbeciles, and they became helpful. They gave us detailed instructions on how to get to our destination, but saw from the dim expression on Joey's face and the meaning-less nodding of his head that he had no idea what they were trying to tell us, so they conferred, and decided to show us the way themselves. "Follow us," one of them commanded, so we did, to Joey's great delight. He was wreathed in smiles at the thought of having a police escort. "Bloody hell," he chuckled, "I bet Bill Haley didn't get a police escort to his gig!"

Stuart immediately put him in his place. "That's because their driver didn't lose the fuckin' piece of paper with the ad-dress on it!"

Suddenly we were there. We piled out of the van to stand in awe looking at the impressive Star Palast building before us. We had finally found the Holy Grail at the end of our journey. It was huge with four sets of double doors leading into it and a short flight of steps that stretched the length of the building. We gleefully congratulated our leader for getting us here and for having got us on a tour that would put us on stage at such a fantastic venue.

With the help of an employee we finally had our equipment stacked on the stage, and could relax and take in our new surroundings. Joey lit a cigarette and was roughly reprimanded by our helper, "Nein! Rauchen verboten!" he exclaimed. Joe stumped it on his amplifier and looked irritated. I sat on a drum and stared around me in awe. The place was huge. The dance-floor must have had room for a thousand dancers, and around it were numerous tables and chairs standing on lush red carpeting. There was also an upstairs area with a veranda sticking out, and the walls had enormous murals that depicted Arabs with lecherous grins and sexy women as naked as the day they were born.

"Ah, gentlemen, there you are!" a voice called from the room, and I looked up to see someone approaching us. "I am Manfred Müller," he said. He was younger than I had thought, and stocky. He wore a sharp dark-blue suit and had rings on every finger. His hair was sleeked back and a smile played around his clean-shaven face, but it was his eyes that fascinated me, for although the smile reached them, there was something more sinister hiding behind them.

"I have heard good reports about you from Schleswig and Lüneburg," he told us, "but even so, I would like to hear you myself, so do you mind?" He indicated now, and he was obviously not used to being disappointed, so we plugged in and gave him a vocal harmony rendition of the Beatles' *If I fell*. Judging by the expression on his face he seemed to enjoy it. Apparently someone else also fell for it, for we heard clapping coming from th back of the hall, and watched as a tall woman with a mass of black curly hair and a pout the size of a monkfish wriggled towards us in a very tight and short purple dress.

"This is Magda, my wife," Manfred introduced her, and took a grip looking pleased with himself, "and she is a very sexy lady." To prove the point, she sat down on a chair and crossed her legs provocatively revealing acres of thigh and jerking her leg up and down as she let the heel of her shoe slip to dangle in mid-air. She smiled wickedly, showing more teeth than a piranha, for she knew full well the effect her presence was having on us.

The next person to come out of the shadows to join our happy throng was as black as spades. He didn't walk, but gracefully glided across the floor. "This is my friend and partner, Bob," Manfred announced.

So this was Black Bob of whom Lonnie had warned us. I had never seen anyone so black before. Apart from the whites of his eyes and his pearly whites, one of which had a diamond screwed into it, he was completely black. He wore a jet-black suit, black shirt and black tie, and everything inside them was as black as black could be. He circled us slowly looking us over without embarrassment, smiling to himself as he assessed our assets. It was obvious that Black Bob was no threat to the ladies, and I certainly felt uncomfortable under his scrutiny, feeling like a slave in the marketplace and not liking it.

"You will be sharing the bill with another group called Mozzletof and alternate with them every hour," Manfred informed us. "You will start at seven and finish at one thirty." He positively beamed at us, perhaps expecting applause for this announcement. It was heartbreaking news for it meant we would be stuck there for six and a half hours and not be finished until well into the night when we would be tired and the girls would have departed.

He then ordered our happy helper to show us to our quarters, and we were led down a long corridor, then down two flights of stairs to find our place of rest. The sight that greeted us was a staggering shock to the system, that made our home in Schleswig seem like Buck House. The room was twenty feet long and six across with two double iron-framed bunk beds, one small table and one chair. The décor was soul destroying with walls painted in dark grey gloss paint, the floor was concrete and there were two large pipes suspended from the ceiling.

For our further delight we were shown to the toilet which was in the corridor under the stairs. It was so small you would have to crawl out to have a fart, the mirror was cracked and there were two dirty towels and a block of Wehrmacht issue soap.

As I lay on my chosen lower bunk I closed my eyes and thought, Fucking hell! This is terrible! I felt like a prisoner banged up for a long stretch, but I'm sure they would have had better accommodation in jail. Could life get any more depressing than this? We were to play from seven to late in the night, and only have this grey grotto to fall back on and find some relaxation. Judging by the moaning around me the others felt as badly as I did. Stuart was whining about having to sleep in the upper bunk, claiming that he couldn't stand heights, but the one moaning most was Dave, who was quite adamant that he wasn't kipping in this castle, saying, "How d'ya expect me to bring a girl back here? I'd have to give her a leg up before I could even get me leg over! That's hardly romantic, now is it?"

"It might have helped if we had some windows to look through once in a while," Stu pointed out.

"And look at what exactly?" Joe wondered.

"I don't know," said Dave now getting really depressed, "anything, I suppose."

Actually we did have some windows. They were two thin strips of frosted glass that allowed us the view of peoples feet as they walked by, for we were below pavement level, deep in the bowels of the building.

Stu moved his ample body on the bunk above me and demanded that I pass his guitar to him. He struck a couple of chords then launched into Tom Jones' latest offering. *As I sit and look around me, at these four grey walls that surround me, I think yeah I'm only dreaming, as I walk down the lane with hairy Mary, feeling like a Black Bob fairy ...*

We all laughed at his impromptu performance and realised that moaning and groaning was going to get us nowhere, and that we would just have to get on with it and get through it all somehow, for someday we would look back on this and laugh, hopefully.

To escape from our prison cell, we decided to reconnoitre the area to find a watering hole, and soon found one that suited our requirements. Our noisy entrance did attract attention but by now we were used to the stares of curiosity so we just let it ride and ignored them. The waitress came over to take our order. As it happened, she was blonde and blue-eyed, but fortunately for me, this time, not attractive, which was a blessing considering the emotional upheaval other blonde blue-eyed waitresses had caused me recently.

Our first spot in Kiel was exactly as feared. We began by playing to an empty hall completely devoid of customers with only the bouncers cum waiters idly chatting away at the back of the hall without taking a blind bit of notice of us. I reckoned that the invisible man would have had a higher profile. Consequently, the enthusiasm of our performance never rose above the ordinary, for after all, what was the point? People began to drift in during our time on stage but despite this, not one dancer appeared on the dance-floor before us. I sat behind my drums and fervently wished that the stage would swallow me up and take me away from the misery of it all. When it was finally over, I slunk off the stage and found a table right at the back of the hall to drown my sorrows and watch as the Mozzletoff battled on.

Our second set was a good deal better than the first simply because there were actually some dancers on the floor, which always helps. However, we still had no reason to feel any great enthusiasm for there was little enough of it inside the building and certainly not enough to go around and spread any cheer. The next break found me sitting at a table with Joey, both more or less despondent. Stu and Dave had disappeared to try to lure any available frauleins to their charms. "Tell you what, Joe," I offered, "we'll go to the bar across the road for our next break, just to get away from this place for a bit." He found this to be an agreeable suggestion, not least because the drinks were cheaper there than where we were.

As Dave and Stu were still desperately prowling the forest of heaving humanity in the hope of finding a suitable prey, Joe and I crossed the road alone to enjoy some peace in the bar there. Compared to the heaving hordes of the Star Palast this was an oasis of calm, but after Lüneburg it was very lonely, and we spent our break in monosyllabic conversation.

When we had finally finished for the night we found our way back to the bar to try to deaden the depression we both felt at the prospect of spending our first night in our new penthouse suite. Despite the late hour there were quite a few revellers chatting and laughing and generally enjoying themselves, which only seemed to widen the gap between their exuberance and our own mood of despondency. I thought, *don't these people know that they are in the same room as Joey The Nose, the unassuming carrot-topped superstar and a veritable legend within the confines of his own esteem!*

Joe had gone very quiet again as he stared blankly through the haze of smoke from his umpteenth cigarette. Wherever he was, it wasn't where I was sitting. "Missing Maria, Joe?" I ventured to enquire.

Jolting back from wherever he had been, he replied, "What do you think?" and frowned. I had rarely before seen Joe looking so frail and, dare I say it? Human. "What about you" he asked, "don't you miss that Heinke?"

"Yeah," I sighed, "she was a lovely lass and I really do miss her," I admitted.

Before our conversation could develop into a misty-eyed meeting of the lonely hearts club, Dave and Stu arrived looking considerably gloomier than when we had last seen them, so then the lonely hearts club band was complete and we could set the meeting.

"What's up with you two?" Joey enquired, suddenly brightening at the sight of their crestfallen expressions.

"We never got as much as a nibble all night," Stu moaned.

"The girls didn't want anything to do with me, either," Dave whined. He seemed to be in shock, and his eyes were wide in amazed disbelief. This kind of thing had obviously never happened to him before. It was a first, and therefore a new experience that he didn't know how to deal with.

The dynamic duo's fall from grace had Joe back in high spirits and he was chuckling away again enjoying their misery. Joe was back! "There's always another day," he comforted them, "and we'll all get lucky tomorrow," he assured us.

"Tomorrow's a Sunday, and the place is closed," Stuart pointed out, "so there's no chance." He had been unhappy before, but after hearing his own words and realising their implication, he became even more morose.

I consoled myself by thinking, *Does it really matter? Do we really need all this shit, anyway?* It had been a depressing day!

Whatever was coursing through the pipes was certainly producing enough heat, for the temperature in our cell was akin to a sauna. The sweat was pumping out of me by the bucketload and my mouth was so dry that I could barely feel my tongue. I rushed to the sink tap to try to quench my thirst but on tasting the water I immediately spat it out again for it tasted foul. I had to have something down my throat in a hurry, so I quickly got dressed and headed for the door hoping to find a café that was open. Joey heard me, and promised to follow in my footsteps.

Porthos and D'Artagnan had apparently also found the prospect of remaining in the cell too daunting, and they arrived with Joe to partake of some breakfast. Joey informed me that Dave had been studying the map before he left our abode.

"I know they speak funny English here, Dave," I told him, "but if you're still confused, then rest assured, we are nowhere near Carlisle."

"I know that, you bugger!" he snapped back. "If you must know, I was looking to see how far we are from Schleswig." This stopped us for a moment. "I just thought that with us being here, and Schleswig being not that far, we might, well, you know, sort of drive up there and, you know, meet up with a few old friends, like."

"A few old friends!" Stuart snorted, having left none behind after his love-life debacle there. "You mean, like Doris, right?"

"Well, yeah," Dave grudgingly admitted, and seemed ill at ease.

"Your daft!" Stu decided. "It's Sunday so the dancehall's closed and you'd have to go and knock on her door. Now who do you think will be there to open it, eh? It'll be her old fellah, who almost killed you last time you met him. Now what are you going to say to him? *Please can Doris come out to play with me?*" He mimicked the words then snorted derisively. Then he began to chuckle. "Or perhaps Adolf will be at the door to finish his meal."

Dave had become quite morose, but he blanched visibly at the mention of Adolf, and I thought I saw a slight tremble to his mouth. That dog had certainly made an impression on his mind as well as his body. Stuart's reminder of Adolf's existence had blunted Dave's enthusiasm for a sentimental journey back in time, and he was going down quicker than a punctured inner tube.

Schleswig was only thirty miles away from where we were and wouldn't take too long to reach in the van, should it actually make it there at all, but even Joey's suggestion that we could just go and pop into Otto's bar was met with little enthusiasm from Stu.

Joey clearly wasn't happy that Stuart had put the brakes on his bright idea, for it was his van, and if he wanted to go, then why not? He knew that his first Maria would probably be found in Otto's place whether the dancehall was closed or not. I was with him on this one, for if Maria was there, then Trudi would be there with her, and perhaps the beautiful Henni would also put in an appearance? I smiled at some memory and enthused, "I'm with you, Joe. Let's go for it!"

But as always it was Stu, the voice of reason, who brought us back to earth with a bang. "Listen, you load of misty-eyed, love-sick morons," he charmingly addressed us. "You're forgetting something here. Things move on and never stay the same. Other groups have been there since we left, including Bodger and his mob, and the girls will be hooked up with somebody else by now." He was really laying it on thick, and we slid further down in our seats at each word he spoke. "Do you really think they'll be sitting around twiddling their thumbs pining impatiently hoping that we might condescend to return?" He was derisive in his assault. "Well, I don't think so, and if you do then you're all a bigger load of idiots than I thought!"

The smug bugger was right, of course, and we knew it. The next few minutes were spent in silent reflection with the only sound coming from the spoons as they stirred the coffee and the occasional match that was struck to light yet another cigarette. It was going to be a long day.

To try to cheer us up, we found our way to a bar to have a drink or two, but even that failed to produce any spark between us, for we had all day to do nothing, and nothing isn't much when you have all day to do it. Everyone seemed to become lethargic. It was hardly surprising, when we had come from the warmth and friendship of some wonderful girls to the cold and unwelcoming misery we had so far received here.

The spiral of depression deepened when I broached the subject that had been nagging me for a day or two, for we would soon be going back home, and apart from the doubts about the van's reliability there was the important issue of how we were going to pay for the ferry. I therefore informed my audience, that although we had some coins in our pockets for the moment, we would have to become more prudent with its use in the next couple of weeks, in order to put aside sufficient capital to get us home.

Our finances had hardly been sufficient on the trip, and we had been forced to choose between food and drink, and had therefore eaten very little, but times were now about to become even harder.

The lads rather reluctantly agreed with my reasoning, as we really had no option but to save if we were ever going to get back home, and by now, I think we were all ready to make that journey. So overnight, life went from not too good, to pretty damned lousy as we saved what we could and doing so by doing nothing. Even less of nothing than we had been doing before. Our main pastime was to lie in our bunks in the cell, idly chatting about nothing in particular, sleeping, waking up, scratching and fallen back to sleep again, all interspersed with moaning, groaning and whining.

Who said rock and roll on the road was a high?

After a day or two of constant misery we could finally stand it no longer, and found our way to a bar, where the warmth and chatter brightened our spirits considerably. As the evening wore on we were relaxed and happy for the first time in days, and especially so when a group of frauleins came to sit at a nearby table. This had Stu and Dave vibrating and trying to attract their attention as best they could. Although they were pleasant enough towards us, Stuart's winsome smile and Dave's electric sexuality didn't seem to impress them, and they soon left, leaving Stu miserable and Dave dejected and in shock, wondering if he had lost his magic.

After this night out of our cell it was back to basics, which meant being locked in a cycle of boredom, playing the long hours into the night and spending the rest of the time alone in our cell waiting for our sentence to pass and longing for the freedom that would follow.

Mozzletoff were replaced on the bill by Tony Jackson's All Stars. He had been in the Searchers and I was looking forward to seeing him perform. Unfortunately I never got the chance because the group turned up without Tony, and the All Stars were a useless band of nobodies, and Manfred sent them packing after only two nights. In a brief meeting with Manfred and the dubious Black Bob, we were informed that because The All Stars had been sacked, he would be bringing in Tony Sheridan and his group for one night only on Saturday.

Posters were plastered all over town with pictures of Germany's top musical pin-up, and people seemed to be very excited about the fact that he would be putting in an appearance. I knew of him because of his association with The Beatles when they had been over here battling there way through similar slogging sessions as we were now. It was the record they had made with him that had first brought them to the attention of Brian Epstein.

Saturday arrived and I found myself looking forward to the evening when Tony Sheridan would be gracing us with his presence, a fact that was generating considerable excitement among the Star Palast staff, which I found odd since they must have had bigger stars there before.

We afforded ourselves a cup of coffee at a café, but Dave had pressing engagements elsewhere and wandered off promising to see us before the show, leaving us wondering what was what. Stu offered the suggestion that he had finally found himself a woman, then admitted that he himself had caused some female interest the previous evening and thought that his chances were good for the night. This news weighed heavily on Joey as he had no prospects himself. I wasn't too happy to hear it either, because if they were lined up it would mean that I would be stuck with Joey for company, and that could be trying at the best of times.

To my surprise, Stu agreed to take a walk though the town to pass the time. Stuart, walking? It was a miracle! It didn't take long before he decided he had walked far enough, so we stopped at a café for a coffee. There were tables and chairs outside on the pavement where people sat as they enjoyed their meal. Looking at them, Stu commented, "This used to be a regular occurrence back in Liverpool when I was a kid, with people eating and drinking on the pavement," he told us, "only then it was called eviction."

As expected, the Star Palast was heaving that evening with excited fans waiting to see Tony Sheridan, and his arrival on stage was greeted with wild enthusiasm, and he milked his popularity for all it was worth, although on hearing him play, I couldn't really understand why he was so popular at all. It must have had something to do with the fact that he had rubbed shoulders with the Fab Four, because he really wasn't all that good.

I spotted him later in the foyer as he sat with a young sex-goddess draped all over him like a curtain. She was quivering with excitement that he had actually chosen her to grope, for his hands were all over her nubile young body and she was loving it. By the smug look on his face this was just another willing fraulein and one of many.

This romantic interlude was suddenly interrupted as he pushed the girl from him and sprang towards me with an angry glare on his face, and accused me of throwing peanuts at him. Peanuts? He must have been nuts himself, for I wouldn't touch them. I was somewhat taken aback by this sudden confrontation, and thought that he was about to bop me, but Manfred came over and smoothed things over by informing him that it had been the toilet lady. One look at her was enough to drive him back into the arms of his lady of the night, and forget my existence.

I wandered across the road to the bar and soon found myself in pleasant conversation with the group of girls we had met a few days earlier. We were really getting along quite well, and I was especially making contact with a dark-haired girl with an easy laugh and an interest in what I had to say, which was unusual. In fact, things were going so well that they had to be spoiled, which they were on Joey's untimely arrival. On seeing me in convivial female company, he jumped in with both feet and took full control, placing himself firmly in the middle of the ring and the centre of attention. Unfortunately, his audience was not impressed by his performance, but he kept trying regardless of the lack of response.

Stu entered with a girl on his arm. "Let me introduce you to, er, Astrid," he said. I had to smile. We seemed to be picking the girls by name, so we would remember them without too much difficulty. Schleswig Astrid had been ample but the Astrid who now stood before me was slim and attractive with an engaging smile, and very pleasant. "Is Joe having any luck with those frauleins?" he asked me.

I looked over at him, busy at work. "I doubt it, mate," I said, "but you have to give him ten out of ten for trying!"

The dark-haired girl slid along the bench towards me. She smiled and indicated Joey. Doesn't he ever stop?" she asked with a chuckle.

"Only when he's asleep," I told her, and knew it to be the truth.

We were getting along like a house on fire and I was thinking that I had actually managed to make another conquest, feeling the adrenalin pumping, when she suddenly informed me that she had to go because her fiancée had finished his shift. I watched as she walked away with the barman, and felt even more dejected and stupid than usual. Joey's captive audience had also had enough and took to the road leaving the two of us looking like Laurel and Hardy on a bad day.

I woke up with the smell of Joey's feet in my nostrils, which hardly made a good start to the day, and the memory of what might have been but wasn't, still clinging to me from the night before. The ginger man was fast asleep with a stupid grin still on his face. The silence from the upper bunks confirmed that the dubious duo had spent the night elsewhere, and the only movement came from the occasional sets of feet that passed by the slits of glass that claimed to be windows. It promised to be another day of misery.

Monday and Tuesday flashed by in another blur of boredom as we remained in bed until we could stand it no longer then got up to sit around sighing. It was a depressing time. Even Joey seemed down in the mouth and didn't try to hide the fact. "The last few days have driven me round the bloody bend with boredom," he told me. "The others are staying in bed all day, but I'm not hanging about to listen to them moaning." So we wandered out into much-needed fresh air.

"At times like these, I wish I had a really good dose of diarrhoea," he said as we walked to the car park, "at least I'd have something to occupy my mind." Then he brightened up. "I know," he exclaimed with glee, "we can take a trip in the van!"

"Is that wise?" I countered, thinking about the state of it, and the fact that we were due for home in a few days.

"No problem!" he insisted. "What's the worst that could happen? I keep telling you, you've got no sense of adventure!"

"Joe," I sighed, "in the past weeks I've had enough adventures to last me a lifetime."

"Then one more aint gonna make any difference!" he exclaimed, and claimed the point. He rubbed his hands together like Scrooge at the sight of a penny. "Right, then, we're off to Schleswig!"

I looked at him as if he had grown another nose. "Schleswig," I howled, "that's sixty miles there and back!"

He shuffled his feet and mumbled, "Yeah, but I miss Maria and want to see her again." He glanced at me and sheepishly admitted, "I've been thinking a lot about her lately."

So with the argument won, he started the van and we headed for Schleswig with Joe in particularly high spirits even to the extent of singing the song Stu had once taunted him with, *Maria*. I thought I was going to be sick!

However, how long was Adam in paradise? I have no idea, but I know that our stay with our heads in the clouds was short-lived, for no sooner had we left the city of Kiel behind us when a grinding sound came at us from under the van followed by a dramatic drop in speed, before Joey stopped to ascertain what the problem was. He stuck his head into the engine, and he rolled under the vehicle, and would probably have stood on his head if he thought it would help, but came out from both areas looking bewildered and quite obviously didn't have a clue about what he was looking for or where he might find it.

Even Joe had to agree when I decided that Schleswig was now out of the question and we should make our way back to Kiel, assuming of course, that we could manage to start the motor at all. After a little prayer and a lot of patience, the motor did eventually start, and we limped our way back at the top speed of fifteen mph, accompanied from start to finish by the continuous grinding noise that jarred our nerves and rattled our tonsils.

We had just crossed the bridge spanning the Kiel Canal when Joey's rust-heap went bang and smoke immediately filled the van. There was a shudder, then it gave up the ghost. As it happened, we were on a downhill slope that allowed us to drift to within walking distance of our lodgings before the van came to a final standstill.

Joe sat still and silent for several minutes, gripping the steering-wheel as he stared blankly into the distance. Not a word was said as the awful reality began to sink in; we were due to leave for England in three days and our faithless van had finally expired in the gutter in Kiel.

I eventually broke the silence by stating the obvious. "That sounded pretty terminal to me, Joe." There was no reaction.

Wherever he was, it was obvious that he preferred to stay there. "So what, if anything, do we do now?" I asked to try to get some kind of response.

He considered this for some time, weighing the pros and cons before he delivered his verdict. "We can push it," he said.

"Push it?" I gasped. "What, all the friggin' way home?"

"No, just to The Star Palast. You push and I'll steer it." The bugger had it all worked out. Some passing people kindly came to our assistance and we finally managed to manoeuvre the dead beast back to its temporary home and probable final resting place.

When I had got my breath back I demanded to know, what now?

"Sop panicking, will you," he said, trying to reassure me. "I'll fix it. I'm good with me hands. Don't you remember how I fixed that bog back in Schleswig?"

I had to concur, but made the point that the toilet had not had four wheels, a blown engine and a broken gearbox.

"Don't worry," he said, "I've got a toolbox so I'll fix it, I promise!"

This information added to my gloom, for I knew that the toolbox contained a seven pound lump hammer, a moveable spanner that didn't actually move, a chisel, a screwdriver, an assortment of rusty spanners and an empty oil can. Here was a ginger-haired idiot who had never thought to put oil into the vehicle when it was still alive and more or less kicking, and who didn't even know where to put it when the suggestion had been made, and now he was going to "fix it" and bring it back to life … I always wanted to have faith in Joey, but frankly I now saw us all having to hitch-hike back to Blighty.

To really make my day, Manfred informed me that I would have to fill in for the drummer in the other group because he had fallen ill. This meant that I would be playing none-stop from seven to one-thirty in the morning, first with my own band and then with the other. The only offering he was prepared to make was to allow me a ten minute break between each session. Needless to say I was completely shattered by the end of this marathon session, and I honestly thought that my wrists were broken. I was so tired that I fell asleep in the bar at the end of the night, only to be woken by my comrades when it was my turn to buy. Heartless buggers!

At least we didn't have to bother our brains about how to spend our time the next day, for that was unfortunately already pre-ordained; the three of us were to sit on the wall outside, chain-smoking while we watched Ginger Joe fix the van as promised.

Because of the predicament we now found ourselves in, we were up with the larks and ready to go. I cast a glance or two in Joey's direction and noticed that he wasn't exactly brimming with confidence. In fact, he looked more like someone on a one-way trip to the gallows. "You alright, Joe?" I asked. "D'ya reckon you can manage to fix it?"

He shrugged his shoulders and gave a weak smile. "I don't know. I honestly don't."

This was not what I wanted to hear, because I was relying on him to do so, and if he didn't, then, quite frankly, we were up the river without a paddle or a boat.

We watched as Joe dismantled various bits and pieces from the engine with his limited range of tools. We offered some words of encouragement to ginger him up a little. "Loosen the flange bracket! Try from a different angle with the differential! Tighten the foo-foo valve, it's probably loose! Many more suggestions were made as more bits and bobs began to mount up on the ground around him. From the withering glares and expletives he sent in our direction, we gathered that our words of encouragement were not welcome, so we paused once in a while before coming with new suggestions, just to keep him on his toes.

Amid the sound of dropped spanners, he swore loudly as the oil can fell out of his hands and he kicked it right out of the car park in a fit of pique, which wiped the smiles off our faces to be replaced by expressions of concern, for if Joey didn't manage to fix it we would be in serious trouble.

We sat on the wall without a single titter or comment as Joe reassembled what he had recently dismantled, and I began to think that rigor mortis had set in because my bum was so numb, then he grinned in triumph and exclaimed, "That should do it!" and got into the van to start the engine as we waited with bated breath for the result.

There was a frighteningly loud *ker-lunk* accompanied by a cloud of smoke, so we were still up the creek. The only good news was that the windscreen wipers worked perfectly which was quite comforting as it had begun to rain.

Joe jumped out of the van with a wild look on him and began to kick the van in sheer frustration cursing vehemently, then proceeded to take out all the bits and bobs he had bolted into position only minutes earlier. In doing so a spanner slipped, taking the skin off his knuckles in the process and, accompanied by a might yowl of pain, he aimed another hefty kick or two at the bodywork.

With this and the fact that the rain was getting heavier, Stu and Dave lost interest and wandered off in the direction of a bar. I was sorely tempted to join them but felt an obligation to remain as moral support for our desperate mechanic, who was still striving to fix the problem. However, it was by now becoming patently obvious that he would never be able to fix it, and by the look on his face this fact was slowly beginning to dawn on the man of the hour, too. He joined me on the wall and lit a cigarette. "It's no good, Biffo," he sighed, "I've given it my best shot, but we have to face the fact that the van's a gonner."

Just then a huge white Cadillac pulled up outside The Star Palast and out stepped the long legged Magda teetering along on her high heels and looking for the world like a gangster's moll in a Hollywood film, accompanied by the slimy Black Bob and Kiel's number one bad-guy, Manfred Müller, who wondered what our problem was.

Joe gave him the short version. He glanced at the tools and informed us that we would need professional assistance, to which Joe replied that there was an acute cash-flow crisis that made such assistance unattainable, so Manfred took a break to discuss tactics and finances with his partner in crime.

In the meantime, Magda gave Joe an enticing smile and asked, "Are you always this hot, dirty and sweaty?"

Joe knew a come-on when it came, and cheekily replied, "Whenever I get a chance, I am!" and gave her what he considered to be his seductive smile, but which only served to make him look dafter than usual.

Manfred came back to inform us that they had a proposal for us. "You help us with a small thing and we'll help you a lot," he said. Joey eyed Black Bob nervously, and waited to hear more. I could see his mind working, knowing that we had to have the van to get back home, but at what price? He looked decidedly dubious as his glance flew from Black Bob to Manfred and back again.

"We've had a cancellation, so if you guys fill in from Saturday to Tuesday, then we will pay to get the van repaired. A deal? Yes?"

"It certainly is!" Joey agreed on the spot without consulting me, and his relief showed plainly on his face. The van fixed, and no Black Bob! He was happy.

It was a huge disappointment not to be finally leaving on Saturday after having looked forward to it for some time, but even I realised that without Manfred's deal, we wouldn't have been going anywhere anyway. So we were in high spirits when we found the others in the bar, and we all agreed that it was a relief to know that, although our departure would be delayed a few days, we would at least be getting home, eventually.

The next day I went into town on my own and bought a couple of postcards. I addressed one to the café in Schleswig. The other was sent to a girl in Liverpool with laughing eyes and an accent exceedingly rare who I had not seen for a couple of years. I didn't know her address, so my card would simply be a message in a bottle bobbing about on the waves in the hope that it would reach her, and that she might hopefully reply, for I was keen to see her again and missed her even more now than I had when I had been at home. I popped the cards in a box and crossed my fingers.

The End
is Very Nearly in Sight

Knowing my luck or lack of it, I seriously considered spending the day in bed as it was Friday the Thirteenth, which by all accounts was a day to be particularly careful. However, Joey made me change my mind, or should I say, his feet put another perspective to my options. I couldn't recall that he had removed his striped socks once in the course of the past two weeks, and I now awoke to find them only inches from my face and about to black me out with their smell. It was no wonder that the frauleins had kept their distance during his stay in Kiel. The one lady he had managed to get close to must have had serious sinus problems or she wouldn't have survived the encounter. Bad eyesight too, by my reckoning, but that's another story.

So with my eyes swimming, and gasping for breath, I retreated from the bunk and decided to escape and risk the dangers Friday the Thirteenth represented for me rather than remain within the confines of the cell to be gassed by the fumes from Joey's feet.

Unfortunately, before I had been able to tip-toe to the door, Joey came awake, and Stuart's voice demanded to know what day it was and what date it was, which I found to be a strange way to start the day. So I told him. "Bloody hell," he exclaimed with some dismay, "it's the wife's birthday and I've forgotten to send her a card!" I then heard him muttering something about being unlucky, which certainly suited the day.

"Just say it must have got lost in the post," Joey suggested, showing by the look on his face what he thought about Stu concerning himself with such trivialities.

"Yeah, but how do I explain that I haven't sent her any money for the past couple of weeks?" Stuart said miserably. "She's gonna have me guts for garters when I get home."

"It's certainly been an unlucky day for me!" came a voice from Dave's bunk where Dave was not supposed to be. We were so surprised that we jumped to our feet to confirm that it actually was the blonde bass player up there, for he had been spending his nights elsewhere of late. It was, and he was sulky and offended because his latest conquest had shown him the door, which must have been a first for him. "She said I was selfish!" he whined with a disbelieving expression on his face that clearly showed his opinion that such a claim was nothing short of ridiculous.

"That's probably because you spent all your time preening yourself in the bathroom mirror, instead of showing her some interest, you vain bugger!" Stu suggested.

"No it wasn't!" Dave replied huffily. "Actually it was my sexual demands, that did it," he primly informed us.

"What have you been up to now, you pervert?" Joey demanded, rubbing his hands in gleeful anticipation of all the gory details.

Dave was back to being huffy. "It was nothing like that," he assured us, "but she was satisfied, and I wanted more, then she kicked me out saying I was selfish! Can you believe that?" He was hurt and bewildered, and certainly not used to having his charms refused.

So now Dave was also without a fraulein, which seemed to cheer up Stu considerably. He had a wide grin on his face as he mockingly used cricket parlance to describe the situation as he now gleefully saw it. "It would seem that I'm the last man in, the only one still batting for England. The golden-boy opener has been bowled out after scoring a sixty-nine, whereas the ginger man is out after a derisory single leg-over and the ugly drummer never even got on the field."

"Very droll," we told him, and didn't even laugh, because he was right, and the England team certainly was having a lousy innings in the testing time spent in Kiel.

To escape from the confines of the cell, we headed for town. It was snowing and slippery, and there was a heavy wind that pressed the cold through our clothes and into our very bones, but we battled on. Waiting to cross the road was a frail old lady carrying her shopping bags. She was obviously not very good on her legs as she waited patiently for a gap in the traffic. Joey didn't hesitate, and took command of the situation, handing the bags for us to carry, he took her gently by the arm, stopped the traffic with his arm outstretched and guided her carefully to the other side.

Dave was quite pleased with our good deed for the day. "We were like four cub scouts in the pee-wee patrol," he said happily.

"Bollocks!" Joey retorted, once again back to being just Joe.

"It must be awful getting old," Dave warbled on. "You feel the cold more, your joints ache, and most of all it's the loneliness that gets you in the end."

"You don't have to be old for all of that," I pointed out. "I'm freezing right now, my joints ache from all the drumming, and I haven't felt so lonely for a long time."

"There's a good reason for that, though, isn't there, Biffo?" Stu piped in.

"Yeah? And what's that?" I asked warily, knowing something was coming, but not what.

"Your bloody ugly!" he sniggered. He was probably right.

There seemed to be more traffic than usual in the town and there were people thronging about all over the place, and I couldn't understand why. This mystery was solved when Stuart retrieved a newspaper that had been left by a customer at a nearby table. He looked at it, then handed it to me. "It's not Friday the Thirteenth, you chuff," he told me, "it's Saturday the Fourteenth!"

I couldn't believe it, and tried to remember what had happened the previous day, but couldn't remember a thing. Tuesday, yes. Wednesday and Thursday, no problem. But yesterday was gone, apparently without me being part of it, for there was no memory of it having happened. I must have been there or my compadres would have told me. But I couldn't remember a single thing from the previous day. It was blank, and it worried me.

I decided to see the positive side, and brightened as I realised that this meant that we were now one day closer to our departure for home than I had thought. I brightened even more as I recalled that we would be receiving our pay-packets that evening. Things were looking up. The down side was that we would be playing for free for the next few days to pay for the van-repairs.

To our relief and great delight the van arrived back the next day. We were once again mobile, which meant freedom, and more importantly, we now had the means to return to our homes and families. "Let's go somewhere," Joey suggested to me. "Anywhere will do, but Schleswig would be better!" He gave me a wink, eager to be off before Stu could put in an appearance and spoil the opportunity. Dave was also enthused by the thought of returning to first base now that his local romance was over, but then Stu spoiled it all by popping up to chastise us once again, pointing out that we were idiots to even think of going back, which finally took the buzz out of our collective bee. His finger-wagging lecture grudgingly brought us around to his way of thinking, but by then I was past caring.

Instead we decided to take a drive somewhere else. Anywhere, just to be doing something. I looked at the map and suggested we could visit a place called Shiksee, but Stu wasn't enthusiastic about that either. "And do what exactly?" he wondered.

I shrugged my shoulders and replied, "I dunno, but there should be a good view of the sea," I offered lamely.

He snorted derisively. "So what you're suggesting is that we go to this place we know nowt about just to stare out at the sea," he sneered.

Having effectively scuttled all our hopes and aspirations for the day, we finally found ourselves in a bar with four beers on the table before us, which was probably what he had been hoping for all along.

Having grouped us in our normal alcoholic environment, he then demanded that we should all pool our money for the ferry-crossing to ensure that we didn't spend it and have to wave the boat goodbye from the Continental side of the North Sea.

"Twelve quid!" we howled when it dawned on us what the fare would be, for that was a small fortune in our present financial state, but we had no option but to pop our coins in the kitty.

"Then there's the petrol money," Joey pointed out, so we had to keep emptying our purses as we grumbled at the injustices of life. My battered wallet was considerably lighter after these arrangements had been made, but my heart was considerably heavier when I saw how little was left.

It was a tremendous relief to take the stage knowing it was our last night and we would be going home in the morning. We gave it our best shot and did a really good and enthusiastic show that had the dancers on the floor, but the joy I felt before commencing our final number had me all a quiver knowing that it was only three or four minutes to go before our miserable fortnight in Kiel would be over. On the conclusion of the final song, Joe had us all to the front of the stage to take a bow, and announced, "Guten nacht from The Charters and aufwiedersehen Kiel!" which brought forth some enjoyable applause, but then he began to wave and blow kisses at the crowd which annoyed Stuart sufficiently to send him a glare that threatened damnation and worse.

We changed from our sweaty group gear into our well-worn on-the-road, scruffy casuals, and headed for the local bar to celebrate that it was finally over and that we were free again. The three musketeers with D'Artagnan in tow together to celebrate that we had somehow, together, managed to get through it all and survive. It was a good feeling!

We had a fantastic buzz going those last few hours in the bar. Joey was in particularly high spirits, finding fun and amusement in everything and nothing, and generally laughing uproariously most of the night. On spotting a group of frauleins he immediately joined them to regale them with his Star-Spangled Bullshit hoping for a final hit before leaving. Dave went with him for a last gasp try before the final whistle, leaving Stu and myself alone with our beer.

"The wife's gonna kill me when I get home," he moaned looking quite miserable.

"I doubt it," I reassured him. "I'm sure she loves you really."

"D'ya reckon?" he said, bucking up a little.

"Yeah, definitely!" That seemed to put the smile back on his face. "Anyway, it's Dave who should be worrying," I told him, "because he can't find his wedding ring." It had been six weeks since he had it on, and now he couldn't remember where he had put it. He had already begun to consider possible excuses, the present candidate being that his finger had swollen up because of all the playing and he had to take it off.

Stu chuckled as he looked across at where Dave was working his wiles with the women, "That's not the only thing that's swollen," he guffawed. "Have you seen his face? All the colour's drained from it!" He took a swig of his beer and informed me,

"That's why his brain doesn't work. All the blood's pumping down below and there's nowt left for his brain cells."

He looked across at Joey and smiled. That smile told more than a million words about the bond we had between us. "Rejection never seems to bother carrot-head over there, does it? I mean, look at him now, leering and laughing and chopsing away nineteen to the dozen when it's patently obvious that he's wasting his time."

"Aye," I agreed, "but you have to remember that Joey's a one-off, and they threw the mould away after they'd made him, deciding that one mistake was enough. He's impervious to criticism and rejection, and do you know why? Because he simply doesn't give a damn," I told him. "Joey's a very rare specimen indeed and the last of a threatened species." I'm sure we both loved the grinning idiot.

Wednesday arrived and we were alive and kicking and raring to go, for we were finally free. Dave dragged his feet before leaving the room, wondering if there was anywhere he had forgotten to look for the lost wedding ring, but we eventually manoeuvred him outside where the van was waiting, loaded and pointing to Blighty and home.

I stood at the top of the steps of The Star Palast, threw out my arms and shouted for all the world to hear, "Biffo has now left the building!" but Joey's strident voice rasping out from the open van window telling me to get me arse in gear and stop being an idiot, somehow spoiled my moment.

We found the Autobahn without difficulty, and with me navigating and signs popping up to guide us on our way, I felt confident that even Joey couldn't get lost, so we headed for the blue wiggly thing that had baffled Joe at the beginning of our adventure, glad to be leaving Kiel and all its traumatic memories and happy to be going home to clean bedclothes and four meals a day.

Dave and Stu were soon asleep in the backseat, and their snores combined with the steady droning of the engine soon had me nodding. I was awakened by the van horn being punched repeatedly as Joe's frustration took control after not being able to pass a big articulated lorry that threw plumes of spray to our windscreen.

"Wind your window down, Biffo, and tell me when it's safe to pass this bloody thing, because I can't see with us driving on the right side of the road."

I wound down my window and felt the rain lashing against my face as I waited for a gap in the traffic. Eventually, I nodded my head and shouted, "Right! Now!" and Joe swung the wheel and almost hit a van that came shooting out of the rain from nowhere. It would have wiped us out but Joe's instant reaction saved us. It wasn't just a near accident. It was an unavoidable and fatal accident that some miracle had saved us from, with a little help from Joe.

We sat in complete silence for a full ten minutes. Despite his blotchy red face, Joey was still ashen when he finally spoke. "Bloody hell, that was lucky," he said quietly. That must have been the understatement of the year, because by rights, we should have been dead.

Snitch and Snatch slowly came to life in the backseat having slept comfortably through what should have kept them asleep permanently, and were far from happy when they were told of the incident, and Joey had to take a verbal beating, but took it like man, without complaining.

On arriving in Bremerhaven we discovered that the boat was delayed, which was a shame since we had got there early and this meant several hours of uninvited waiting, but after the last few weeks we were used to wasting time, so we managed to live through it, and we were finally allowed to approach the officials on the way into the vessel. Stuart, of course, couldn't find his passport, and we watched with growing concern as he searched his pockets several times without success. "I think I must have left it in Kiel," he announced. "I kept it under the mattress so I wouldn't lose it." He searched through his bag in the back, then his guitar case, then under the seat, but the passport was nowhere to be found. On a final desperate body-search it turned up in his back pocket much to everybody's relief.

Joey only had one comment. "Chuff!" he said, and chose to leave it at that.

Having boarded the vessel I decided to change my coins to British cash, and found my acquaintance from the previous crossing still behind the counter. She remembered me. I wonder why? "You've lost some weight," she pointed out, smiling at me pleasantly. I couldn't disagree with this observation for I had eaten little during the past weeks, and my belt was pulled in several notches as testament of the fact.

She counted out the money, and there before me lay what I had left after six weeks of slogging work and much privation. I counted it. Five pounds, eighteen shilling and four and a half pence! And I still wasn't home!

We found an empty cabin and I dropped on the nearest bunk and promptly fell asleep.

It was past midnight by the time I woke up. I could feel the ship moving through the waves. I was alone in the cabin but didn't have to be a detective to know where I would find the others, so I went to the bar to join them there.

The journey over had been lively and fun, but it was different now. We were all very quiet. The spark had gone. I suppose there had to be a reaction after all we had been through, and it seemed to have set in now that we were on board ship, finally realising that what lay behind us was gone, a dead flame that could never be reignited. We were lost in our own thoughts and the memories they held for each of us, and chose to keep them closed to ourselves.

Back in Blighty the first thing on the menu was an eager return to Sid's Café on the docks, and sausage, eggs, mushrooms and two slices of bread all burnt to a frazzle. Proper food at last!

With this inside us we then began the final journey home through the back roads of Suffolk, where Joey, not surprisingly, promptly got lost. Driving in ever widening circles we finally found our way, but his unscheduled detour meant that it took us five hours just to get to the Midlands, where we crossed the motorway which confirmed that we were going more or less in the right direction.

This discovery put some cheer back into us, but unfortunately it was short-lived, for we got a puncture and had to wobble along at zero miles an hour for three or four miles to the sound of flapping rubber slowly shredding itself, before we found a suitable place to do the necessary repairs.

We all piled out and watched with some interest and a little trepidation as Joe inspected the tyre. "Shit!" he screamed, and kicked it violently. There followed a stream of colourful expletives, for the tyre was a shredded mess virtually hanging off the rim and completely beyond repair. He kicked the van again, then did a tribal dance hopping about on one foot like a Hopi Indian and screaming like a stuck pig, claiming he had broken his toe.

As Joe struggled to fit the jack in place, the rest of us casually walked off to the nearby café. "And just where do you think you shower are going?" he demanded in tearful desperation. "Aren't you going to give me a hand?"

"Nah," Stu replied, "you don't need us, you've done it before, remember?" We were caring creatures.

From the café window we could follow Joey's progress while enjoying a coffee and smoke. Stuart kept us abreast of developments with a football commentary. "Good, he's got it off. Well done, Joe! My, my, that tyre's a mess. Here he comes with the spare. Easy does it, mate. He's got it on. Now! Here comes the tricky it. Oh, no! He's slipped with the wheel-brace again. I can see blood! He's just thrown the brace down. No, Joe, no! Too late! He's kicked the van again, and now he's jumping. He's getting quite good at that! He's wrapping his handkerchief around his knuckles, and now he's looking around. It's there, Joe. There where you threw it, remember! He's found it. Just one more turn now, and Yes! He's done it! The jack's off and the van's ready to go!"

Stuart calmly finished his coffee. "Come on you lot, let's go," he said. "You know how tetchy he can get if we keep him waiting."

Back in the van I noticed that Joey's eyes were watering. Looking at the blood seeping through the handkerchief I could understand why. "You alright, Joe," I asked, feeling some concern, for he was in obvious pain.

"Yeah," he insisted, "and that wheel-change was a piece of cake, no problem at all."

"Yeah, right," I said. "I just thought I'd ask."

The rest of the journey was uneventful, and we could finally pull up at Dave's place. He had a pained expression on his innocent face as he prepared to face the realities of life with the wife but without a band of gold on his finger. I called him over and brought some joy to his day by informing him that he would find the ring in his pharmacy bag somewhere among the pink pills, and his face lit up as he scrambled for his case to find it.

Stuart was quite understandably in an anxious frame of mind as we rapidly approached his abode. He was thinking of the birthday card he hadn't sent and the money he had spent on necessities like beer and cigarettes rather than on keeping his wife and family alive. As it turned out, his fears were unfounded for his good lady embraced him warmly and was obviously overjoyed at having him back again.

And then there were two. Joey began to hum *Maria* as we drove on to our next port of call. Unfortunately this turned out to be the *Sound of Music* version, which didn't quite seem to go with his rough and ready personality, for you would have to look far and wide to find anyone less saintly than Joe, and somehow it was difficult to imagine him in a nunnery, although knowing him, I'd bet that he would even fancy his chances there.

The night was not over, for we were pulled over by a police car. They apparently thought that the rust-heap we were driving was so battered that it had to contain something criminal. They did what policemen do under such circumstances and wandered around the vehicle kicking the tyres and looking serious. Joey denied being an IRA gun-runner before they had even asked, just to be on the safe side.

Frankly, I was more concerned with the interest one of the constables was showing for the tax disc on the windscreen as he held a torch to it. The thing was, that Joey had not had time to apply for a tax disc when he had acquired the van, and being Joey, had simply forged one, and now the forgery was under examination by what I assumed to be an expert.

I gazed at the roof of the van and prayed for divine intervention. So far and so close, I thought, and now to be stopped and arrested for a dastardly crime and end up in yet another cell. It was just before I cried mother and admitted all. *It's a fair cop, Guv!*

I suppose that the dirt saved us, for the van was covered in it, and it must even have been difficult to see the tax disc in daylight, so in the darkness of night it would have been close to impossible. I sighed with relief as they waved us on, but

Joey just chortled and gave extra acceleration just for show.

It was one thirty by the time the van stopped outside my home, and everything was quiet. Given the racket we made while unloading my drums and cymbals it was a wonder that we didn't wake up the whole neighbourhood with our shouting and laughter, but the only houselights that came on where those in my house.

"It was fun, wasn't it?" Joey said.

"Aye, I suppose so. At least some of it was," I agreed.

"We'll have to do it again another time," Joey shone up at the thought, but I didn't.

"I don't think so, mate. Once was enough for me."

"There you go again, you miserable bugger," he chided, "you've got no sense of adventure!"

As usual, Joey wasn't listening. "I'll call the agent and get things sorted out." He was already raring to go. "It'll be a gas, and just think of all the frauleins waiting for us," he enthused. "I'll call the agent tomorrow!" he called as the van started running.

I watched it as it disappeared around the corner, and I thought, *Yeah, Joey, you do just that!*

"Stan, put the kettle on and make us a nice cup of tea," my mother ordered, then turned to study me. "You've lost weight, son," she said, haven't you been eating properly?"

"Of course," I told her, "we were in the café every day."

The old fellah sat himself down by the kitchen table. "Well, are you going to tell us how you got on?"

Blowing out my cheeks, I told him, "Well, it's a long story, and I really don't know where to start."

"In my experience, son, the beginning is usually a good place to start."

So I did.

And Then
What?

I became a mini personality in the tap room of my local watering hole, The Peacock, as I regaled my mates and cronies, and anyone else who happened to be listening, with tales of daring do on our German adventure.

When he thought my mother wasn't listening, my Old Fellah asked me, "Did you have any luck with … er … the thingy's … you know what I mean, don't you … the frauleins?"

I couldn't lie, and I wouldn't if I could, so I told him the truth. "Not as much as the others," I admitted. "You know what I'm like, slow on the uptake, but I did get to know a couple of quite nice girls."

I don't think that was what he wanted to hear, but throughout the years it has been the memories of the nice girls that have remained strongest in my mind. Wonderful girls like Henni and Heinke, who I fell in love with without any invitation.

Perhaps the hardest part after our return to England after those weeks of carefree freedom, was to return to work and follow the clock. Rock star one week, Manweb labourer the next, but then I suppose that's life.

We were soon back on the local circuit playing the same venues as before, but somehow they didn't quite hold the same glamour after having played The Star Palasts of the world. The local newspapers sent reporters and photographers to do stories on our German escapades, so we were heroes and personalities one day, and fish and chip wrappings the next. Just like real life; here today, gone tomorrow.

We had many interesting bookings and even had another jaunt across the sea when we were booked for a weekend booking at a club in Dublin. They lined everything up, and all we needed to take with us was the guitars and our own charming selves. Even the remnants of Joey's van could remain at home, which was as well or we might have ended up in Scotland instead. We were even put up in a first class hotel which was as far removed as possible from the humble quarters we had suffered through in Germany.

We would sometimes dust off the memories and have a chuckle or two as we remembered what we had been through together, knowing that memories was all we had left from our little adventure. That is until Joey one day airily announced that we had been offered another six week stint back in Germany, and he had accepted and we were to leave in three weeks.

"Well, that'll be without me, because I'm not going," I wailed, paling at the very prospect, for once was enough for fond memories, whereas twice would probably kill me. I was adamant, and for once in my life I actually managed to remain steadfast, so I remained at home when the others left on a new adventure, this time with a replacement drummer.

If the truth be told, The Charters was quite a good group, and definitely capable of playing solid rock and roll that had people jumping. There was even some serious interest from record companies, agents and music publishers in London. Unfortunately we never followed up on their interest and will therefore never know how far we might have got. Probably nowhere, but then now we'll never know.

The message in a bottle I had sent back from Kiel actually found its way to the one person I hoped it would reach, and I renewed my friendship with the girl with the laughing eyes and the accent exceedingly rare. So at least something good came from our German jaunt.

I had promised myself that I would someday make a sentimental journey back to Schleswig where it had all started for me and where my fondest memories were born. After many years, the opportunity finally offered itself when I went to northern Germany with a friend of mine, Derek Fawkes.

As the plane dropped into Hamburg I peered through the window and saw the blue wiggly thing, known to others than Joey as the River Elbe. From the sky it looked quite impressive and very wide, just as I remembered. We took the Autobahn on the way to our destination, which was the World Speedway Final in Denmark, and the further we progressed the more things began to jog my memory.

I noticed the signs: Neunmünster, Kiel, Flensburg, and Schleswig! We were on the very same route I had travelled down all those years ago. I gulped as we crossed over the Nord Ostsee-Kiel Kanal near Rendsburg for I knew that this was only a dozen miles from the place I had promised myself that I would sometime return to.

As we neared the turn-off point I actually found myself speaking my thoughts out loud. "1000 metres, 500 metres, 200 metres, 100 metres. There! There's the turning, Joe! I wonder how Henni's going on these days?" I didn't know it, but I was back in time.

Derek looked at me askance. "What the hell are you on about?" he asked.

I hadn't realised that I had excitedly been speaking my thoughts, so I explained. "I was just thinking about a young girl I met here in Schleswig," I told him. "She was sweet and beautiful and her name was Henni."

"When was this, then?" he wondered, puffing away at his pipe and probably not all that interested.

"It was when I was over here with The Charters in sixty-six," I told him and couldn't quite hold back the sigh that followed this information.

"That's years ago," Derek pointed out. He began to chuckle. "Far be it for me to shatter your dreams of things that might have been, but she'll be a grandmother by now."

Of course he was right, but I couldn't let such an irrelevancy destroy the memory of a lifetime. "In my mind, she's still the same sweet smiling waitress I first met in a café and fell in love with," I insisted. And that's the way she was going to stay.

Derek gave me a glance and a wry smile. "Yes, but how could you fall for a girl called Henry? That's a terrible name for a girl."

We approached a sign that showed the road to Schleswig. "Shall we take a trip in and have a look around?" Derek asked, knowing that I wanted just that.

My eyes never left the road ahead as I replied. "No, just keep driving," and we drove past the road that lead back to Schleswig without me even blinking an eye.

As Stuart had once said, "You can never go back." He had been right, as usual. It was better to leave the memories untarnished.

So I never returned. Neverland would never see me again, but would always remain in my heart as a fond memory that will linger with me until the final chord of the last song ends and the curtain closes on the farce that was my life.